THE GELLER PAPERS

THE GELLER PAPERS

Scientific Observations on the Paranormal Powers of Uri Geller

Edited by Charles Panati

Illustrated with photographs, diagrams, and charts

HOUGHTON MIFFLIN COMPANY BOSTON · 1976

Library of Congress Cataloging in Publication Data

Main entry under title:
The Geller papers.

Includes bibliographies.
1. Geller, Uri, date —Addresses, essays, lectures.
I. Panati, Charles, date
PF1283.G4G44 76-3701
ISBN 0-395-24351-3

Printed in the United States of America

c 10 9 8 7 6 5 4 3 2 1

For my mother
and Stan

PREFACE

THERE HAS BEEN much debate in the last few years over the "powers" or, as some prefer to say, "prestidigitations" of the thirty-year-old Israeli Uri Geller. Can he bend metal by gently stroking it — or not touching it at all? Can he clairvoyantly "see" the uppermost face of a die that has been shaken in a sealed metal box before the lid of the box is opened? Can he telepathically read the thoughts of others?

A growing number of professionals, most notably physical scientists, believe Geller can do these things. They have tested him. They have observed events for which there are no present scientific explanations. Other people, however, among them magicians, see Geller as tremendously talented, lightning-fast in his deceptions, and disarmingly humble over his many failures. They take him to task not because of his talent and theatrics, but because, according to them, he pawns off what he does as "the real thing" — the product of innate paranormal abilities.

The purpose of this book is to present firsthand observations on the talents of Uri Geller and, in doing so, to bring to light and offer for public scrutiny much material that has either never before appeared in print or has surfaced only piecemeal in the popular press. The book is written — through papers, reports, diary entries, and letters — by the scientists and professionals who, in various ways, have scrutinized Geller's talents, and feel that Geller is an individual who deserves further scientific attention.

Since 1972, when he first came to worldwide attention, Geller has been tested in seventeen laboratories in eight different countries. The scientists who have worked with him have watched him deform solid steel rods without touching them, cause part of an exotic crystal to vanish from within a sealed container, alter the memory of a rare metal alloy, erase information from computer tapes, set Geiger counters ticking with only his thoughts, and read the thoughts of others while he is sealed in a room that blocks out all types of radio waves. They are men and women of probity, affiliated with major universities and research centers throughout the world. To prevent fraud the scientists have searched Geller for metals that might be hidden under his fingernails and magnets sewn into his clothing, x-rayed his teeth for evidence of minute electronic devices, bound his hands, blindfolded his eyes, all but stripped him naked. Many of the scientists flatly stake their reputation on the genuineness of Geller's paranormal talents.

But scientists, it is rightfully said, should not be the final arbiters in separating what is psychic from what is magic. And they have not been. Four magicians have worked closely with Geller, applied their own standards to prevent any sleight of hand, and have observed inexplicable events. It is their unanimous opinion that Geller either has paranormal abilities or is acquainted with a form of magic unknown to the entire brotherhood of magicians. Their observations are presented here along with those of the scientists.

Some of the papers in this book were originally meant for publication in reputable scientific journals — and several were submitted to these journals. In each case it was the scientist's hope that publication of his work with Geller would provide a platform for healthful debate and would generate further and more exhaustive experimentation. To date, however, only one paper has appeared in a major scientific journal. It is not the purpose of this preface to examine the procedures of scientific publishing, least of all for such a highly unorthodox subject as parapsychology. Suffice it to say that all of those papers appear here. No material in them has been altered; no terminology diluted; the reports contain all the original charts, diagrams, pictures, and references that support the research. Geller's failures as well as his successes are discussed.

Some of the papers are heavily detailed, giving all the specifics necessary for a scientific investigation. Others are short sketches, informal notes, or personal observations about the hours and days a particular researcher spent with Geller. Fourteen papers are by physicists, mathematicians, and engineers; three by parapsychologists; four by magicians; one by a professional photographer (who witnessed Geller take a "thought photograph"); and one (a letter that appears in the Introduction) by a dentist who x-rayed Geller's mouth for evidence of hidden devices. These men and women who have tested Geller are convinced that he is a phenomenon worthy of, indeed, demanding, the serious attention of science. As the prestigious British technical journal *Nature* editorialized, Geller "has clearly created a *prima facie* case for further investigation."

Who are the professionals who have investigated Geller? What are their credentials? How rigorous or casual were their investigations? Exactly what did they do? And, of course, what did they discover? These questions will be examined, in part, in the Introduction. It should be noted, however, that the Introduction is not meant to be an evaluation of the papers; the papers stand or fall on their own contents. Rather, because of the technical nature of many of the papers and the sheer volume of the material they contain, the Introduction will serve as a general review, for the layman, of the major highlights of the research that has been done with Geller.

There can be no doubt that this research will affect different people in radically different manners. Geller-advocates who read this collection of firsthand observations may feel confirmed in their present opinion of him. His critics will dissect these papers and will find large loopholes and countless faults with the experiments and descriptions they contain, for all of the evidence presented here is certainly not of equal quality. There is nevertheless a considerable amount of new and impressive information — from responsible scientists and professional magicians alike. Their observations taken as a whole are hard to dismiss on the grounds of simple fraud or mass delusion. But whatever one's opinion of the events described in this book, the thoughtful reader should give these reports a careful review before drawing final conclusions on the phenomena associated with Uri Geller.

CONTENTS

THE GELLER PAPERS

INTRODUCTION

Thirty-five miles south of San Francisco is the Stanford Research Institute, a giant think-tank that conducts wide-ranging research for government and for private industry. Over the years SRI staff scientists have made major advances in computer technology, genetics, and laser communications. The institute has a reputation to uphold, and it does not thoughtlessly plunge into new areas of research. In late 1972 SRI invited Geller to visit its laboratories for six weeks of testing. The visit was arranged by former astronaut Edgar Mitchell, who since his Apollo space flight has been interested in psychical research; the actual tests at SRI were to be conducted by two laser physicists, Dr. Harold E. Puthoff and Russell Targ, who for years had been interested in parapsychology.

Puthoff and Targ had heard stories about Geller's alleged telepathic talents and about his even more remarkable ability to bend forks and spoons without touching them (psychokinesis). Now they were going to get a chance to test him. For six weeks Geller was put through the laboratory wringer, never knowing from one day to the next what would be expected of him. He came out of the ordeal exhausted, and the SRI scientists came out with a statement: "We have observed certain phenomena . . . for which we have no scientific explanation. All we can say at this point is that further investigation is clearly warranted."

More testing did take place about a year later, and this time the SRI scientists made a startling statement: "As a result of Geller's success in this experimental period, we consider that he has demonstrated his paranormal perceptual ability in a convincing and unambiguous manner." What had Geller done to draw such an endorsement?

In their paper "Information transmission under conditions of sensory shielding," Puthoff and Targ present their investigations into Geller's perceptual talents of telepathy and clairvoyance. For most of thirteen experiments, Geller sat in a room that shielded him, visually, acoustically, and electrically, from the outside world. In another room down the hall, one scientist opened a dictionary at random, selected a word, and drew a picture of what it suggested. Geller's task was to "see" telepathically, and draw on paper, each target picture. When, for example, the word chosen was *grape,* the scientist drew a bunch of grapes. Minutes later Geller said over a one-way intercom that he " 'saw' . . . drops of water coming out of the picture," and he spoke of "purple circles." Finally, when he was quite sure he "had it," he drew a bunch of grapes. The target and Geller's rendition of it both contained exactly twenty-four grapes. (For all target pictures and Geller's responses, see Plates 1 and 3.)

This mental impression had come to Geller easily, but, for reasons still unknown, at other times he had to strain and concentrate for up to half an hour before all the bits and pieces he perceived came together to form a complete picture. In their paper "The Record," a sort of daily log kept by Puthoff and Targ during experiments conducted in August 1973, we see the difficulty Geller had one time when the target picture was a devil with a pitchfork. During a thirty-minute period Geller got impressions (and drew pictures) of "Moses' Tablet containing the Ten Commandments," the earth and a pitchfork, a worm crawling from an apple, a snake and a leaf. Puthoff and Targ speculate that the negative religious connotations of the target picture might have been the reason Geller drew "thematic" rather than "direct" responses to the target.

The degree of success in these experiments was high, so the difficulty of Geller's task was heightened. For three tests he sat in a double-walled copper-screen Faraday cage — a housing that blocks out virtually all radio waves and magnetic fields. If Geller could score "hits" in this room too, then the hypothesis that his impressions were carried by standard electromagnetic radiation would be greatly weakened. To further complicate Geller's task, the scientists did not draw the target pictures on paper. In one test a computer drew a picture of a kite on the face of a cathode-ray tube (a device similar to a TV screen); Geller drew a kite. (See Plate 2(a).) Next a picture of a church was drawn and stored in a computer's memory bank; Geller drew a picture vaguely resembling the target. (See Plate 2(b).) In the third test a picture of a heart pierced by an arrow was drawn on the screen of the cathode-ray tube and then the device was turned off. Geller perceived it correctly. (See Plate 2(c).) From a total of thirteen such perceptual experiments the SRI scientists concluded that the odds for Geller's success being due merely to chance were more than a million to one.

"Information transmission under conditions of sensory shielding" was published in *Nature* on October 18, 1974. It was the first parapsychological research paper to appear in a major scientific publication. An editorial accompanying Puthoff and Targ's article said in part: "We publish a paper . . . that is bound to create something of a stir in the scientific community . . . [The claims made are] bound to be greeted with a preconditioned reaction among many scientists. To some it simply confirms what they have always known or believed. To others it is beyond the laws of science and therefore necessarily unacceptable. But to a few — though perhaps to more than is realized — the questions are still unanswered, and any evidence of high quality is worth a critical examination."

The paper did cause the stir that the *Nature* editors thought it would, and there remains much misunderstanding about the views of the three independent judges who voted on whether the paper should be published. For this reason the full text of the *Nature* editorial "Investigating the paranormal" appears in this book, preceding Puthoff and Targ's article.

That article is detailed and scientific, but its two companion pieces, "The Record" and "Experiments with Uri Geller," contain more experiments related in a simple and personal way.

An ordinary die was placed in a small steel box; the box was shaken and placed on a table. Before the box was opened Geller wrote down his impression of the uppermost face of the die. This is called a "double-blind" experiment because neither the subject nor the researchers know the number until the box is opened. The test was performed ten times, with Geller "passing" twice because he received no psychic impressions. But the eight times he did record a number, he was right every time. The odds: about a million to one. In another test, also under double-blind conditions, Geller located a hidden object placed in one of ten aluminum cans. He did this correctly twelve times in a row, with odds of over a trillion to one. He also mentally altered the reading of an electrical scale and disrupted the workings of a magnetometer, a device that generates an electric current from a radioactive source.

When Geller is pressed for an explanation of how he performs telepathic and clairvoyant feats, he gives a simple, if frustrating, answer: "I put a screen in my mind, like a television screen. Even when I talk or listen, it is still there. When I am receiving something, the image appears there as a picture. I don't feel it; I actually *see* it." But Geller himself is at a loss when it comes to accounting for his psychokinetic talent.

*

He demonstrated this ability for physical scientist Eldon Byrd at the Naval Surface Weapons Center, Silver Spring, Maryland, by deforming an unusual metal alloy called nitinol. Nitinol wire is composed of approximately 55 percent nickel and 45 percent titanium. It has a physical memory. That is, a piece of nitinol wire actually "remembers" the shape in which it was manufactured. No matter how much it is crumpled or bent, a nitinol wire, when heated, springs vigorously back to its original shape. Byrd is quite familiar with the properties of nitinol. He knows that no simple, ordinary forces can alter the wire's memory; he wanted to see if Geller could.

Geller arrived at the Naval Surface Weapons Center in October of 1973. In one test Byrd held a five-inch straight piece of nitinol by its ends while Geller "gently stroked" the middle of the wire with his thumb and index finger. After twenty seconds Geller felt a "lump" forming in the wire. He removed his fingers and there was a sharp "kink" at the wire's center. Byrd placed the wire in boiling water, which should have removed the kink. It did not vanish. "Instead of [the wire] snapping back with some force into a straight shape," Byrd writes, "[it] began to form approximately a right angle." Byrd then placed the kink over a flame, but still it did not straighten out.

In his paper "Uri Geller's influence on the metal nitinol," Byrd states that a crystallographic analysis of the kinked section showed that the crystals that contain the wire's memory had actually increased in size. Such a change requires that the wire be reannealed by being heated to a temperature of about 900° F. "There is absolutely no explanation as to how Geller bent the wire by gently touching it," says Byrd.

Perhaps not, but the metallurgists at the Naval Surface Weapons Center were intent on removing the kink. They put the wire under tension in a vacuum chamber, and heated it by passing an electric current along its length until the wire was glowing and almost molten; in other words, they reannealed it into a straight shape. When the wire was removed from the chamber and laid on a plate to cool it was indeed straight; it appeared to have regained its original memory. But when the wire cooled to room temperature, the kink spontaneously returned. "The day following the experiment" writes Byrd, "I took another piece of nitinol wire and tried to bend it into as tight a kink as Geller had formed: I used the point of a screwdriver . . . It was impossible for me to [do it] without using Bunsen burners and pliers." Byrd also tried various chemicals on pieces of nitinol wires to see if the wire could be temporarily "softened" so that a kink might be formed without extreme heat and sizable force. The nitinol proved impervious to all the chemicals tested.

But experimentation between Geller and nitinol does not stop there. Byrd realized that anomalous effects can occur in the best of experiments. Perhaps the wires Geller altered (there were several of them) had a structural defect: Is this why Geller had been able to change their memory? Byrd pondered this question for eleven months before he got another chance to test Geller. This time it was not at the Naval Surface Weapons Center, but in an informal setting at the home of a friend of Geller's in Connecticut. Byrd brought with him three pieces of nitinol wire; all had been thoroughly tested at the lab to make sure that on being heated they sprang back to straight configurations. Geller rubbed the wires one at a time, and all three became deformed. (See Plates 4–7.) Heating would not straighten them out. On later examination, nitinol experts at the lab concluded that the only way "permanent deformation" could have occurred was through the use of intense heat and mechanical stress. "All of the bends that Geller has produced thus far in nitinol wires have been *permanent* deformations," says Byrd. "The wires can be . . . twisted into any shape by hand, but on being heated . . . [they always] return to the shape Geller had imposed upon them."

Could Geller have somehow cheated to achieve the results he did? Because of the unusual nature of nitinol, the scientific controls essential for an unambiguous investigation are, for the most part, built into the testing material. Byrd and his colleagues conclude that Geller would have had to either "palm" a Bunsen burner or substitute his own pieces of nitinol, manufactured to his specifications, if deception is to be the explanation for the events that took place. Geller had to deform the wire, Byrd thinks, by paranormal means.

*

Working with nitinol was a new and novel experience for Geller, but in the physics laboratory of Kent State University, he bent metals with which he was more familiar: steel and platinum. He fractured four metal objects in the presence of Dr. Wilbur Franklin, a physicist, and his associates: two stainless steel spoons, a stainless steel needle, and a platinum ring. (One of the spoons was to serve as a control, but it bent spontaneously, without being touched.) The bending of the objects, reports Franklin, was amazing in itself (an associate of Franklin's held the ring while Geller concentrated on it and its surface cracked), but Franklin's primary interest was an analysis of the fractured surfaces under the probing eye of a scanning electron microscope, a device that can achieve extremely high magnifying power and very fine resolution of detail.

Until Franklin's work with Geller, as far as any scientist could discern, all of the fractures Geller had induced in metals resembled "fatigue fractures" — ruptures caused by excessive wear and tear (even though many of the objects Geller had broken were brand new). But Franklin's analysis revealed something new and unusual. To the naked eye the platinum ring appeared to have a single crack in its surface, but the scanning electron microscope showed that there were actually two cracks; they were spaced a hundredth of an inch apart. (See Plates 13–17.) Yet despite their extreme proximity, they appeared to have been produced by two entirely different conditions. One crack resembled a type that typically occurs at the temperature of liquid nitrogen, $-195°$ C. The other was typical of the melting point of platinum, $1773°$ C. In his paper "Fracture surface physics indicating teleneural interaction," Franklin concludes that it would be extremely difficult, even under the best laboratory conditions, to produce two so totally different fractures at sites so close to one another.

In another paper printed in this book, Franklin gives more details of his work with Geller and offers some theoretical models in an attempt to understand how Geller's powers might operate. In one model, Franklin concentrates on the interactions we know to exist between living systems and matter, then extrapolates them to include psychokinesis. Using another approach, he looks at information theory — a powerful tool that has been invaluable in computer and satellite communications — and considers how it might be used to explain paranormal phenomena. The net result of all of Franklin's experimentation and theorizing can be stated briefly: "The evidence," he writes, "based on metallurgical analysis of the fracture surfaces, indicates that a paranormal influence must have been operative in the formation of the fractures."

*

Shall we one day be able to *see* that paranormal influence? Actually detect and measure the energy that many scientists feel must be traveling from Geller to the metals he bends, breaks, or shatters? At UCLA, medical psychologist Dr. Thelma Moss has taken some unusual photographs, which she thinks capture on film "hints" of evidence that a paranormal influence emanates from Geller's fingers.

The photographic technique Moss uses is known as Kirlian photography, named after two Soviet scientists, S. D. and V. Kirlian, who first demonstrated its operation in 1939. The process is simple enough. The object to be photographed (in Geller's case it was his fingertips) is placed in direct contact with regular black-and-white or color film. An electrical discharge is sent through the back of the photographic plate to the object. When the film is conventionally developed, there is a halo, or corona, surrounding the image. The color of the halo, its intensity, and its geometrical configuration appear to vary markedly with the mental and physical states of the subject photographed.

Moss observed something unusual with Geller. A key lay on a photographic plate a few inches from Geller's fingertip. While Moss took the photograph Geller was to try to bend the key at a distance. Moss hoped to photograph some "emanations" traveling from Geller's finger to the key. She did. Several times. (See Plates 22 and 23.) The sequence of Kirlian photographs first shows a brilliant halo around Geller's finger, then light flaring outward from the center; the light detaches itself and travels away from Geller toward the key. What is the "blob" of light traversing the film? Moss calls it "a spurt of energy," and believes that it may be related to a form of "bioenergy" or "psychic energy," which may be responsible for physical phenomena.

Moss is no novice in the Kirlian technique. She was one of the first American scientists performing psychical research to observe the Kirlian process, during a trip to Russia in 1970. She was so impressed with what she saw that, on returning to the U.S., she and her assistant, Kendall Johnson, built their own Kirlian device. Since 1970 Moss and Johnson have refined their equipment and have taken several thousand pictures. Although Moss observed many "strange" things in her laboratory during Geller's two visits in June of 1975, in her paper "Uri's Magic" she is careful to state that her scientific controls were not rigorous enough to rule out the possibility of deception on Geller's part: for example, black-and-white Kirlian photographs must be taken in a room lit with only a dim red bulb, and for color pictures there must be no light. Moss discusses the drawbacks of these facts in her paper and states that her goal is to "present a subjective description of the events that took place in our laboratory."

But what interested Moss even more than those events were incidents that occurred after Geller's several public appearances on the West Coast. "Since Geller's appearance in Los Angeles," she writes, "our lab has been visited by several persons who claim that they, too, can bend metals by stroking them. And they have successfully demonstrated their ability." The phenomenon of certain individuals' being able to duplicate Geller's feats after watching him perform has been called the "Geller Effect" and has been reported by many researchers. Moss tested several children, boys and girls, and is convinced that they were able to deform heavy metal objects (see Plates 31–33) for a certain period of time after having seen Geller. British physicists Dr. John Hasted and Dr. John Taylor have also studied children who spontaneously developed similar abilities (Taylor's research is presented here), and Dr. E. Alan Price of the South African Institute of Parapsychology has conducted an extensive statistical field study of the phenomenon (his paper "The Uri Geller Effect" details his investigations). Manifestations of the Geller Effect are treated in many of the papers here, and the phenomenon will again be discussed later in the Introduction.

❋

During one of his trips to the West Coast Geller visited Ronald Hawke, an engineer working at the Lawrence Livermore Laboratory, one of the top physical research centers in the U.S. The meeting occurred in late 1974 and no formal testing with Geller was undertaken. But Hawke and his colleagues did observe events in their laboratory that they feel call for further scientific investigation. The targets of Hawke's informal tests with Geller were four computer cards with magnetic programs permanently stored on their surfaces under a plastic coating. Geller's goal was to alter or entirely erase the programs. Twice he failed: once when a card given to him was sealed in a glass bottle and again when he was not allowed to touch a card. Two other cards were handed to Geller and he was allowed to rub his fingers gently across their surfaces. Hawke states that mere rubbing of the cards cannot alter their magnetic programs, but when the cards were taken from Geller and fed into a computer, they were immediately rejected, indicating that their magnetic programs were now "ambiguous." Hawke writes: "Subsequent inspection with a magnetic viewer after the meeting with Geller revealed that the magnetic patterns had been altered." (See Plates 37 and 38.) Hawke's paper, "Magnetic Pattern Erasure," first tells of the laboratory events that took place with Geller, and then suggests a method to investigate, without danger of ambiguity, whether Geller can indeed erase information from magnetic cards and tapes.

❋

Geller has demonstrated his talents for some scientists in an informal manner. These scientists have not been able to impose the rigorous controls required to make a "demonstration" an actual "experiment." But often a scientist is so impressed by what Geller has done, and so sure that it did not involve trickery, that he wants to speak out. Such is the case with Dr. Thomas P. Coohill, a biophysicist at Western Kentucky University.

Geller had been invited there to deliver a lecture to the student body. Afterward, Coohill asked Geller if he would like to try some "tests" in the university's physics laboratory. (Coohill had planned the tests in advance.) Geller agreed. Several members of the physics and psychology departments were present that day. Geller successfully duplicated target drawings and deflected the needle of a compass. But what Coohill found most interesting was Geller's attempt to influence a magnetometer. Geller worked hard at the task, Coohill reports, "clenching his fists, holding his breath, waving his hands, and visibly straining himself." Several times Geller turned to Coohill and asked, "Are you sure it's working?" He had a gut feeling that the needle of the device should be moving — as he said, he was confident that he was "making contact" with it. But nothing moved. After twenty minutes the test was called off. "Are you sure it's not broken?" Geller asked. To satisfy him, Coohill checked the magnetometer. It was broken; nothing Geller or any of the physicists present could have done would have influenced the device.

After the tests, which are described in "On Uri Geller's visit to Western Kentucky University," Geller accompanied Dr. Coohill, his wife, and some faculty members to the Coohills' home for lunch. In the second part of his report Coohill tells of a spoon that "mysteriously" fell to the floor during lunch, though no one was near it. But what amazed Coohill most was that the spoon landed with a metallic "clink," despite the fact that the floor was thickly carpeted. Coohill picked the spoon up by its handle; to his astonishment, "it began to bend in my hand as if it were melting."

Geller then asked Mrs. Coohill to place the spoon between her hands. He held his hands slightly over hers. Suddenly a "pop" was heard and the spoon was found to be broken in two. "At no time," says Coohill, "did Geller touch the spoon."

Coohill is sure that what he and his colleagues witnessed that day is genuine. He is no magician, but he is a highly qualified scientist who has performed biophysical research at the Veterans' Administration Hospital in Pittsburgh and at the Marine Biology Laboratory in Woods Hole, Massachusetts. I say this only to give some perspective to the event that Coohill and his wife witnessed two days *after* Geller's visit. In Coohill's own words: "I was about to put some sugar in my coffee when suddenly I noticed that the sugar spoon was bent. Since my wife and I had carefully checked all of our silverware after Geller's departure and found none of it damaged, we were alarmed . . . The spoon continued to bend slightly . . . for about the next fifteen minutes."

Admittedly this is only an anecdote, but it is not the first or only time that an inexplicable event took place in the wake of a Geller visit and was reported by a reliable source. Although Coohill admits the possibility of deception in the laboratory tests with Geller, he is certain that there was none involved in what occurred two days later in his own home. He feels that what happened was another manifestation of the Geller Effect.

*

William Cox is a research associate at the Institute for Parapsychology in Durham, North Carolina; he is also a magician. In fact, Cox has been interested in psychical research and magic for forty years. A long-standing member of the Society of American Magicians, he organized a committee made up of fellow magicians to investigate fraudulent ESP claims. Cox is well versed in the art of sleight of hand and he is convinced that sleight of hand is not what Geller performed one day in April of 1974.

The session took place in Geller's East Side New York apartment, where, as Cox carefully points out in "A preliminary scrutiny of Uri Geller," Geller could have plotted any kind of deception. As a matter of fact, Cox was doubtful of Geller's alleged psychic talents and thought that the informal setting of the apartment would give Geller an easy opportunity to cheat if, indeed, that was how he achieved his results.

Cox had carefully planned his experiments in advance. He brought with him some newly purchased keys, a mirror, and a pocket watch that had been cleverly rigged not to work. One key, untoothed, was made of thick steel. Cox had previously determined that forty pounds of pressure were required to bend the key. He placed it on a glass-topped table in Geller's living room and held one finger on the key's head; with his other hand he held the mirror beneath the table. The arrangement gave him a top and bottom view of the object and its immediate surroundings. Geller stroked the middle of the key gently. After about a minute the key had bent upward at an angle of about twelve degrees. (See Plate 42.) Cox reports that he kept his finger on the key, and at no time did he feel pressure being exerted by Geller. The fact that the key bent upward from the table raises an interesting point.

Is there a preferred direction, that is, with or against gravity, to Geller's metal-bending ability? In some of the papers here, spoons, forks, letter openers, and a variety of laboratory props influenced by Geller appear to "melt" in the middle and slowly droop *downward* under the force of gravity. But it is also clear from the papers that at other times, as in Cox's test, a metal object touched (and sometimes untouched) by Geller inexplicably seems to defy gravity and turn *upward.* Why? At present no one knows if the apparent arbitrariness (if it really is arbitrary) has to do with the type of metal used or the particular experimental setup or if it is related to Geller's mood at the time of the experiment. In Cox's second paper, "On the issue of Uri Geller and his claims," he suggests some other areas of research, which he feels could reveal the scope, if not the source, of Geller's talents. Can Geller, for instance, heal wounds that have been intentionally inflicted on laboratory mice? Can he affect the growth rate of plants? Can Geller, by his mere presence, transmit a temporary paranormal ability to a person physically near him — a phenomenon, if it exists, called telergy?

Cox performed other experiments with Geller that afternoon. In one, Geller was able to start the pocket watch in which Cox had inserted a physical obstruction to hold down the balance wheel. (See Plate 43.) Cox had arrived at Geller's apartment a skeptic, prepared to catch Geller in some clever sleight of hand, but he left with different feelings: "If he is not, in fact, possessed of inordinate psi [paranormal] abilities, then he is unquestionably more expert a magician than any professional twice his age — if my experience during four decades in the fields of both magic and parapsychology is any criterion."

*

Cox is not the only magician who has tested Geller. In June of 1975 two professional magicians and members of the Society of American Magicians, Artur Zorka and Abb Dickson, ran Geller through some of their own "controlled" experiments. "I emphasize the word *controlled*," writes Zorka in "A magician's investigation of Uri Geller," "because the type of control put on by a magician is different from that of any other investigator. It is a control designed specifically, by those very people who are professionally trained in the art of deception, to prevent fraud."

The tests took place in a room that contained no mirrors and no windows; only Geller, Zorka, and Dickson were present. The first test involved Geller's attempt to bend a fork, made of forged steel with a nylon-reinforced handle, that belonged to Zorka. The fork, which had been selected because of its extreme resistance to physical force, was placed in Geller's hand while the two magicians watched for what they were certain would be an attempt at trickery. Geller curled his fingers around the fork and within seconds, Zorka reports, the nylon handle exploded, sending fragments across the room. (See Plate 45.) "Since it was my fork," says Zorka, "and since Geller had no idea that any tests were going to be conducted with him that day, he could have made no preparations. I was thoroughly amazed at what happened."

Zorka and Dickson were equally amazed at the successful telepathy tests that were performed that day. Dickson made simple drawings, careful of the sound of his pencil on the paper, the movement of his arm and of the head of the pencil (even though Geller's back was turned away). "After a few false starts," writes Zorka, "Geller was able to make remarkably accurate facsimiles of the target drawings." Geller was also able directly to "read" images that were thought of by Zorka, but were never drawn on paper. (See Plate 46.)

Geller did not know that Zorka and Dickson were magicians (nor had he known about Cox) until after the tests had been completed. Had he known in advance, it is quite possible he would have been unable to perform, as has often been the case. Geller explains this by saying that he must have either the confidence or at least the neutrality of the people testing him. Magicians, he feels, approach him with a negative attitude. Zorka and Dickson conclude their paper, an Official Report to the Society of American Magicians, with a powerful endorsement: "It is [our] unanimous finding that although we, as magicians, can duplicate each of these test results using methods known by us, there is no way, based on our present collective knowledge, that any method of trickery could have been used to produce these effects under the conditions to which Uri Geller was subjected." *

*

Yet another professional magician has been convinced that Geller's accomplishments are not the result of trickery. In January

* Release of Zorka and Dickson's Official Report caused a good deal of controversy and an exchange of letters within the community of magicians. Printed here, following the Official Report, are three of the letters, which shine additional light on the two magicians' investigation of Uri Geller.

of 1974 Geller visited Copenhagen and appeared on a local television show. The show's producer called in a well-known magician, Leo Leslie, who instructed the members of the show in the magic tricks that Geller might attempt to use. For one thing, Leslie felt certain that Geller used mercuric salts to soften metal objects before he attempted to bend them. For the taping of the show certain precautions were taken: members of Geller's personal staff were barred from the studio, and throughout the performance one camera always remained focused on Geller's hands. Although Geller appeared to display telepathy and psychokinesis during the taping, Leslie, a skeptic, still was not convinced that what he had seen was genuine. After the show he and Geller got together in one of the backstage dressing rooms, where, under many precautions taken by Leslie, Geller was able to duplicate a target drawing made by the magician. But what amazed Leslie most was a "trick" that took place in his own hands. Geller had been given a nickel-plated, enameled key to try to bend. After stroking it several times, while a Danish journalist held it by one end, Geller claimed that he did not think the key was going to bend. As Leslie recounts in an excerpt from his book, *Uri Geller*, printed here: "I took the key from the journalist and studied it closely. But while I sat looking at the key the enamel suddenly started to crack, and a second later strips of the nickel plating curled up like small banana peels, while the key actually started to bend in my hand." Leslie states that, so far as he could tell, Geller used no form of magic to accomplish the events he witnessed that day. He concludes by saying that "while Geller was in Copenhagen I did not catch him in any deceptions. Therefore I have to continue to rely on my own judgment and experience as a mentalist; they tell that Uri Geller is genuine."

✲

Psychokinesis and telepathy are the phenomena for which Geller is best known. But on rare occasions he has produced "thought photographs," that is, images projected by the mind on film even though a camera's lens cap is on. A paper by award-winning photographer Lawrence Fried, a past president of the American Society of Photographers in Communications, describes an experience he had with Geller while on assignment for a national magazine. During the photographic session, Geller mentioned that he had once or twice before been able to project his own image onto film through a completely closed camera. He was anxious to try it again, and Fried was curious enough to go along with him. "I fastened the lens cap very securely onto a 50-mm Nikkor lens," writes Fried, "and then, using generous amounts of photographer's gaffer tape (a two-inch-wide . . . clothlike tape), I put two complete layers . . . across the lens cap . . . I then wound another long piece of the tape around the lens barrel . . ."

Fried handed the taped camera to Geller, who held it at arms length, pointed at his forehead, and began tripping the shutter. He repeated this at various distances from his head while Fried, with another camera, continually photographed Geller's movements. Two of Fried's photographic assistants were present throughout the event.

When Geller had "exposed" the entire roll of film Fried took the camera, removed the film, and put it in his pocket. When it was processed the next day, all of the frames were black except for number 10: it contained a blurry but discernible picture of Geller at the exact location where he had been sitting the day before. (See Plate 48.) In his report, "Thought photography: a photographer's account," Fried tells of the precautions he took to prevent fraud on Geller's part. He believes that the image on frame 10 was produced by paranormal means.

*

It is understandable that Geller is often accused of producing the effects he does by legerdemain: paranormal talents are not commonplace, and many people find it difficult to fit psychical events into their world view. Some scientists are convinced that Geller is a fraud and that their colleagues who have investigated him have been royally deceived. One such scientist is physicist Dr. Joseph Hanlon, an editor of the British magazine *New Scientist.* "Like witnesses to a motor accident," wrote Hanlon in one article,* "people who have seen Uri bend a spoon or do a drawing by telepathy tell widely differing stories about the same event." Hanlon criticized Geller and the work of two scientists who investigated him: Harold Puthoff and Russell Targ. One of the theories Hanlon puts forward to account for the success of the SRI telepathy experiments was that Geller might have a small receiving device implanted in a tooth. This device could pick up broadcasts and transmit them, through nerves in the teeth, to Geller's brain. Of course, one of the SRI scientists, or someone else present in the room, would have had to be an accomplice in the scheme of deception, whispering descriptions of the target pictures softly into a hidden microphone. Because the James Bond-like device Hanlon described does exist, and was invented by Dr. Andrija Puharich, the man who first brought Geller to the U.S., Hanlon's suggestion that Geller might indeed use a tooth-receiver has become popular with Geller's critics. Hanlon gave the idea more credence by writing that Geller refuses to have his teeth x-rayed. It is true that Geller had not had his teeth x-rayed at the time Hanlon wrote that statement. But since then Geller's entire mouth has been checked for evidence of hidden receiving devices. Here are two paragraphs from a letter from dentist John K. Lind of the Columbia-Presbyterian Medical Center in New York City:

Mr. Uri Geller was examined in my office on December 7, 1974. He was given a routine clinical examination of the hard and soft tissues, and a full-mouth series consisting of fourteen dental radiographs was taken. Our examination revealed no prior dental restorations and only three moderately sized carious lesions: mesial of his lower right first molar, occlusal of his upper right first molar and the mesial of his upper right central incisor.

* *New Scientist,* October 17, 1974, pp. 170–85.

I can attest to the fact that clinical and radiographic examination of his mouth, teeth and jaws reveal no foreign objects implanted such as transistors, metal objects, etc.

Several months had elapsed between Hanlon's suggestion that Geller might use a tooth-receiver and Dr. Lind's examination. Could Geller have had the device removed in the meantime? That possibility is ruled out by one statement in Lind's letter: "Our examination revealed no prior dental restorations . . ." Thus, none of Geller's teeth had ever been drilled, not even for minor cavities.

*

Geller has been observed by scientists not only in the United States, but in Germany, Japan, Switzerland, France, England, and Canada. In Canada, observations of Geller's talents were made by Dr. A. R. G. Owen, executive director of the New Horizon Research Foundation in Toronto and former head of the Department of Genetics at Cambridge University, England. Owen, who has published scores of technical papers on genetics and mathematics, has long been interested in paranormal phenomena. When he heard that Geller would be in Toronto to tape a television show, he decided that he would prepare his own type of test for Uri.

On Friday, March 8, 1974, Geller arrived at the CITY-TV studio in Toronto. He was greeted by the studio staff, by several members of the Toronto Society for Physical Research, and by Owen. It had been agreed in advance that objects would be collected from the TV audience before the show, and that once the program began Geller would try some of his metal bending. Owen, who wanted to "test" Geller, planted three of his own objects among those taken from the audience: his were rare, almost one of a kind items. Also on the tray was a variety of ordinary keys, nails, spoons, and forks. Owen examined each object, and once the tray was placed on a table between Geller and the TV show's host, he kept a careful watch over it. He was curious to see if Geller would select an ordinary nail, a common key, or an undistinguished fork to bend — for which a sleight-of-hand substitution could be made — or if Geller would go for one of the rare items.

Geller, as anyone who has worked with him will agree, is unpredictable. Sometimes he prefers to work with an ordinary object, and other times the novelty of an item will strike his fancy. Geller claims that when he is confronted with a variety of objects, certain ones "suggest themselves" to him. That afternoon at the studio, Geller singled out three objects on the tray that he would try to bend: a fork and two keys tied together by a string. He stroked the fork and it bent some forty degrees; he held the keys up by the string (never touching them) and soon one key began to bend before a close-up TV camera. (See Plate 49.) Ironically, they were Owen's items. Geller claims that he picked them because they looked so different from the others on the tray. The fork was rare: stamped on its back was, "Koba, Stainless, Japan."

The two keys belonged to private rooms at Cambridge University. In his paper, "Uri Geller's metal phenomena: An eyewitness account," Owen argues that a magician would have selected the most common object on the tray; a standard sixpenny nail, perhaps — he could have such a nail, already bent, palmed or up his sleeve. But Geller had quickly, and without deliberation, selected the three unique objects on the tray. "The phenomena," writes Owen after much consideration, "were paranormal and totally genuine."

*

It is one thing to watch Geller bend a metal object, and quite another experience to have a "Gellerized" object become plasticlike and bend in your own hand. Thomas Coohill experienced this twice under very informal conditions, but at Birkbeck College, the University of London, four scientists who tested Geller observed this phenomenon. A metal spoon, which had been previously tested and carefully weighed, began to bend in Geller's hand. Not believing his eyes, Dr. John B. Hasted, a physicist, took the spoon from Geller. "The center was floppy . . . plastic . . . [like] a heated glass tube," writes Hasted in "Experiments on psychokinetic phenomena." When the spoon hardened, it spontaneously broke in two. When the pieces were weighed, and a microscopic examination of the break was made, the possibility that chemicals could have been used by Geller to corrode the spoon was ruled out. But during Geller's three visits to Birkbeck, Hasted, along with world-renowned physicist Dr. David Bohm, Dr. Edward Bastin, and researcher Brendan O'Regan, observed some phenomena that had not occurred in the other labs in which Geller had worked.

The phenomenon of dematerialization really needs no defining. And, of course, it is clearly impossible to have objects suddenly vanish (except on "Star Trek," "The Twilight Zone," and "Space 1999"). This is what Hasted thought just a year ago. But today he is not so sure.

Dematerialization of an object had not been among the tests Hasted and his colleagues had prepared for Geller. For one of his visits to the college, the scientists had prepared two encapsulated crystal discs — about 2.0 mm in diameter and 0.4 mm thick, with central orifices surrounded by thinned sections. Each crystal had been specially sealed in a pharmaceutical plastic capsule about 1 cm long. Geller's task was to try, without touching a capsule, to influence the atomic structure of the crystal. Hasted held his own hand directly above the capsules, and Geller's hand was above Hasted's. Suddenly, Hasted felt a warm sensation, and a moment later one of the capsules moved "like a jumping bean." That capsule was taken to another laboratory and opened: half of the crystal was missing. (See Plate 52.) Hasted feels certain that a portion of the crystal atomically decomposed and vanished. "It did disappear under circumstances that led us to think that conjuring was out of the question," writes Hasted. The next day the remaining portion of the crystal was examined under an electron microscope; the examination confirmed that no substitution of material had taken place. In an unpublished manuscript, *My Geller*

Notebooks, Hasted goes into great detail about why he now believes in the possibility of dematerialization of physical objects; he claims that since the incident with the crystal several other "dematerializations" have occurred in Geller's presence, under informal conditions. Two excerpts from Hasted's *Notebooks* are printed here. They concern two of Geller's visits to Birkbeck, and present important details concerning the circumstances surrounding the events reported in the first paper by Hasted and his colleagues. Hasted candidly evaluates the "controlled conditions" (they were not so controlled as they should have been) under which some of the testing was done, and some of the shortcomings of the experimental procedures. Anyone wishing to evaluate for himself the tests recounted in the paper "Experiments on psychokinetic phenomena," will also have to read the two excerpts from Hasted's *Notebooks*. One of them considers the dematerialization event, and the other discusses, at length, the influence Geller had on a Geiger counter which registered higher than normal radiation levels when Geller touched the device.

In working with Geller on four different occasions (one did not take place in the laboratory), the Birkbeck team reached some general conclusions: (1) In attempting to produce psychokinetic phenomena under laboratory conditions the attitude of the scientists is crucial; they must be in a relaxed state. Tension, fear, or hostility can communicate itself from members of the research team and affect Geller's performance. (2) The probability of success is higher when all present actively want things to work well — a sort of team spirit. (3) Geller works best with experiments that challenge his imagination. Hasted also found that, in working with Geller, it is difficult to produce a predetermined set of phenomena. Fixed conditions are what any scientist strives for; thus, the spontaneous nature of many of the phenomena produced by Geller places a serious handicap on research efforts — one that unfortunately has not yet been satisfactorily resolved.

*

Dr. John G. Taylor, a mathematician at King's College, University of London, was the first scientist to design experiments to measure the pressure applied by Geller when he bends metal. Taylor took two approaches in his tests. In one experiment he employed a scale of the type used to weigh letters. It was sensitive enough to measure weights to a quarter of an ounce. A brass strip, about 20 cm long, was taped horizontally to the platform of the scale. Geller had to stroke the strip, attempting to bend it, while an automatic reading device monitored the downward pressure Geller applied.

In one attempt, the strip bent, *upward*, by about ten degrees. The recording device showed that the maximum amount of pressure Geller applied when rubbing the strip was half an ounce (20 grams). "It was out of the question," Taylor writes, "that such a small pressure could have produced the deflection." What was totally unexpected, though, was that while the brass strip was bending upward the needle of the scale bent about seventy degrees away from the scale's face.

Hoping to get additional information on the pressure exerted by Geller, Taylor devised a more elaborate experimental setup. He used a small cylinder that was embedded in a strip of aluminum; one end of the cylinder was covered by a pressure-sensitive diaphragm. When pressure is applied to the diaphragm as a result of the strip's being rubbed gently with a finger, an electric current of an amount proportional to the pressure is generated by a device inside the cylinder.

Geller held the strip in one hand, and he did make it bend. But as the bending occurred the mechanism in the cylinder suddenly stopped functioning. "I took the apparatus from Geller," writes Taylor, "and observed, to my horror, the pressure-sensitive diaphragm begin to crumble. A small hole appeared in its center and spread across its whole surface till the diaphragm had completely disintegrated, the entire process taking about ten seconds."

Geller was in peak form at Taylor's laboratory, for he was able to influence objects without direct contact, something he cannot always do. He held his hands over a plastic container in which Taylor had placed a small crystal of lithium fluoride; within ten seconds the crystal split into a number of pieces. "There was absolutely no chance of Geller's having touched the crystal," says Taylor. "Throughout the experiment I could see a gap between his hands and the container holding the crystal." Geller also buckled a small disc of aluminum without touching it.

What happened after this, reports Taylor, surprised even Geller. He was taken to another laboratory where other experiments had been set up. One of these involved a strip of copper onto which was glued a very thin wire. Distortion of the strip would cause a change in the electrical properties of the wire, which could be accurately measured. Geller tried to bend the copper strip without direct contact, but after several minutes he had not done so. He became very frustrated and Taylor decided that it was best to call off the test. That decision sparked a rash of unusual happenings. In Taylor's own words:

> We broke off [the experiment to bend the strip] . . . but, turning around a few moments later, I saw that the strip had been bent and the thin wire was broken.
>
> Almost simultaneously I noticed that a strip of brass on the other side of the laboratory had also become bent. I had placed that strip there a few minutes before, making sure at that time that it was quite straight. I pointed out to Geller what had happened, only to hear a metallic crash from the far end of the laboratory, twenty feet away. There, on the floor by the far door, was the bent piece of brass. Again I turned back, whereupon there was another crash. A small piece of copper, which had earlier been lying near the bent brass strip on the table, had followed its companion to the far door. Before I knew what had happened I was struck on the back of the legs by a perspex tube in which had been sealed an iron rod. The tube had also been lying on the table. It was now lying at my feet with the rod bent as much as the container would allow.

Taylor insists that "none of the flying objects could have actually been thrown by Geller as he was some distance away from them and would not have been able to get close to them without being spotted." Taylor had been ready, indeed expecting, objects to bend under Geller's influence, but he was not prepared for flying objects. "These events seemed impossible to comprehend . . ." he writes in "A visit by Uri Geller." "I should certainly have dismissed reports of them as nonsense if I myself had not seen them happen. I could always try taking the safe line that Geller *must* have been cheating, possibly by putting me in a trance. I had no video tape to support my own direct observations . . . Yet I was sufficiently *compos mentis* at the time to monitor various pieces of scientific equipment while these objects were 'in flight.' I certainly did not feel as if I were in an altered state of consciousness."

Since his work with Geller, Taylor has found fifteen children in England, all under the age of sixteen, who can deform metal as Geller does. He has named this ability the Geller Effect, since the children have developed this talent after having seen Geller perform on British television shows. In his paper "Analyzing the Geller Effect," Taylor gives experimental evidence and states that the Geller Effect, as produced by Geller and the fifteen children, is genuine. He also looks at the metal-bending phenomenon from a physical standpoint. What variables are present in the Geller Effect? Are there changes in temperature? Does current flow? Are magnetic fields present? What type of energy produces the deformations? And what is the range of metals that can be bent?

Taylor gives answers to some of these questions. He has found that copper, aluminum, brass, several forms of steel, tin, lead, zinc, and silver all respond to the Geller Effect. He has never observed a temperature change during bending greater than two degrees — what one would expect from the gently rubbing of metal by hand. Using sophisticated equipment, he has determined that during psychokinetic deformation of metal there is no flow of electrical current in the test object; no ionizing radiation is given off; there is no ultraviolet or infrared radiation; and no static magnetic fields are present in the vicinity of the subject or the object being bent. The lack of ionizing radiation is particularly disturbing to Taylor and to the scientists at Birkbeck, because they all observed Geller set a Geiger counter ticking by merely touching it. In Taylor's case, the ticking indicated the presence of ionizing radiation up to 500 times that of the normal background level.

*

On one of his visits to Europe in April 1975, Geller was invited to INSERM, the National Institute for Higher Studies and Medical Research of the Foch Hospital in Suresnes, France. Seven experiments were conducted under the direction of Dr. Albert Ducrocq, in the presence of five other scientists. Some of the tests were successful, others were not; two of them raise some interesting questions.

Without touching a compass (his hands were held by two scientists, see Plate 55), Geller was able to deflect its needle "slightly" and with only "great difficulty." After several unsuccessful attempts to get more motion from the needle, he asked the scientists and technicians in the room to form a tight circle around him. The people gathered together (three now held his hands). Geller encouraged them to come closer and closer until he "felt" they were at the right distance. He then concentrated on the compass and immediately there was an increase in the movement of the needle. Did Geller draw some form of energy from the people around him to help him move the needle? The scientists are unsure of the answer, but Geller himself feels certain that he draws his psychokinetic powers from others. "I have never been able to bend or break an object unless there are at least one or two other people in the room," he says. "When I am alone I don't seem to have this power. I feel that in some way I am taking energy from the people in the room." Besides the presence of people, Geller sometimes needs around him metals other than the one he is trying to bend. At the Foch Hospital he was able to bend a key only slightly until it was placed on a metal plate. Then, claims Ducrocq in "The Uri Geller Report," the key bent without Geller's touching it.

*

Uri Geller visited South Africa from mid-July to mid-August 1974, giving lecture-demonstrations in Johannesburg, Pretoria, Durban, Cape Town, and Port Elizabeth. "From the beginning of his visit," writes Dr. E. Alan Price of the South African Institute for Parapsychology, "it became apparent that numerous phenomena occur outside the direct physical presence of, or contact with, Mr. Uri Geller. I then decided to launch a project that would attempt to collect, record, and analyze the various experiences that were reported to be taking place throughout the country." Thus Price's paper, "The Uri Geller Effect," is a "field study," similar to the type of research that characterized the earliest days of parapsychological investigation. To get his data, Price appealed to people through the press and radio to report to the institute any phenomenon that may have occurred in association with Uri Geller's visit to their area.

The unavoidable subjectivity in all field-study work makes most physical scientists balk. There are no unambiguous electric currents to be measured, no temperatures or pressures to be recorded — only the word of some individual about an ill-understood event. How can you trust the reports that are submitted to you? How can you be certain that an event, even if it did actually take place, is related to the propinquity of Uri Geller? Despite the obvious difficulties in field-study work, it is a well-established investigative tool, which has long served such subjects as sociology, psychology, and anthropology; and Price has conducted his investigation in a thorough manner. I will not go into the specifics of collecting data and determining the reliability of a source (Price does these things in great detail in his paper). In short, after considerable sifting and screening of correspondence, Price ended up with 137 "reliable case reports." The elements of each case and the facts about the individuals who reported them were then analyzed by computer for correlations on such parameters as age, sex, I.Q., social status, income. Here I will briefly summarize a few of Price's results:

Age: The number of people who experienced the "Uri Geller Effect" (as Price calls it) increased with age. However, those who *continued* to claim that they could bend metal some time after Geller's visit were all under the age of twenty.

Sex: Psychical researchers in England have determined that spontaneous cases of ESP occur about 19 percent of the time among males and 81 percent among females. The American Society for Psychical Research in New York City has come up with similar figures: 24 percent for males, 75 percent for females. However, Price found that manifestations of the Uri Geller Effect in the South African population had no sex-dependence.

Marital Status: A large percentage of widowed and divorced persons experienced spontaneous ESP phenomena. "The possibility exists," writes Price, "that certain psychological factors, such as tension, stress, frustration, and loneliness, may play a part in facilitating psychokinetic ability or stimulating greater interest in the paranormal."

Being married did not significantly influence a person's reported psychokinetic ability.

Occupation: "A considerably larger proportion of professional persons," writes Price, "than is present in the general population responded to the Uri Geller Effect. A rather small proportion of tradesmen and civil servants, on the other hand, reported such an effect."

Type of Experience: 16.99 percent were telepathic experiences; 83.01 percent were of a psychokinetic nature.

Sensory Feelings: Only 43.15 percent of those reporting mentioned an associated sensory or emotional experience coupled with the psychokinetic experience. 56.02 percent experienced nothing.

Sense of Conviction: About the same number of cases of ESP were reported by confirmed believers as by confirmed skeptics.

After presenting all his data Price weighs the relevance of the information. Is the Uri Geller Effect nothing more than mass hysteria in the population, and are the people who report it consciously or unconsciously cheating or lying? He concludes by stating: "The present investigation is presented not as final and conclusive evidence of the existence of the Uri Geller Effect, but rather claims that enough evidence is present to suggest that the Uri Geller Effect exists and is genuine." That conclusion has been reached independently by Dr. John Hasted, Dr. John Taylor, and Dr. Thelma Moss as well — all worked directly with individuals who developed spontaneous paranormal ability after having seen or heard of Uri Geller. If the Geller Effect does indeed turn out to be proved true, says Price, it may be the most significant happening in the history of parapsychology. "Thus, it would seem possible that a large number of 'experient-percipients' in a sizable population group," writes Price, "could be activated through mass media and a psychic with the personality and ability of Uri Geller, and PK phenomena could be produced. The discovery of mini-Gellers, who may then be subjected to laboratory investigations, would open up a completely new avenue, a new prospect and dimension in psi research. This could produce as near a repeatable laboratory experiment as is possible in biological science."

At the moment, however, the only evidence we have on the Geller Effect — and on Uri Geller — lies in the papers that follow. They raise many more questions than they answer, which must be expected at this early stage of investigation. But they are a start. The papers are here to read and evaluate, and it is hoped that they will generate more scientific research on Uri Geller.

INVESTIGATING THE PARANORMAL

This editorial appeared in Nature *and is referred to in the Introduction. Not only does it explain why the British journal decided to publish the Stanford Research Institute investigations of Geller, but it articulates the hesitations and doubts, obligations and responsibilities of scientists toward the field of psychical research. The writer of the editorial does not limit his comments to the work of the SRI scientists with Geller; he discusses perceptual experiments with other psychic subjects.*

Published in Nature, *Vol. 252, No. 5476, Oct. 18, 1974, pp. 602–607.*

WE PUBLISH this week a paper by R. Targ and H. Puthoff that is bound to create something of a stir in the scientific community. The claim is made that information can be transferred by some channel whose characteristics appear to fall "outside the range of known perceptual modalities." Or, more bluntly, some people can read thoughts or see things remotely.

Such a claim is, of course, bound to be greeted with a preconditioned reaction among many scientists. To some it simply confirms what they have always known or believed. To others it is beyond the laws of science and therefore necessarily unacceptable. But to a few — though perhaps to more than is realized — the questions are still unanswered, and any evidence of high quality is worth a critical examination.

The issue, then, is whether the evidence is of sufficient quality to be taken seriously. In trying to answer this, we have been fortunate in having the help of three independent referees who have done their utmost to see the paper as a potentially important scientific communication and not as a challenge to, or confirmation of, prejudices. We thank them for the considerable effort they have put into helping us, and we also thank Dr. Christopher Evans of the National Physical Laboratory, whose continued advice on the subject is reflected in the content of this leading article.

A general indication of the referees' comments may be helpful to readers in reaching their own assessment of the paper. Of the three, one believed we should not publish, one did not feel strongly either way, and the third was guardedly in favor of publication. We first summarize the arguments against the paper.

1. There was agreement that the paper was weak in design and presentation, to the extent that details given as to the precise way in which the experiment was carried out were disconcertingly vague. The referees felt that insufficient account had been taken of the established methodology of experimental psychology and that in the form originally submitted the paper would be unlikely to be accepted for publication in a psychological journal on these grounds alone. Two referees also felt that the authors had not taken into account the lessons learned in the past by parapsychologists researching this tricky and complicated area.

2. The three referees were particularly critical of the method of target selection used, pointing out that the choice of a target by "opening a dictionary at random" is a naive, vague, and unnecessarily controversial approach to randomization. Parapsychologists have long rejected such methods of target selection and, as one referee put it, weaknesses of this kind reveal "a lack of skill in their experiments, which might have caused them to make some other mistake which is less evident from their writing."

3. All the referees felt that the details given of various safeguards and precautions introduced against the possibility of conscious or unconscious fraud on the part of one or other of the subjects were "uncomfortably vague" (to use one phrase). This in itself might be

sufficient to raise doubt that the experiments have demonstrated the existence of a new channel of communication that does not involve the use of the senses.

4. Two of the referees felt that it was a pity that the paper, instead of concentrating in detail and with meticulous care on one particular approach to extrasensory phenomena, produced a mixture of different experiments, using different subjects in unconnected circumstances and with only a tenuous overall theme. At the best these were more "a series of pilot studies . . . than a report of a completed experiment."

On their own these highly critical comments could be grounds for rejection of the paper, but it was felt that other points needed to be taken into account before a final decision could be made.

1. Despite its shortcomings, the paper is presented as a scientific document by two qualified scientists, writing from a major research establishment apparently with the unqualified backing of the research institute itself.

2. The authors have clearly attempted to investigate under laboratory conditions phenomena that, while highly implausible to many scientists, would nevertheless seem to be worthy of investigation even if, in the final analysis, negative findings are revealed. If scientists dispute and debate the reality of extrasensory perception, then the subject is clearly a matter for scientific study and reportage.

3. Very considerable advance publicity — it is fair to say not generated by the authors or their institute — has preceded the presentation of this report. As a result many scientists and very large numbers of nonscientists believe, as the result of anecdote and hearsay, that the Stanford Research Institute (SRI) was engaged in a major research program into parapsychological matters and had even been the scene of a remarkable breakthrough in this field. The publication of this paper, with its muted claims, suggestions of a limited research program, and modest data, is, we believe, likely to put the whole matter in more reasonable perspective.

4. The claims that have been made by, or on behalf of, one of the subjects, Mr. Uri Geller, have been hailed publicly as indicating total acceptance by the SRI of allegedly sensational powers and may also perhaps now be seen in true perspective. It must be a matter of interest to scientists to note that, contrary to very widespread rumor, the paper does not present any evidence whatsoever for Geller's alleged abilities to bend metal rods by stroking them, influence magnets at a distance, make watches stop or start by some psychokinetic force, and so on. The publication of the paper would be justified on the grounds of allowing scientists the opportunity to discriminate between the cautious, limited, and still highly debatable experimental data, and extravagant rumor, fed in recent days by inaccurate attempts in some newspapers at precognition of the contents of the paper.

5. Two of the referees also felt that the paper should be published because it would allow parapsychologists, and all other scientists interested in researching this arguable field, to gauge the quality of the Stanford research and assess how much it is contributing to parapsychology.

INFORMATION TRANSMISSION UNDER CONDITIONS OF SENSORY SHIELDING

by Harold E. Puthoff, Ph.D., and Russell Targ,
Stanford Research Institute, Menlo Park, California.

Harold E. Puthoff is a senior research engineer at the Stanford Research Institute and a specialist in laser physics. He holds patents in the areas of lasers and optical devices, and is coauthor of Fundamentals of Quantum Electronics, *a text bridging quantum mechanics, engineering, and applied physics.*

Russell Targ is a senior research physicist at the Stanford Research Institute and an expert in the field of plasma physics. He is the inventor of the tunable plasma oscillator at microwave frequencies, the FM laser, and the high-power gas-transport laser. His publications include more than two dozen articles on lasers, plasma physics, and psychic research.

Published in Nature, *Vol. 252, No. 5476, Oct. 18, 1974, pp. 602–607.*

For completeness, all of the investigations conducted at SRI on Geller and on other subjects are presented here.

We present results of experiments suggesting the existence of one or more perceptual modalities through which individuals obtain information about their environment, although this information is not presented to any known sense. The literature[1-3] and our observations lead us to conclude that such abilities can be studied under laboratory conditions.

We have investigated the ability of certain people to describe graphic material or remote scenes shielded against ordinary perception. In addition, we performed pilot studies to determine if electroencephalographic (EEG) recordings might indicate perception of remote happenings even in the absence of correct overt responses.

We concentrated on what we consider to be our primary responsibility — to resolve under conditions as unambiguous as possible the basic issue of whether a certain class of paranormal perception phenomena exists. So we conducted our experiments with sufficient control, utilizing visual, acoustic, and electrical shielding, to ensure that all conventional paths of sensory input were blocked. At all times we took measures to prevent sensory leakage and to prevent deception, whether intentional or unintentional.

Our goal is not just to catalogue interesting events, but to uncover patterns of cause-effect relationships that lend themselves to analysis and hypothesis in the forms with which we are familiar in scientific study. The results presented here constitute a first step toward that goal; we have established under known conditions a data base from which departures as a function of physical and psychological variables can be studied in future work.

Remote Perception of Graphic Material

First, we conducted experiments with Mr. Uri Geller in which we examined his ability, while located in an electrically shielded room, to reproduce target pictures drawn by experimenters located at remote locations. Second, we conducted double-blind experiments with Mr. Pat Price, in which we measured his ability to describe remote outdoor scenes many miles from his physical location. Finally, we conducted preliminary tests, using EEGs, in which subjects were asked to perceive whether a remote light was flashing, and to determine whether a subject could perceive the presence of the light, even if only at a noncognitive level of awareness.

In preliminary testing Geller apparently demonstrated an ability to reproduce simple pictures (line drawings) that had been drawn and placed in opaque sealed envelopes he was not permitted to handle. But since each of the targets was known to at least one experimenter in the room with Geller, it was not possible on the basis of the preliminary testing to discriminate between Geller's direct perception of envelope contents and perception through some mechanism involving the experimenters, whether paranormal or subliminal.

So we examined the phenomenon under conditions designed to eliminate all conventional information channels, overt or subliminal. Geller was separated from both the target material and anyone knowledgeable of the material, as in the experiments of Reference 4.

In the first part of the study a series of thirteen separate drawing experiments was carried out over seven days. No experiments were deleted from the results presented here.*

At the beginning of the experiment either Geller or the experimenters entered a shielded room, so that from that time forward Geller was at all times visually, acoustically, and electrically shielded from personnel and material at the target location. Only following Geller's isolation from the experimenters was a target chosen and drawn, a procedure designed to eliminate pre-experiment cueing. Furthermore, to eliminate the possibility of pre-experiment target forcing, Geller was kept ignorant as to the identity of the person selecting the target and as to the method of target selection. This was accomplished by the use of three different techniques: (1) pseudorandom technique of opening a dictionary arbitrarily and choosing the first word that could be drawn (Experiments 1–4); (2) targets, blind to experimenters and subject, prepared independently by SRI scientists outside the experimental group (following Geller's isolation) and provided to the experimenters during the course of the experiment (Experiments 5–7, 11–13);

* For all target drawings and Geller's responses see Plates 1 and 2.

Table 1. Summary: Remote perception of graphic material

Experiment	*Date*	*Geller location*	*Target location*	*Target*	*Figure*
1	8/4/73	Shielded room #1[a]	Adjacent room (4.1 m)[b]	Firecracker	la
2	8/4/73	Shielded room #1	Adjacent room (4.1 m)	Grapes	lb
3	8/5/73	Shielded room #1	Office (475 m)	Devil	lc
4	8/5/73	Room adjacent to shielded room #1	Shielded room #1 (3.2 m)	Solar system	ld
5	8/6/73	Room adjacent to shielded room #1	Shielded room #1 (3.2 m)	Rabbit	No drawing
6	8/7/73	Shielded room #1	Adjacent room (4.1 m)	Tree	No drawing
7	8/7/73	Shielded room #1	Adjacent room (4.1 m)	Envelope	No drawing
8	8/8/73	Shielded room #1	Remote room (6.75 m)	Camel	le
9	8/8/73	Shielded room #1	Adjacent room (4.1 m)	Bridge	lf
10	8/8/73	Shielded room #1	Adjacent room (4.1 m)	Seagull	lg
11	8/9/73	Shielded room #2[c]	Computer (54 m)	Kite (computer CRT)	2a
12	8/10/73	Shielded room #2	Computer (54 m)	Church (computer memory)	2b
13	8/10/73	Shielded room #2	Computer (54 m)	Arrow through heart (computer CRT, zero intensity)	2c

[a] *EEG Facility shielded room (see text).*
[b] *Perceiver-target distances measured in meters.*
[c] *SRI Radio Systems Laboratory shielded room (see text).*

and (3) arbitrary selection from a target pool decided upon in advance of daily experimentation and designed to provide data concerning information content for use in testing specific hypotheses (Experiments 8–10). Geller's task was to reproduce with pen on paper the line drawing generated at the target location. Following a period of effort ranging from a few minutes to half an hour, Geller either passed (when he did not feel confident) or indicated he was ready to submit a drawing to the experimenters, in which case the drawing was collected before Geller was permitted to see the target.

To prevent sensory cueing of the target information, Experiments 1 through 10 were carried out using a shielded room in SRI's facility for EEG research. The acoustic and visual isolation is provided by a double-walled steel room, locked by means of an inner and outer door, each of which is secured with a refrigerator-type locking mechanism. Following target selection when Geller was inside the room, a one-way audio monitor, operating only from the inside to the outside, was activated to monitor Geller during his efforts. The target picture was never discussed by the experimenters after the picture was drawn and brought near the shielded room. In our detailed examination of the shielded room and the protocol used in these experiments, no sensory leakage has been found.

The conditions and results for the ten experiments carried out in the shielded room are displayed in Table 1 and Plate 1. All experiments except 4 and 5 were conducted with Geller inside the shielded room. In Experiments 4 and 5, the procedure was reversed. For those experiments in which Geller was inside the shielded room, the target location was in an adjacent room at a distance of about 4 m, except for Experiments 3 and 8, in which the target locations were, respectively, an office at a distance of 475 m and a room at a distance of about 7 m.

A response was obtained in all experiments except Numbers 5–7. In Experiment 5, the person-to-person link was eliminated by arranging for a scientist outside the usual experimental group to draw a picture, lock it in the shielded room before Geller's arrival at SRI, and leave the area. Geller was then led by the experimenters to the shielded room and asked to draw the picture located inside the room. He said that he got no clear impression and therefore did not submit a drawing. The elimination of the person-to-person link was examined further in the second series of experiments with this subject.

Experiments 6 and 7 were carried out while we attempted to record Geller's EEG during his efforts to perceive the target pictures. The target pictures were, respectively, a tree and an envelope. He found it difficult to hold adequately still for good EEG records, said that he experienced difficulty in getting impressions of the targets, and again submitted no drawings.

Experiments 11–13 were carried out in SRI's Engineering Building, to make use of the computer facilities available there. For these experiments, Geller was secured in a double-walled, copper-screen Faraday cage 54 m down the hall and around the corner from the computer room. The Faraday cage provides 120 dB attenuation for plane wave radio frequency radiation over a range of 15 kHz to 1 GHz. For magnetic fields the attenuation is 68 dB at 15 kHz and decreases to 3 dB at 60 Hz. Following Geller's isolation, the targets for these experiments were chosen by computer laboratory personnel not otherwise associated with either the experiment or Geller, and the experimenters and subject were kept blind as to the contents of the target pool.

For Experiment 11, a picture of a kite was drawn on the face of a cathode-ray tube display screen, driven by the computer's graphics program. For Experiment 12, a picture of a church was drawn and stored in the memory of the computer. In Experiment 13, the target drawing, an arrow through a heart (see Plate 2(c)), was drawn on the face of the cathode-ray tube and then the display intensity was turned off so that no picture was visible.

To obtain an independent evaluation of the correlation between target and response data, the experimenters submitted the data for judging on a "blind" basis by two SRI scientists who were not otherwise associated with the research. For the ten cases in which Geller provided a response, the judges were asked to match the response data with the corresponding target data (without replacement). In those cases in which Geller made more than one drawing as his response to the target, all the drawings were combined as a set for judging. The two judges each matched the target data to the response data with no error. For either judge such a correspondence has an *a priori* probability, under the null hypothesis of no information channel, of $P = (10!)^{-1} = 3 \times 10^{-7}$.

A second series of experiments was carried out to determine whether direct perception of envelope contents was possible without some person knowing of the target picture.

One hundred target pictures of everyday objects were drawn by an SRI artist and sealed by other SRI personnel in double envelopes containing black cardboard. The hundred targets were divided randomly into groups of twenty for use in each of the three days' experiments.

On each of the three days of these experiments, Geller passed. That is, he declined to associate any envelope with a drawing that he made, expressing dissatisfaction with the existence of such a large target pool. On each day he made approximately twelve recognizable drawings, which he felt were associated with the entire target pool of 100. On each of the three days, two of his drawings could reasonably be associated with two of the twenty daily targets. On the third day, two of his drawings were very close replications of two of that day's target pictures. The drawings resulting from this experiment do not depart significantly from what would be expected by chance.

In a simpler experiment Geller was successful in obtaining information under conditions in which no persons were knowledgeable of the target. A double-blind experiment was performed in which a single ¾-inch die was placed in a 3 x 4 x 5-inch steel box. The box was then vigorously shaken by one of the experimenters and placed on the table, a technique found in control runs to produce a distribution of die faces that does not differ significantly from chance distribution. The orientation of the die within the box was unknown to the experimenters at that time. Geller would then write down which die face was uppermost. The target pool was known, but the targets were individually prepared in a manner blind to all persons involved in the experiment. This experiment was performed ten times, with Geller passing twice and giving a response eight times. The eight times he gave a response, he was correct each time. The distribution of responses consisted of three twos, one four, two fives, and two sixes. The probability of this occurring by chance is approximately one in 10^6.

In certain situations significant information transmission can take place under shielded conditions. Factors that appear to be important and are therefore candidates for future investigation include whether the subject knows the set of targets in the target pool, the actual number of targets in the target pool at any given time, and whether the target is known by any of the experimenters.

It has been widely reported that Geller has demonstrated the ability to bend metal by paranormal means. Although metal bending by Geller has been observed in our laboratory, we have not been able to combine such observations with adequately controlled experiments to obtain data sufficient to support the paranormal hypothesis.

Remote Viewing of Natural Targets

A study by Osis[5] led us to determine whether a subject could describe randomly chosen geographical sites located several miles from the subject's position and demarcated by some appropriate means (remote viewing). This experiment carried out with Price, a former California police commissioner and city councilman, consisted of a series of double-blind, demonstration-of-ability tests, involving local targets in the San Francisco Bay area, which could be documented by several independent judges. We planned the experiment believing that natural geographical places or manmade sites that have existed for a long time are more potent targets for paranormal perception experiments than are artificial targets prepared in the laboratory. This is based on subject opinions that the use of artificial targets involves a "trivialization of the ability" as compared with natural pre-existing targets.

In each of nine experiments involving Price as subject and SRI experimenters as a target-demarcation team, a remote location was chosen in a double-blind protocol. Price, who remained at SRI, was asked to describe this remote location, as well as whatever activities might be going on there.

Several descriptions yielded significantly correct data pertaining to, and descriptive of, the target location.

In the experiments a set of twelve target locations clearly differentiated from each other and within thirty minutes' driving time from SRI had been chosen from a target-rich environment (more than 100 targets of the type used in the experimental series) prior to the experimental series by an individual in SRI management, the director of the Information Science and Engineering Division, not otherwise associated with the experiment. Both the experimenters and the subject were kept blind as to the contents of the target pool, which were used without replacement.

An experimenter was closeted with Price at SRI to wait thirty minutes to begin the narrative description of the remote location. The SRI locations from which the subject viewed the remote locations consisted of an outdoor park (Experiments 1 and 2), the double-walled copper-screen Faraday cage discussed earlier (Experiments 3 and 4, and 6–9), and an office (Experiment 5). A second experimenter would then obtain a target location from the division director from a set of traveling orders previously prepared and randomized by the director and kept under his control. The target demarcation team (two to four SRI experimenters) then proceeded directly to the target by automobile without communicating with the subject or experimenter remaining behind. Since the experimenter remaining with the subject at SRI was in ignorance both as to the particular target and as to the target pool, he was free to question Price to clarify his descriptions. The demarcation team then remained at the target site for thirty minutes after the thirty minutes allotted for travel. During the observation period, the remote-viewing subject would describe his impressions of the target site into a tape recorder. A comparison was then made when the demarcation team returned.

Price's ability to describe correctly buildings, docks, roads, gardens, and so on, including structural materials, color, ambience, and activity, sometimes in great detail, indicated the functioning of a remote perceptual ability. But the descriptions contained inaccuracies as well as correct statements. To obtain a numerical evaluation of the accuracy of the remote viewing experiment, the experimental results were subjected to independent judging on a blind basis by five SRI scientists who were not otherwise associated with the research. The judges were asked to match the nine locations, which they independently visited, against the typed manuscripts of the tape-recorded narratives of the remote viewer. The transcripts were unlabeled and presented in random order. The judges were asked to find a narrative that they would consider the best match for each of the places they visited. A given narrative could be assigned to more than one target location. A correct match required that the transcript of a given date be associated with the target of that date. Table 2 shows the distribution of the judges' choices.

Among all possible analyses, the most conservative is a permutation analysis of the plurality vote of the judges' selections, assuming assignment without replacement, an approach independent of the number of judges. By plurality vote, six of the nine descriptions and locations were correctly matched. Under the null hypothesis (no remote viewing and a random selection of descriptions without

Table 2.

Distribution of correct selections by judges A, B, C, D, and E in remote viewing experiments

Descriptions chosen by judges		*Places visited by judges* *1*	*2*	*3*	*4*	*5*	*6*	*7*	*8*	*9*
Hoover Tower	1	**ABCDE**				D				
Baylands Nature Preserve	2		**ABC**	E				D		D
Radio Telescope	3			**ACD**		**BE**				
Redwood City Marina	4		CD		**ABDE**		E			
Bridge Toll Plaza	5						**ABD**		**DCE**	
Drive-In Theater	6			B		A	C			E
Arts and Crafts Garden Plaza	7							**ABCE**		
Church	8				C				AB	
Rinconada Park	9		CE							**AB**

Of the 45 selections (5 judges, 9 choices), 24 were correct. Bold type indicates the description chosen most often for each place visited. Correct choices lie on the main diagonal. The number of correct matches by Judges A through E is 7, 6, 5, 3, and 3, respectively. The expected number of correct matches from the five judges was five; in the experiment 24 such matches were obtained. The *a priori* probability of such an occurrence by chance, conservatively assuming assignment without replacement on the part of the judges, is $P = 8 \times 10^{-10}$.

replacement), this outcome has an *a priori* probability of $P = 5.6 \times 10^{-4}$, since, among all possible permutations of the integers one through nine, the probability of six or more being in their natural position in the list has that value. Therefore, although Price's descriptions contain inaccuracies, the descriptions are sufficiently accurate to permit the judges to differentiate among the various targets to the degree indicated.

EEG Experiments

An experiment was undertaken to determine whether a physiological measure such as EEG activity could be used as an indicator of information transmission between an isolated subject and a remote stimulus. We hypothesized that perception could be indicated by such a measure even in the absence of verbal or other overt indicators.[6,7]

It was assumed that the application of remote stimuli would result in responses similar to those obtained under conditions of direct stimulation. For example, when a normal subject is stimulated with a flashing light, his EEG typically shows a decrease in the amplitude of the resting rhythm and a driving of the brain waves at the frequency of the flashes.[8] We hypothesized that if we stimulated one subject (a sender) in this manner, the EEG of another subject (a receiver) in a remote room with no flash present, might show changes in alpha (9–11 Hz) activity, and possibly EEG driving similar to that of the sender.

We informed our subject that at certain times a light was to be flashed in a sender's eyes in a distant room, and if the subject perceived that event, consciously or unconsciously, it might be evident from changes in his EEG output. The receiver was seated in the visually opaque, acoustically and electrically shielded double-walled steel room previously described. The sender was seated in a room about 7 m from the receiver.

To find subjects who were responsive to such a remote stimulus, we initially worked with four female and two male volunteer subjects, all of whom believed that success in the experimental situation might be possible. These were designated "receivers." The senders were either other subjects or the experimenters. We decided beforehand to run one or two sessions of thirty-six trials each with each subject in this selection procedure, and to do a more extensive study with any subject whose results were positive.

A Grass PS-2 photostimulator placed about 1 m in front of the sender was used to present flash trains of ten-seconds' duration. The receiver's EEG activity from the occipital region (O_z), referenced to linked mastoids, was amplified with a Grass 5P-1 preamplifier and associated driver amplifier with a band pass of 1–120 Hz. The EEG data were recorded on magnetic tape with an Ampex SP 300 recorder.

On each trial, a tone burst of fixed frequency was presented to both sender and receiver and was followed in one second by either a ten-second train of flashes or a null flash interval presented to the sender. Thirty-six such trials were given in an experimental session, consisting of twelve null trials — no flashes following the tone — twelve trials of flashes at six flashes per second and twelve trials of flashes at sixteen flashes per second, all randomly intermixed, determined by entries from a table of random numbers. Each of the trials generated an eleven-second EEG epoch. The last four seconds of the epoch were selected for analysis to minimize the desynchronizing action of the warning cue. This four-second segment was subjected to Fourier analysis on a LINC 8 computer.

Spectrum analyses gave no evidence of EEG driving in any receiver, although in control runs the receivers did exhibit driving when physically stimulated with the flashes. But of the six subjects studied initially, one subject (H.H.) showed a consistent alpha blocking effect. We therefore undertook further study with this subject.

Data from seven sets of thirty-six trials each were collected from this subject on three separate days. This is all the data collected to date with this subject under the test conditions described above. The alpha band was identified from average spectra; then scores of average power and peak power were obtained from individual trials and subjected to statistical analysis.

Table 3. EEG data for H. H. showing average power and peak power in the 9–11 Hz band, as a function of flash frequency and sender

Flash Frequency	0	6	16	0	6	16
Sender	Average power			Peak power		
J.L	94.8	84.1	76.8	357.7	329.2	289.6
R.T.	41.3	45.5	37.0	160.7	161.0	125.0
No sender (subject informed)	25.1	35.7	28.2	87.5	95.7	81.7
J.L.	54.2	55.3	44.8	191.4	170.5	149.3
J.L.	56.8	50.9	32.8	240.6	178.0	104.6
R.T.	39.8	24.9	30.3	145.2	74.2	122.1
No sender (subject not informed)	86.0	53.0	52.1	318.1	180.6	202.3
Averages	56.8	49.9	43.1	214.5	169.8	153.5
		−12%	−24% ($P<0.04$)		−21%	−28% ($P<0.03$)

Each entry is an average over 12 trials

Of our six subjects, H.H. had by far the most monochromatic EEG spectrum. Plate 3 shows an overlay of the three averaged spectra from one of this subject's thirty-six-trial runs, displaying changes in her alpha activity for the three stimulus conditions. (See Plate 3.)

Mean values for the average power and peak power for each of the seven experimental sets are given in Table 3. The power measures were less in the sixteen-flashes-per-second case than in the zero-flashes-per-second in all seven peak power measures and in six out of seven average power measures. Note also the reduced effect in the case in which the subject was informed that no sender was present (Run 3). It seems that overall alpha production was reduced for this run in conjunction with the subject's expressed apprehension about conducting the experiment without a sender. This is in contrast to the case (Run 7) in which the subject was not informed.

Siegel's two-tailed *t* approximation to the nonparametric randomization test[9] was applied to the data from all sets, which included two sessions in which the sender was removed. Average power on trials associated with the occurrence of sixteen flashes per second was significantly less than when there were no flashes ($t = 2.09$, d.f. $= 118$, $P < 0.04$). The second measure, peak power, was also significantly less in the sixteen-flashes-per-second conditions than in the null condition ($t = 2.16$, d.f. $= 118$, $P < 0.03$). The average response in the six-flashes-per-second condition was in the same direction as that associated with sixteen flashes per second, but the effect was not statistically significant.

Spectrum analyses of control recordings made from saline with a 12 kΩ resistance in place of the subject with and without the addition of a 10 Hz, 50 μV test signal applied to the saline solution, revealed no indications of flash frequencies, nor perturbations of the 10 Hz signal. These controls suggest that the results were not due to system artifacts. Further tests also gave no evidence of radio frequency energy associated with the stimulus.

Subjects were asked to indicate their conscious assessment for each trial as to which stimulus was generated. They made their guesses known to the experimenter via one-way telegraphic communication. An analysis of these guesses has shown them to be at chance, indicating the absence of any supraliminal cuing, so arousal as evidenced by significant alpha blocking occurred only at the noncognitive level of awareness.

We hypothesize that the protocol described here may prove to be useful as a screening procedure for latent remote perceptual ability in the general population.

Conclusion

From these experiments we conclude that:

1. A channel exists whereby information about a remote location can be obtained by means of an as yet unidentified perceptual modality.

2. As with all biological systems, the information channel appears to be imperfect, containing noise along with the signal.

3. While a quantitative signal-to-noise ratio in the information-theoretical sense cannot as yet be determined, the results of our experiments indicate that the functioning is at the level of useful information transfer.

It may be that remote perceptual ability is widely distributed in the general population, but because the perception is generally below an individual's level of awareness, it is repressed or not noticed. For example, two of our subjects (H.H. and P.P.) had not considered themselves to have unusual perceptual ability before their participation in these experiments.

Our observation of the phenomena leads us to conclude that experiments in the area of so-called paranormal phenomena can be scientifically conducted, and it is our hope that other laboratories will initiate additional research to attempt to replicate these findings.

REFERENCES

1. Pratt, J., J. B. Rhine, C. Stuart, and J. Greenwood, *Extrasensory Perception after Sixty Years* (New York: Henry Holt, 1940).

2. Soal, S. and F. Bateman, *Modern Experiments in Telepathy* (London: Faber and Faber, 1954).
3. Vasiliev, L. L., *Experiments in Mental Suggestion* (Hampshire, England: ISMI Publications, 1963).
4. Musso, J. R. and M. Granero, *Journal of Parapsychology*, 37, 13–37, 1973.
5. Osis, K., *ASPR Newsletter*, No. 14, 1972.
6. Tart, C. T., "Physiological Correlates of Psi Cognition," *International Journal of Parapsychology, V*, No. 4, 1963.
7. Dean, E. D., *International Journal of Neuropsychiatry, 2*, 1966.
8. Hill, D. and G. Parr, *Electroencephalography: A Symposium on Its Various Aspects* (New York: Macmillan, 1963).
9. Siegel, S., *Nonparametric Statistics for the Behavioral Sciences* (New York: McGraw-Hill, 1956), pp. 152–56.

THE RECORD: EIGHT DAYS WITH URI GELLER

by Harold E. Puthoff, Ph.D., and Russell Targ,
Stanford Research Institute, Menlo Park, California.

The following paper is not a technical report. Rather, it is a daily log kept by the SRI scientists on their observations of Geller during the experimental period from August 4 through August 11, 1973. Most of the scientific results in "The Record" appear in the preceding paper, "Information transmission under conditions of sensory shielding." However, "The Record" is printed here because it shows the ease or difficulty with which Geller received his psychic impressions of target pictures.

Published here for the first time, with the permission of the authors.

Objective

The objective of this first group of experimental sessions is to verify Geller's apparent paranormal perception under unambiguous and carefully controlled conditions. A second objective is to achieve an understanding of the physical and psychological variables underlying his apparent ability.

Experimental Program

In each of the eight days of this experimental period we conducted picture-drawing experiments. In these experiments Geller was separated from the target material either by an electrically isolated, shielded room or by the isolation provided by having the targets drawn on the East Coast. We have continued to work with picture-drawing tasks in an effort to achieve repeatability, so that we could vary the experimental conditions to determine the effect of physical parameters on the phenomena. As a result of Geller's success in this experimental period, we consider that he has demonstrated his paranormal perceptual ability in a convincing and unambiguous manner.

Saturday, August 4.

Two drawing experiments were conducted this day. In both of these, Geller was closeted in an opaque, acoustically and electrically shielded room. This room is the double-walled shielded room used for EEG research in the Life Sciences Division of SRI. It is locked by means of inner and outer doors, each of which is secured with a refrigerator-type locking mechanism.

The two drawings used in this experiment were selected by the experimenter's randomly opening a large college dictionary and choosing the first word that could reasonably be drawn. The first word obtained in this manner was *fuse* and the object drawn was a firecracker. All target selection and picture drawing was done with Geller already in the shielded room. Geller was notified via intercom when the target picture was drawn and taped to the wall outside his enclosure.

His almost immediate response was that he saw "a cylinder with noise coming out of it." (He was continuously monitored by a one-way audio circuit.) His drawing to correspond to the target was a drum, along with a number of other cylindrical-looking objects. (See Plate 1(a).)

The second word selected was *bunch*, and the target was a bunch of grapes. Geller's immediate response was that he saw "drops of water coming out of the picture." He then talked about "purple circles." Finally, he said that he was quite sure that he had the picture. His drawing was indeed a bunch of grapes. Both the target picture and Geller's rendition had twenty-four grapes in the bunch. (See Plate 1(b).)

In this work the target picture is never discussed by the experimenters after the picture is drawn or brought near the shielded room. The intercom operates only from the inside of the room to the outside, except when the push-to-talk switch is depressed on the outside of the room. In our detailed examination of the shielded room and the protocol used in these experiments no sensory leakage has been found, nor has any defect in the protocol been brought to our attention.

Sunday, August 5.

Geller is locked in the shielded room and the target is drawn in the experimenter's office about a half mile away. The target selected from the dictionary was an outline drawing of a man, which evolved through the drawing process into a devil with a pitchfork. To start the experiment, Puthoff, who was with Geller, called Targ, who was with the drawing. Geller spent almost a half-hour working on the drawing before producing the first of several responses.

His drawings were as follows. (1) "Moses' Tablets"; i.e., Ten Commandments, inside the world with a trident on the outside. (2) Apple with a worm coming out of it. A snake was in the same picture. (3) Composite picture with the Ten Commandments on top of the world, God inside the world, and the pitchfork on the outside, along with a neatly drawn leaf. One is led to speculate that the Garden of Eden representation in these three drawings is perhaps associational material triggered by the target. The inability on Geller's part to draw the devil may be culturally induced.

With regard to the pictures, Geller did draw the pitchfork from the target picture, but he did not draw the man who was holding it. From this it seems, then, that Geller does not simply copy lines from the target picture, but rather does perform some mental processing on them before drawing them himself. (See Plate 1(c).)

The second target picture was drawn by an experimenter while he was inside the shielded room, and Geller outside the room with another experimenter. In this case the target was a representation of the solar system, drawn without the orbit lines. His immediate verbal reaction before drawing was one of "space." (See Plate 1(a).) Geller's drawn response to the target while outside the room also omits the conventional orbit lines and appears to have many similarities to the target drawing. The block in the center of Geller's picture, according to his statement, was his afterthought, suggested by the movie *2001*, and was drawn as an addition just before comparing target with response.

Monday, August 6.

The experiment to be done this day was a pure clairvoyance task. A picture was drawn by a scientist outside the usual experimental group. The picture was locked in the shielded room before Geller's arrival at SRI. Geller was then led by the experimenters to the shielded room, and asked to draw the picture inside the room. He drew a number of pictures, all of which he rejected as not being applicable. He said that he got no clear impression, and passed. The target was a rabbit, and nothing Geller drew in any way resembled a rabbit. It should be added that the picture was drawn by a scientist whom Geller considers a skeptic, and Geller asked at the outset if this was the case. The experimenters said that this was not the case, since they did not know who had drawn the picture. Geller felt vindicated to some extent when he found out that his initial guess as to the artist had been correct.

Tuesday, August 7.

This day two target pictures were attempted with Geller in the shielded room. He was connected to an EEG apparatus to allow measurement of his brain waves at the time that he was attempting to perceive a hidden picture. The two target pictures were a tree and an envelope. He experienced difficulty, did not make a drawing that corresponded to either drawing, and passed. Also, he found it very difficult to hold adequately still to make good EEG records. We will repeat the EEG experiment another time to try to obtain better data.

Wednesday, August 8.

Three targets were drawn during the course of this day's work. For the first, the experimenters closed the outer door of the laboratory in which the shielded room is located (in addition to the inner double doors) and worked in an adjoining room.

The target picture in this case was a camel. Geller felt unsure and passed, but his first-choice drawing was a horse. (See Plate 1(e).)

The experimenters then returned to the room outside the shielded room and drew the second picture, which was of the Golden Gate Bridge. Geller inside the shielded room drew some curved lines with some squares underneath. He said that he didn't know what the picture was, and passed. (See Plate 1(f).)

The third picture was a flying sea gull. Geller almost immediately said that he saw a flying swan over a hill. He drew several birds and said that he was sure that his drawing was correct, which it was. (See Plate 1(g).)

In these experiments conducted with this shielded room, six days' work was done. Good results were obtained on the four days when there was no openly skeptical observer (except the experimenters, whom Geller had learned to accept).

Thursday, August 9.

We moved the experiments to a new shielded room from the Life Sciences to the Engineering building in order to make use of the computer facilities available there.

After Geller was secured in a shielded room about 150 feet down the hall and around a corner from the computer room, a picture was drawn on the face of the TV screen, driven by the computer's graphics program. The picture drawn was a kite. Shortly after Geller was notified that the picture had been drawn, he had the computer room called to determine if the target picture was a geometric picture or an object. We told him by talking to an intermediary who was ignorant of the target picture, that it was an object. Geller's first drawing in this case was a square with the diagonals drawn in. He then also drew some triangular airplanes, and passed. His first drawing was a good representation of the actual target picture. (See Plate 2(a).)

Friday, August 10.

Two pictures were drawn and stored in the computer memory so that no visible evidence was available in the computer room after the picture was drawn.

The first picture was a church. The picture was drawn and stored in the memory of the computer. Geller's responses are shown in the collection of drawings. It is clear that both of his attempts have some elements in common with the target drawing, but he had no idea that it was a church and he passed. (See Plate 2(b).)

The second target picture was stored on the face of the TV tube with the intensity turned off so that no picture was visible with the room lights turned on. Geller immediately drew an arrow under a rounded brick and then drew another arrow inside a suitcase. We consider the arrow in the suitcase similar to the target, which was an arrow through a heart. (See Plate 2(c).)

These latter two experiments admit of at least two hypotheses, which will require further work to differentiate: (1) clairvoyant perception of information stored in the computer, or (2) telepathy, since there were several people in the computer room, all of whom knew the nature of the target that was stored.

A long-distance telepathy experiment was also done on Friday. An East Coast scientist was called and asked to draw a simple representational object for Geller to copy. Following the experiment he indicated that he drew two peaked mountains with a sun in the upper right. Geller drew two arches side by side with a circle in the upper right. Geller's picture also had a trainlike object running through it. We consider this to be suggestive of communication but not conclusive. We do not have the East Coast original.

Saturday, August 11.

A lengthy long-distance experiment was performed with another East Coast scientist. In this case the man chose to draw a cross-sectional view of the brain. (In retrospect we consider this to be an unsuitable target since Geller would not recognize the drawing even if he were successful.) Geller began by writing down the words *medical, organic,* and *living* on the top of his paper. Later he wrote the words *aviation* and *architecture.* He made two drawings, one of which was complex and indescribable. The second did somewhat resemble an anatomical cross section. These responses are being sent to the originator for comparison.

EXPERIMENTS WITH URI GELLER

by Harold E. Puthoff, Ph.D., and Russell Targ,
Stanford Research Institute, Menlo Park, California.

During Uri Geller's visits to the Stanford Research Institute, he took part in certain experiments that do not appear in either of the foregoing two papers by Harold Puthoff and Russell Targ. What follows is the narration to a half-hour film, shot at the SRI laboratories, that contains these additional tests. The research presented here was conducted during Geller's first visit to SRI — a five-week period in late 1972. The film was sponsored jointly by the Mind Science Foundation, the Science Unlimited Research Foundation, and EDMA, all of San Antonio, Texas. It was first shown publicly on March 9, 1973, at a physics colloquium at Columbia University. Because a film itself cannot offer proof of genuine paranormal abilities, Puthoff and Targ made the following remark at the end of the narration: "What we've demonstrated here are experiments that we performed in the laboratory and should not be interpreted as proof of psychic functioning." Since the film also depicts some experiments that have been reported in the previous two papers, the text of the film has been edited, with the consent of the SRI researchers, to avoid repetition.

The following narrative is published for the first time, with the permission of the researchers.

THROUGHOUT mankind's history there has existed a belief that certain gifted individuals have been capable of producing physical effects by means of some agency generally described as psychic or psychoenergetic. Substantiation of such claims by accepted scientific methodology has been slow in coming, but recent laboratory experiments, especially in the Soviet Union and Czechoslovakia, and more recently in our own laboratory, have indicated that sufficient evidence does exist to warrant serious scientific investigation. It would appear that experiments could be conducted with scientific rigor to uncover not just a catalogue of interesting events, but rather a pattern of cause-effect relationships of the type that lend themselves to analysis and hypothesis in the forms with which we are familiar in the physical sciences. The SRI considers this to be a valid area for scientific inquiry.

As scientists we consider it important to examine various models describing the operation of these effects so that we can determine the relationship between extraordinary human functioning and the physical and psychological laws we presently understand. It is not the purpose of our work at the SRI to add to the literature another demonstration of the statistical appearance of these phenomena in the laboratory, but rather we seek to achieve an understanding more compatible with contemporary science, and more useful to mankind.

Here we describe partial results of a five-week investigation conducted at the Stanford Research Institute with Uri Geller. It was set as an absolute that experiments, to be worthy, had to be under institute control and not Geller's.

We conducted a double-blind experiment in which someone not associated with the project came into the experimental room, placed an object into a can chosen at random from ten aluminum cans. The randomizer then left the area, and the experimenters entered the room with Geller — neither the experimenters nor Geller knowing which can contained the object. In one case, the target was a ¾-inch steel ball bearing. The ten cans had been arranged neatly, and Geller's task was to determine which of the ten held the steel ball bearing. He was not permitted to touch the cans or the table. The experimental protocol called for the experimenter to remove the cans one at a time in response to Geller's instructions. Eventually, there were just two cans left, and Geller indicated by gesture and in writing which one of the remaining cans contained the target. He was correct. It was only at the end of the experiment that Geller touched the can that he believed contained the object. The protocol included the possibility that he might touch a can accidentally. In such a case, that would count as a miss.

After repetition of this experiment several times, using different objects, Geller was finally able to walk into the room, look at the cans lined up on the table, and just pick up the one that contained the target. We have no hypothesis at this point as to whether this is a heightened sensitivity of some normal sense, or whether it is some paranormal sense.

In another case, one can contained room-temperature water. Again, the can had been filled by an outside person who randomized the position of the cans in a box. Then the box was rotated by a second person so that there was no one person in the room who knew the location of the target can. Geller entered the room and had no difficulty picking out the can that contained the water. We repeated this type of experiment fourteen times; five times involving a target, which was a small permanent magnet, five times also involving a steel ball bearing as the target. Twice the target was water. Two additional trials were made — one with a paper-wrapped ball bearing, and one with a sugar cube. The latter two targets were not located. Geller felt that he did not have adequate confidence as to where they were, and he declined to guess, and passed. On each of the other twelve targets — the ball bearing, the magnet, and the water — he did make a guess as to the target location and was correct in every instance. The whole array of this run had an *a priori* probability of one part in 10^{12}, or odds of a trillion to one.

In another double-blind experiment a die was placed in a metal file box (both box and die being provided by the SRI). The box was shaken up with neither the experimenter nor Geller knowing which face landed up. Out of ten trials, in which he passed twice and guessed eight times, the eight guesses were correct. It gave us a probability of about one in a million. We again point out that there were no errors when Geller made guesses.

We also performed two experiments in psychokinesis. In one test a one-gram weight was placed on an electric scale. It was covered by an aluminum can and by a glass cylinder to eliminate deflection due to air currents. The first part of our protocol involved our tapping the bell jar; next tapping the table; then kicking the table; and finally jumping on the floor, with a record made of what these artifacts looked like so that they could be distinguished from actual signals. Geller's task was to try to influence the scale merely by holding his hands above the bell jar (never touching it) and concentrating. He was able to do this. Once our recording device showed an apparent weight decrease of 1500 mg, and another time an increase of 800 mg. These two readings had not been observed as possible artifacts. In fact, in no case were our intentional artifact readings similar to the signals produced by Geller, nor could anyone else duplicate the effects Geller produced.

We have no ready hypothesis about how these signals might have been produced. It is of interest to note that Geller's ability to influence the scale improved over the period of experimentation, starting with 50 mg deflections and arriving at 1500 mg.

In another experiment Geller attempted to influence a magnetometer, either directly or by generating a magnetic field. The full-scale sensitivity of the instrument was 0.3 gauss. Throughout the experiment Geller's hand did not come into contact with the instrument. The magnetometer itself was used as a probe to go over his hands and person to make sure that there were no magnetic objects in his hands or on him.

Geller had no apparent difficulty in influencing the magnetometer. He caused fluctuations — almost full-scale in certain cases — whose direction was uncorrelated with the motion of his hands. He was very interested in the experiments we were doing because he had never taken part in laboratory work of this kind before.

Another experiment was performed; in retrospect we consider it unsatisfactory as it did not meet our protocol. In this case Geller's task was to deflect a compass needle, which he did. Before and after the experiment he was gone over with a magnetometer probe, and his hands were photographed from above and below during and following the experiment, so we were sure there were no obvious pieces of metal or magnets in his possession. However, according to our protocol, if we could in any way debunk the experiment and produce the effects by any other means, then that experiment was considered null and void even if there were no indications that anything untoward happened. In this particular experiment, we found later that the type of compass needle deflections we observed could be produced by a small piece of metal, so small, in fact, that it could not be detected by the magnetometer. Therefore, even though we had no evidence that Geller might have employed this means, we still considered the experiment inconclusive and an unsatisfactory type of experiment altogether.

There are a number of unconfirmed physical effects that need further investigation. One of Geller's main attributes that had been reported to us was that he was able to bend metal from a distance without touching it. In the laboratory we did not find him able to do so. In a more relaxed protocol, he was permitted to touch the metal, in which case the metal did indeed bend. However, it becomes clear in watching this demonstration on film that simple photo-interpretation is insufficient to determine whether the metal is bent by normal or paranormal means.

In the laboratory, these spoon-bending experiments were continually filmed and video-taped. It is evident that some time during the photographic period a stainless steel spoon became bent. However, unlike what we had heard about Geller, it was always necessary for him in the experimental situation to have physical contact with the spoon or, for that matter, any other object that he bends. It is not clear whether the spoon was bent because he has extraordinarily strong fingers and good control of micromanipulatory movements or whether, in fact, the spoon "turns to plastic" in his hands, as he claims.

A number of the spoons were bent by one means or another during the course of our experiments. There is no doubt that the spoons were bent. The only doubt remains as to the manner of their bending. Similarly, we have rings that were bent by Mr. Geller: a copper ring and a brass ring that were manufactured at the SRI and measured to require 150 pounds of force to bend them. These rings were in Geller's hand at the time they were bent.

The following brief recap is a reminder of those experiments we feel were best controlled. They are the perception experiments, including the double-blind-hidden-object experiments, and the double-blind-die-in-the-box experiment. The two psychokinetic experiments — the depression or raising of a weight on an electric scale and the deflection of the magnetometer — also do not seem to admit of any ready counterhypothesis. What we've demonstrated here are the experiments that we performed in the laboratory and should not be interpreted as proof of psychic functioning.

URI GELLER'S INFLUENCE ON THE METAL ALLOY NITINOL

by Eldon Byrd, Physical Scientist
Naval Surface Weapons Center,
White Oak Laboratory, Silver Spring, Maryland.

Eldon Byrd has a B.S. in Electrical Engineering and a M.S. in Medical Engineering. He has written on a variety of subjects; a paper on the telemetry of brain waves was published in the "Proceedings" of the International Telemetering Conference in 1972. He is also the author of the book How Things Work *and a member of the Institute of Electronic and Electrical Engineers and of Mensa.*

This paper recounts two meetings between Eldon Byrd and Uri Geller; the first took place in late October of 1973 at the Isis Center of the Naval Surface Weapons Center in Silver Spring, Maryland, and the second occurred a year later, at the home of a friend of Geller's in Connecticut. Byrd's paper recounts some unique and cogent experiments with Geller and his influence on the unusual alloy nitinol. To cause permanent change in the shape of nitinol wire, which Geller repeatedly did, normally requires that one heat the wire to a temperature of about 900° F and reshape it under considerable tension. However, as Byrd reports, Geller was able to introduce permanent deformations in several pieces of nitinol wire by gently rubbing them between two fingers.

Published for the first time, with the permission of the author.

On the evening of October 29, 1973, I had two pieces of nitinol wire, each with a different diameter, and a nitinol block in the laboratory at the Isis Center. At that time, nitinol was generally not available to the public. It was produced in very small quantities at the Naval Ordnance Laboratory (currently the Naval Surface Weapons Center), where it had been developed by William Buehler, a lab metallurgist. The alloy has been extensively studied and its characteristics are well known, the main one being that nitinol wire has a physical memory for the shape in which it is formed at the time of manufacture. For example, the alloy has been used for satellite antennas. When a satellite is injected into orbit, the nitinol antenna expands from a tightly coiled position within the satellite and blossoms like a flower.

The block of nitinol I had in the laboratory was approximately an inch by three-eighths of an inch square, and was composed of 60% nickel by weight and 40% titanium. The smaller of the two wires I had was 0.5 mm in diameter, and the other was approximately three times as large, or about 1.5 mm in diameter. The wires were composed of 55% nickel by weight and 45% titanium.

I was interested in determining whether Geller could influence nitinol. The block had been previously tested in the laboratory and found to have a Rockwell "C" Scale hardness of 49 to 60 on several test spots on its surface. The nitinol wires had been checked to ensure that they would, when placed in boiling water or heated with a match, assume a straight configuration.

The block of nitinol was very hard and nonmagnetic. Specifically, I wanted to know whether Geller could change either the block's hardness, which is a function of the structure of the material (the lattice arrangement of the atoms) or whether he could influence the material of the block to make it magnetic. In regard to the two wires, I wanted to know whether Geller could cause them to lose or alter their memory of their straight configuration.

The first thing I had Geller do was handle the block. I told him that I wanted to see if he could alter the block's hardness. Also, I asked him if he would try to alter the magnetic properties of the material. He said he would try to do both.

He handled the block for some time. Finally, he said he thought he would not be able to do anything to it because he somehow did not have a "feel" for the material. In a last attempt to influence the block, he asked for a piece of metal of any kind, and a brass plate was given to him. He placed the block on the plate and held his hand over it. Several times he pressed down on the block, but gave up, saying that he did not think he would be able to affect the material.

I put the nitinol block in my pocket and took out the wire with the larger diameter. Geller handled it for a while. He held the palm of his hand over it, placed the wire on the brass plate, picked it up again and held it firmly between his hands, but nothing seemed to happen. I then took out the smaller diameter wire, cut it into three pieces, each approximately five inches in length, and told him that if he could not influence this, he probably could not influence nitinol at all.

Geller asked me to hold the wire. I held it tautly between the thumbs and index fingers of both hands, keeping it very straight. Geller put his thumb and index finger over the wire and started to rub back and forth. After about twenty seconds of rubbing the wire, Geller said he felt a lump forming in the wire. When he removed his fingers, the wire had a definite "kink" in it, which looked like this:

Fig. 1

I asked that some boiling water be brought in. This particular wire was formed, at the time of manufacture, in a straight configuration, and immersion in boiling water should have caused it to spring back vigorously to that shape. *But when I placed it in the water, the wire, instead of snapping back with some force into a straight shape, began to form approximately a right angle.* This was an exciting finding. I lit a match and held it over the kink, but still the wire did not straighten out. Uri then left the lab and had no further contact with this nitinol wire.

Later, I had the wire (with the kink in it) x-rayed along its entire length. The analysis showed no discernible difference between the density of the wire at the kinked section and at other locations.

I also had an x-ray crystallographic analysis made of the wire. (Such a study shows the relative crystal sizes of the material in the form of a diffraction pattern.) The crystallographic analysis of the shaft of the wire that Geller had deformed showed nothing unusual in terms of crystalline size and uniformity. However, the crystal sizes in the kinked section appeared to have changed, but not significantly. The direction of change was one of enlargement, rather than one of shrinkage or of increase in density.

Several metallurgists at the Naval Surface Weapons Center who had examined and tested the wire were intent on removing the kink. They put the wire under tension in a vacuum chamber and heated it by passing an electric current through it until the wire glowed. When they removed the wire from the chamber and laid it on a cooling plate, it was, indeed, straight. But as the wire cooled down to room temperature, the kink spontaneously returned. They had no explanation for this occurrence.

Throughout the experiment with Geller, I had held the wire so tight that it was impossible for him to have pinched it between his thumb and forefinger. Besides, the day following the experiment I took another piece of nitinol wire and tried to bend it into as tight a kink as Geller had formed: I used the point of a screwdriver. But it was clearly impossible for me to duplicate Geller's kink without using Bunsen burners and pliers.

Later, I tried still other experiments with nitinol wires, using chemicals, all in the hope of duplicating the Geller deformation. Mercuric chloride was used to see if a nitinol wire could be temporarily "softened" so that a kink might be formed without extreme heat and sizable force. But nitinol proved to be impervious to mercuric chloride as well as to other chemicals I tried.

October 1974

Anomalous effects can occur in the best of scientific experiments. Is this what had happened during the test with Geller? I had pondered that question for almost a year before I had the chance to work again with Geller. The occasion took place in October 1974, not in the Isis Center, but at the home of writer John Fuller in Connecticut. Present that day were John Fuller, Ronald Hawke (a physicist at the Lawrence Livermore Laboratory in California), my wife, and two friends of Geller and John Fuller, Solvej Clark and Melanie Toyofuku. However, only Geller, Ronald Hawke, and I took part in the events of that afternoon.

Because of the possibility that an anomaly had occurred during the first meeting with Geller, this time I took extra precautions. I had brought with me some nitinol wire that had been physically characterized prior to my departure from the laboratory. The wire contained no known anomalies and was configured to return to a straight shape after being heated. Prior to leaving for Connecticut, I had cut the wire into four pieces, each approximately four inches in length. The diameter of the wire was about 0.5 mm. One piece was used as a control and was not taken to Connecticut. Audio tape recordings were made during all observations.

I held one of the other pieces by both ends as I had previously done and Geller stroked it as before. A kink formed. I took a second piece of wire, held it by one end, and Geller stroked it unilaterally. It, too, developed a kink. The third piece of wire was given to Geller to do with as he pleased. He rolled it between his thumb and forefinger and it kinked sharply. (See Plate 4.)

All three pieces of wire were brought back to the laboratory. X-ray crystallographic analyses of the kinks revealed no discernible structural deformations in the molecular lattice of the wires. A scanning electron microscope photograph of one kinked section failed to reveal any clues as to the mechanism of the bending phenomenon. A shadowgraph of one of the kinked wires (see Plate 5) showed that the radius of curvature of the bend was less than one mm.

Geller had clearly influenced the alloy nitinol in a most unusual way: it was as if the kinks he produced had actually been manufactured into the wires, even though it had been conclusively determined before any experimentation that the permanent configuration of the wires was that of straight lines. No explanation has been given by nitinol experts, who have been consulted as to how kinks could have been formed without using high temperatures and mechanical stress. Mechanically produced kinks in nitinol leave obvious marks on the surface of the wire. Geller-formed kinks do not.

*

In November of 1973 two other pieces of nitinol wire had been given to Geller; he bent them, but not under controlled conditions. However, in light of the work just presented, some interesting observations can be made about those two pieces of wire. One wire (see Plate 6) developed multiple two-dimensional bends and a three-dimensional twist at its end. The other (see Plate 7) developed a three-dimensional bend also, but it took the shape of an ellipse. The only known technique to bring about this result is to twist the wire into an ellipse, constrain it so that it cannot move, and then heat it to 500° C (or 932° F). What is even more remarkable about this particular piece of wire is that it was permanently deformed in *two* planes; that is, it appears as an ellipse when viewed from above, and as one cycle of a sinusoidal wave when viewed from its side.

All of the bends that Geller had produced thus far in nitinol wires have been *permanent* deformations — the wires can be crumpled or twisted into any shape by hand, but on being heated to a temperature of about 210° F. all the wires return to the shape Geller had imposed upon them.

How did Geller achieve such results? At the present I have no scientific explanation for what happened during both testing periods. I can say that the possibility of fraud on Geller's part can be virtually ruled out. Because of the unusual properties of nitinol, the scientific controls essential for any investigation are, for the most part, built into the testing material. Geller would have had to "palm" a source of high heat or substitute his own personally manufactured or previously altered pieces of nitinol if deception is to be the explanation for the events that took place — two highly unlikely possibilities.

I would like to add, for the record, that I have been in the same room and right next to people who were being hypnotized, and I do not believe I am hypnotizable. I also used to be an amateur magician and have studied techniques of magic and sleight of hand. Throughout the tests with Geller, I tried not to let him affect me psychologically.

Neither I nor other experts can offer any scientific explanation of how these deformations may have occurred under the conditions imposed.

The paper appears here with the official approval of the Naval Surface Weapons Center. It was reviewed by Metallic Materials Branch Chief David Goldstein; Head of the Department of Research and Technology Dr. William C. Wineland; Nitinol expert Dr. Frederick Wang; and Security Department Head Ronald Valimaki. The review board checked the paper for (a) technical accuracy, (b) quality and editorial competence, (c) compliance with security regulations, and (d) professional ethics, and recommended its release for publication. The paper represents the first time parapsychological research conducted at a government facility has been released for publication by the Department of Defense.

FRACTURE SURFACE PHYSICS INDICATING TELENEURAL INTERACTION*

by Wilbur M. Franklin, Ph.D., Department of Physics, Kent State University, Kent, Ohio.

Wilbur M. Franklin is Chairman of the Department of Physics, Graduate Division, at Kent State University. He holds degrees in biology, metallurgical engineering, and solid state science and technology. His publications include articles on such subjects as diffusion theory, the properties of liquid crystals, and the nature of fractures in metals; and many papers on teleneural physics. His interest in this last area began in 1972, when he first met and worked with Uri Geller. Since then he has initiated a course in teleneural physics at Kent State, the course is funded in part by a grant from the Ford Foundation. Dr. Franklin is a member of the American Physical Society and is listed in American Men of Science.

Many of the metallic objects bent or broken by Uri Geller have been subjected to analysis under the scanning electron microscope — a device of extremely high magnifying power that gives fine resolution of detail. Almost all of the fractures Geller has induced in metals resemble "fatigue fractures" — ruptures that result from excessive wear and tear. This is true even when the metal object Geller has affected was brand new. However, Dr. Franklin has discovered a remarkable exception. A platinum ring spontaneously developed a fissure in its surface in Geller's presence, but without his having touched the ring. Two breaks, only a hundredth of an inch apart, seem to have been produced by two very different conditions. One of the breaks resembles a cleavage that typically

* The word *teleneural* stems from the Greek prefix *tele*, meaning "far" or "distant," and the Greek word *neuron*, which has to do with the nervous system in the broadest sense.

occurs at the temperature of liquid nitrogen, −195° C; the other fissure is typical of platinum melting at a temperature of 1773° C. Dr. Franklin concludes that it would be difficult, even under the best laboratory conditions, to produce such totally different fractures at sites so close to one another.

In the first of the two papers printed here, Dr. Franklin gives an easily readable and abbreviated account of Geller's influence on the platinum ring and other metallic objects. His second paper is a rigorous treatment of his analysis of the surfaces fractured by Geller, and it presents a theoretical model to account for the observed events.

Published in New Horizons Journal, *Vol. 2, No. 1, April 1975.*

Introduction

The interesting question of what provided the causal influence for the deformation and fracture of metallic objects is raised by the recent reports of Owen (1974a, b) concerning the teleneural interactions with matter that occurred in the presence of Mr. Uri Geller and Mr. Matthew Manning.* Additional evidence, of a metallurgical nature, is given in this report of four metallic objects broken by, or in the presence of, Uri Geller. Most of the metallurgical investigation that is reported here was done at the Stanford Research Institute prior to the initiation of a special research program with Mr. Geller in the fall of 1972 and is reported, in part, in a recent article dealing with information transmission by Puthoff and Targ (1974).**

The investigation reported here is unusual in nature, significant to various fields of science, and casts the physical analysis of fracture surfaces in an important role in the endeavor to understand the

* Matthew Manning is a young English psychic who has demonstrated abilities similar to, though not so spectacular as, Uri Geller's.

** See pages 35–51.

question of the teleneural interaction capabilities of humans. The four fractures that are analyzed reveal two distinct types of fracture surface. One is not widely different from control fractures whereas the other displays significant differences from normal room-temperature fracture surfaces of the metal involved. The fracture surfaces that are analyzed are those of three household items, specifically, two stainless steel spoons, a stainless needle, and a platinum ring.

Fracture Conditions

All four of the metallic specimens, as observed by the author, were fractured in a room-temperature setting. All were handled by the author or coworkers within approximately thirty seconds to a minute after fracture, and no one reported the sensation of uncomfortable heat or cold from the specimens. All four specimens were owned by colleagues of the investigator; none was owned by Geller or his associates. A fracture occurred in the small part of the shank of one of the spoons, as it was observed visually, when the spoon was withdrawn by Geller from a cup in a time of less than three seconds. The fracture in the second spoon was seen to occur as the spoon was held in Mr. Geller's fingers while he bent it in a very gentle manner back and forth five or six times to angles of approximately forty-five degrees from the spoon's original shape. No apparent strain on the part of the subject was observed during the bending or fracture process of the spoons or of the other specimens. In the case of the platinum ring, the fracture appeared as a crack in the ring while an associate of the author's held it gently between the palms of her hands in the proximity of Mr. Geller. Subsequently, Mr. Geller took the ring and gently bent and broke a small segment out of the shank. The fracture in the needle occurred as it lay on a table approximately a meter from Mr. Geller.

From the brief description given above as well as the observation of other fractures seen by the author or reported by others (Owen, 1974a, b), it is apparent that two distinctly different types of fracture occur. In the first type, the metal appears to weaken in mechanical strength and increase in ductility to the point where a small mechanical force can plastically deform the metal. The successive frames of a movie film that shows this kind of fracture have been exhibited by Vaughan (1973). (See Plate 18.) In the second type of fracture a crack appears to develop in the material while it is not being observed visually.

Metallurgical Analysis of Specimens

Of the various instruments available for metallurgical use, the scanning electron microscope (SEM) was chosen to examine the fracture surfaces since the natural "as broken" surfaces could be examined directly, the depth of field was good, and since both high and low magnifications could be utilized easily. A Cambridge Stereoscan Mark 2A SEM was used for the analysis and all of the SEM photographs were taken between November 9 and 22, 1972.

The fractured spoons were of the Heavenly Star brand of Japanese stainless tableware. SEM photomicrographs showed no large differences between the fracture surfaces of specimens broken by Geller and those broken in the laboratory as controls. Microhardness measurements with a Tukon Hardness Tester gave an average hardness of the sample material corresponding to an approximate ultimate tensile surface strength of 109,000 psi ±5% (pounds per square inch). Immediately adjacent to the fracture surfaces in the Geller and control specimens, the microhardness was essentially identical and corresponded to 113,000 psi, which is less than 4% higher than the matrix material and may, in both cases, be attributable to work-hardening during the deformation of the material. However, hardness measurements were not made on the spoon that apparently broke without bending. Since the smallest cross-sectional area of the shank of the spoons was 1.17×10^{-2} in^2, the load required for fracture in tension would have been 1270 pounds. However, the bend load required for fracture is probably of the order of twenty times smaller. (The author could not bend manually another spoon from the same set by more than ten degrees.)

The SEM photomicrographs of the fracture surface of the needle showed no regions of dimpled network typical of ductile failure. The surface showed regions of distinct granular structure, which looked like intercystalline fracture, and a region with small spherical sections similar to those sometimes seen in sintered metal powders. The needle did not "neck down" in the region of fracture as ductile metals do, and there was no evidence of bending deformation or fracture.

The most interesting of the fracture surfaces were those of the first fracture in the platinum ring. There was no evidence of necking down or bending. The SEM photographs showed a widely variable microstructure with regions that appeared to have been distorted by shear, others characteristic of incipient melting, and one that appeared similar to a low-temperature cleavage surface. Rounded-over protuberances around a cavity, which appear similar to specimens that have been heated to near the melting point, are shown in Plate 15. Plate 17 shows a region approximately 10^{-2} inches from the field of view of Plate 15. This region displays a terraced topography, similar to cleavage surfaces at low temperature, with included geometrical forms that are close to hexagonal in structure. The latter are most likely inclusions and/or cavities that reflect the face-centered-cubic symmetry of platinum.

If ductile failure had occurred in the needle or ring the SEM should have shown a dimpled pattern looking like a lacy white filigree network. In addition, necking down should have been evident. The intergranular patterns seen in the needle fracture surface suggest corrosion or stress corrosion. But Geller did not hold the needle prior to fracture, so corrosive chemicals could not have been applied. In addition, an energy-dispersive x-ray analysis was done on the needle's surface and did not indicate the presence of corrosive chemicals. The overall pattern of the surfaces of the needle and ring were not indicative of fatigue or shear failure, either.

Discussion

From the metallurgical analysis of the fracture surfaces it is evident that the type of fracture that occurred in the spoons does not produce any significant differences from room-temperature control ductile fractures. This observation has also been made by Doris Wilsdorf (1974) on specimens that were apparently broken by Geller in a manner similar to that of the spoons. However, a second type of fracture surface, exemplified by those of the needle and platinum ring, is distinctively different from known types of room-temperature fracture surfaces. This conclusion was reached after consulting with professional metallurgists and reviewing the available SEM literature and photographs in the American Society for Metals library. The flat, slightly terraced structure shown in Plate 16 appears similar to low-temperature cleavage surfaces, whereas the hexagonal inclusions and neighboring regions that look like incipient melting are indicative of structures typical of high-temperature creep and localized melting, respectively. Therefore, it is concluded that it would have been extremely difficult to fabricate these surfaces by known laboratory techniques.

Since the mechanism of signal transmission in mental telepathy may not be electromagnetic (Franklin, 1974), it is interesting to speculate that information transmission may be related to teleneural interaction with matter of a nonelectromagnetic nature. There is no known method whereby room-temperature induction or other electromagnetic means could result in fractures of the nature seen. If these observations are correct there is a necessity for the development of new theoretical constructs capable of characterizing the patterns of behavior of the new force or influence function that is operative in the process.

REFERENCES

Franklin, W., "Theory of teleneural communication," *Bulletin of the American Physical Society*, 19, 821, 1974.

Owen, A. R. G., "Uri Geller's metal phenomena: An eyewitness account," *New Horizons*, 1, No. 4, 164–171, 1974.

Owen, A. R. G., "A Preliminary report on Matthew Manning's psychical phenomena," *New Horizons*, 1, No. 4, 172–73, 1974b.

Targ, R. and H. Puthoff, "Information transmission under conditions of sensory shielding," *Nature*, 251, 602–607, 1974.

Vaughan, A., "The phenomena of Uri Geller," *Psychic*, 4, No. 5, 12–18, 1973.

Wilsdorf, D., University of Virginia, personal communication, 1974.

METAL FRACTURE PHYSICS USING SCANNING ELECTRON MICROSCOPY AND THE THEORY OF TELENEURAL INTERACTIONS

by Wilbur Franklin, Ph.D., Department of Physics, Kent State University, Kent, Ohio.

Published for the first time with the permission of the author.

Introductory Background

The recent investigations of neuronal functions utilizing network theory,[1–5] stochastic models of neuroelectric activity,[6] and a tunneling model to describe a neural state vector[7] have provided substantial new insights into the complexities of the functioning of the central nervous system. The question as to whether the comprehensive function of the mind is greater than the measurable sum of the neural interactions that constitute the total brain function has been raised, in part, by Delgado.[8] In his book, *Physical Control of the Mind*, he says, "The mind should not be considered identical with its supporting organ, the brain . . . The mind is related not only to the structure of neurons but also to their spatial-temporal relations and to important extracerebral factors."

Science dwells, in general, on physically measurable quantities. If some of the functions of the mind depend, in part, on fields or influences that are not physically measurable at the present time with contemporary techniques, then sophisticated methods of interpretation of the results of these influences may be needed in order for one to infer the properties of the unknown influence function. Material results of certain altered states of consciousness have been observed; their causal fields have evidently not been measured or isolated in the laboratory. In addition, teleneural interactions between a human being and material objects have been reported with no evidence for an interaction field.[9] In the expansive literature[10] (most of which is popular in vein) dealing with parapsychology, there is no satisfactory explanation or theory of teleneural phenomena, such as bioinformation transfer or retrieval from both living and inanimate objects or teleneural interaction with matter, that correlates theory with experimental observations. This, perhaps, is the *prima facie* reason for the historical rejection by many scientists of most of the observations in the field of parapsychology; the desire for a reasonable explanation seemingly governs, to a certain extent, one's belief. Another reason, to be sure, is the fact that certain of the experimental observations and techniques have been of questionable validity.[11] The points to be made from a review of both the experimental and theoretical work that has been done in the past are that results of a definitive nature have been lacking, for the most part, and that the evidence for teleneural interactions, particularly with matter, has often not been convincing.

In November and December of 1972, laboratory-controlled experiments[9] were conducted at the Stanford Research Institute (SRI) with a young Israeli, Mr. Uri Geller.[12] The author took part in a portion of those experiments.* The SRI results with Mr. Geller were recorded on film and video tape and included the following results of laboratory-controlled experiments: telepathy; reproducing, reasonably well, simple sketches enclosed inside two opaque envelopes; producing a magnetometer reading of approximately ½ gauss without touching the probe; correctly choosing, without touching any of the cans, which of ten small metal cans held an object (twelve correct, two abstain, and zero wrong, giving a chance probability of 1 in 10^{12}); telling which side of a die faced upward

* For the full set of experiments see pages 61–66.

after the die had been shaken inside a closed opaque box (eight correct, zero wrong, giving a chance probability of 1 in 1.68×10^6); and causing a real or an apparent change of weight in a dynamic balance enclosed in a bell jar. The results of the latter experiment were recorded on a strip chart recorder. Certain of the results obtained with Mr. Geller, namely, the latter two experiments, have *no* apparent means of explanation within the accepted framework of theoretical physics. For this reason it is important to consider carefully these experiments and the metallurgical results[13] that are reported here. It will be of equal importance to perform similar experiments in other laboratories with different subjects and to investigate their theoretical implications. It is the author's opinion, based on the observations that have already been made, that theoretical constructs need not await further experimental results to corroborate and extend the SRI experiments, but that the formulation of theoretical models is, in fact, one of the most important considerations in the constructive development of this field. Without the contributions of physicists, engineers, and others in the "hard sciences" who understand physical laws, the field of teleneural phenomena will not become understandable scientifically, but will remain on the fringes of quasi-scientific endeavor, where a large domain of potential usefulness to society may remain dormant.

The material reported here is both theoretical and experimental in perspective. The new theory given is, for the most part, generally applicable regardless of the type of interaction involved. In this sense, it seems wise, at this stage of the development of the field, to find theoretical paradigms that have general applicability, and are not dependent on the type of field or interaction involved, until the nature of the interaction or interactions in certain teleneural phenomena can be ascertained. Known electromagnetic theory is, of course, applicable to certain types of teleneural interactions that are known with reasonable certainty to be electromagnetic in nature. Some electromagnetic aspects will be discussed below.

The experimental investigations that are reported are made up of metallurgical studies of two metal objects that were broken by Mr. Uri Geller. These results are reported in more detail elsewhere.[13] A scanning electron microscope (SEM) analysis of the fracture surfaces and microhardness test results on one of the specimens are reported. While some of the experimental evidence reported here is principally metallurgical in nature, the photographic evidence, which stems from scanning electron microscopy, is, we feel, clear even to the nonspecialist. The metallurgical analysis that has been performed is not as complete as possible. Metallurgical testing of the specimens prior to, and concurrent with, fracture was not performed. One of the reasons for this deficiency is that insufficient funds were available for a complete investigation.[14] However, enough evidence was obtained through the use of the SEM at SRI and through donated services to give the results reported here.[15]

The fracture surfaces studied were those of two common household items, specifically, a stainless steel spoon and a platinum alloy ring. The following section, Fracture Conditions, is a brief statement about the conditions under which fracture was observed to occur.[16] The next section deals with the SEM analysis of the fracture surfaces, and includes fracture photographs of the specimens and their controls. In the theoretical section that follows, some new theoretical constructs are presented, together with a discussion of electromagnetic effects. Finally, a brief summary and conclusions are given.

Regarding the nature of the process or processes involved in the fractures reported on here, the possibilities that have been proposed from the outset of our work with, and observation of, Mr. Geller include the following: (1) magic trickery, (2) perpetrated fraud, (3) group hypnosis of the investigators, (4) self-hypnosis or self-control by the subject in order to facilitate fracture of the specimens, and (5) a real event. From the SEM analysis of the fracture surfaces of two out of four fractures investigated in three different specimens,[17] it was concluded that (1) and (4) are not reasonable possibilities as an explanation of the observations without the inclusion of (2), (3), or (5). In the SRI experiments, which involved manifestations of teleneural interactions other than metallurgical fractures, it was considered highly unlikely that (2) or (3) could have occurred since both film and video-tape records were made of the experiments and since security measures were followed in the processing and storage of the films. Also, the SRI experiments were monitored visually by observers outside the laboratory using direct TV transmission to a neighboring room. Important additional evidence that (2) or (3) is not involved in the fractures induced by Mr. Geller is a movie from which the pertinent frames have been published.[18] It shows a metallic specimen in the process of being fractured with no apparent force being applied by Mr. Geller. (See Plate 18.)

Fracture Conditions

The nature of the energy fields of subjects with special teleneural powers has not been determined except for those categories that are classifiable with reasonable certainty as being within the framework of known electromagnetic theory. The conditions for fracture that are described in this section do not appear to be within the domain of known theoretical physics. Therefore, it is important to consider the conditions under which fracture occurred as well as the analysis of the fractures themselves. However, it must be stated again that the results that are reported here for the fractured specimens deal with the unusual nature of the metallurgical observations and not with the subject of experimental methodology.[16]

The specimens were fractured in a room-temperature setting and were observed by the author and others during the process of deformation and fracture. The spoon was broken with no apparent strain by Mr. Geller, who bent it back and forth for three cycles or less to angles of approximately forty-five degrees from the vertical. (Another spoon from the same set of tableware was also seen to be broken by Geller without bending.) The author tested another spoon from the same set and found it impossible permanently to deform the handle manually by more than about ten degrees.[19] The spoon was made of work-hardened ferritic stainless steel with an ultimate tensile strength of approximately 110,000 psi (estimated from hardness measurements) and was $\frac{1}{16}$-inch thick and $\frac{3}{16}$-inch wide at the point in the shank where fracture occurred.

The platinum ring was fractured as it was held gently by an associate of the author's in the proximity of Mr. Geller. After the appearance of the first fracture, Mr. Geller held the ring and gently bent a segment outward until a second fracture occurred. The surface of the second break appeared to be ductile fracture distorted by shear. The surface of the first fracture was not characteristic of ductile failure, fatigue, or shear, and is described in the next section.

Metallurgical Analysis

The scanning electron microscope (SEM) is especially useful in the examination of fracture surfaces since it has good depth of field, the natural "as broken" surfaces can be examined directly without replication, and since both low and high magnifications can be utilized easily. The possibility of surface distortion, dissolution, or the removal of loose segments was minimized by examining the "as fractured" surfaces with no cleaning of any sort. The Cambridge Stereoscan Mark 2A SEM at SRI was used and all the photographs were taken between November 9 and 22, 1972. In the following paragraphs the nature of the fracture surfaces of the stainless steel spoon and its control and of the platinum ring is described.

The locations of the fracture surfaces of the two breaks in the stainless steel spoon, one of which was induced by Geller and the other made in the laboratory by bending, are shown in Figure 1.[20] The comparison fracture surfaces, shown in Plates 8 and 9, are quite similar in nature and portray a dimpled pattern that is typical, in the metallurgical literature, of ductile failure. It is not known whether the slight differences between Plates 8 and 9 are significant.

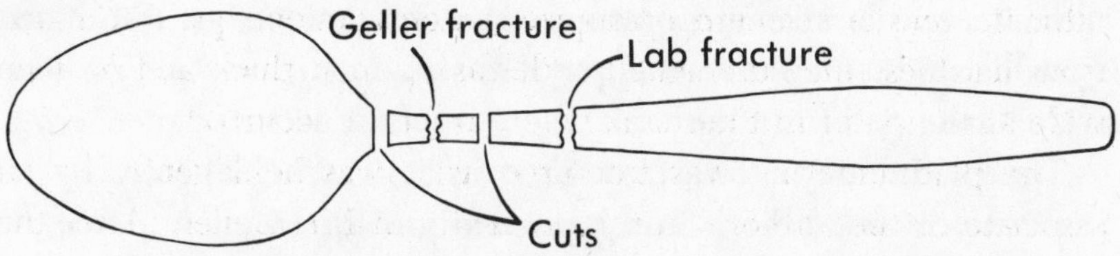

Fig. 1. A common household spoon showing the location of the fracture produced by Geller. In addition, the locations of the laboratory fracture and cuts from the cut-off wheel are shown. Microhardness measurements were made on the three small pieces.

A striking difference from usual room-temperature fractures caused by tension or bending can be seen in Plates 10 and 11, which show a progression of increasing magnification. The shank of the spoon in the foreground of Plate 10 shows a crack along the left vertical edge, which is magnified in the next two figures. The profile of the upper and lower edges of the crack match reasonably well. This, together with the upward displacement of material, indicate that the crack was caused by separation (pulling apart) rather than by a piece's falling out. The bottom of the crack, as shown in Plates 11 and 12, displays an unusual viscous appearance that is not typical of ductile failure from tensile or bending loads at room temperature.

The fracture surface of the first break in the platinum ring was very different from that in the spoon. Plate 13 shows an overview of the fracture surface. There was essentially no evidence of necking down, as is expected in a ductile metal under tensile failure, or of bending. In Plate 13 the higher regions of the fracture surface, especially the left side and the upper right corner, appeared to have been distorted by shear. This may have occurred when the opposing faces of the broken ring, which were in contact, were rubbed, since the ring spread open after the crack was formed.

Plate 14 shows the lower right quarter of the fracture surface and Plates 15–17 show regions taken from the field of view of Plate 14 at a higher magnification. Small rounded-over protuberances are characteristic of the region around the depression shown in Plate 15, which is taken from the upper left corner of Plate 14. Plates 16 and 17 are taken from the lower right corner of Plate 14 and show a terraced structure with distinct geometrical forms that are close to hexagonal in symmetry. The latter are inclusions and/or cavities, which reflect the symmetry of the face-centered-cubic structure of platinum. The fields of view in and around those displayed in Plates 15–17 are unusual in nature, particularly when the possible types of room-temperature fracture are considered. Ductile failure in platinum alloys, such as that caused by tension, results in microstructures similar to those shown in Plates 8 and 9. Usually necking down on a visually macroscopic scale occurs in tension and lateral cracking in bend failure in a metal of this sort. If the fracture occurred by shear, then macroscopic shear deformation should appear adjacent to the fracture surface. The flat terraced surfaces with the included geometrical shapes are difficult to explain as a result of room-temperature fracture. Geometrical shapes of the type shown can occur in high-temperature creep specimens that have had sufficient time for the formation of vacancy clusters and/or inclusions. The flat terraced surfaces have the appearance of low-temperature (liquid nitrogen) cleavage.

Microhardness measurements were made with an 800-gm load on the pieces adjacent to the Geller and laboratory fractures in the spoon. The average of twenty impressions in the matrix material gave an average Knoop hardness of 240, which corresponds to an ultimate tensile strength of 109,000 psi ±5%. The measured values for hardness immediately adjacent to the Geller and laboratory fractures were 254 and 253, respectively, which correspond to an ultimate tensile strength of 113,000 psi. This is less than 4% higher than the hardness of the matrix material. No change of hardness with respect to that of the matrix occurred at the cuts made with the cut-off wheel. Metallographs of the microstructure of the spoon and microhardness measurements with a lighter load (200 gms) indicated that small ($\approx 10\mu$) hard inclusions — probably carbides — were present. There were, however, no regions of significant softening. The steel was a ferritic stainless, which is easier to fracture than one of the austenitic type, but had, nonetheless, a high ultimate tensile strength. The minimum bending load required to bend the spoon by mechanical means was probably greater than sixty pounds. Assuming a 60-pound load, a total bend distance (in three cycles of motion) of six inches, and a time of ten seconds, the minimum required power was roughly 3 to 4 watts. This power is within the capacity of human biomechanics; humans burn energy at the rate of approximately 100 watts ($\approx$ 10 watts for the brain alone) when at rest and 1000 watts in heavy work. From our work with Mr. Geller an upper limit to the diameter of an object that can be bent or broken and the fracture speed (in first Pt fracture) has not been established.

Theoretical Constructs

This section will include some introductory theoretical approaches to the physical understanding of teleneural phenomena that may be applied to interactions between living systems and matter. First an effective stress due to teleneural causes is introduced and is added to the electromagnetic stress-energy tensor. The next section deals with field and information theory concepts. This is followed by a brief presentation of some electromagnetic effects and models of interaction of electromagnetic radiation with a living system.

Effective Stress-Energy Tensor

If the specimens were fractured with less than the mechanical stress for failure required for fractures to occur by normal means, then we can postulate the existence of a force or influence field, exerted by the subject (or due to the presence of the subject), that produces an *effective* stress P_E in the specimen. An effective stress is postulated since the nature of the interaction between subject and specimen is unknown. Let us define a total stress-energy tensor by:

$$T^{\mu\nu} = M^{\mu\nu} + S^{\mu\nu} + P_E^{\mu\nu} \tag{1}$$

where $\overleftrightarrow{M}$, $\overleftrightarrow{S}$, and $\overleftrightarrow{P}_E$ are the stress-energy tensor densities for matter, electromagnetic interactions, and nonelectromagnetic teleneural interactions, respectively. We postulate that the gradients of these densities are given by:

$$\begin{aligned} \partial T^{\mu\nu}/\partial x^\nu &= 0 \\ \partial S^{\mu\nu}/\partial x^\nu &= -f^\mu \\ \partial P_E^{\mu\nu}/\partial x^\nu &= -\zeta_E^\mu \end{aligned} \tag{2}$$

where f^μ and ζ_E^μ are the separate but, perhaps, coupled electromagnetic and teleneural force densities, respectively. Then

$$\partial M^{\mu\nu}/\partial x^\nu = f^\mu + \zeta_E^\mu \tag{3}$$

Following Robertson and Noonan,[21] an equation that represents the conservation of energy in an isotropic fluid [22] is obtained; it is given by:

$$u_\mu(f^\mu + \zeta_E^\mu) = \partial(\rho u^\nu)/\partial x^\nu - (u^\nu/c^2)\,\partial p_0/\partial x^\nu \tag{4}$$

where u_μ is the μ component of the world velocity, c is the velocity of light, p_0 is the pressure, and $\rho = \rho_0 + p_0/c^2$ where ρ_0 is the total proper energy density (including the rest, thermal, nuclear, and teleneural energies). The equation for the force density can also be derived, and is, following Robertson and Noonan,[21] given by:

$$\frac{F^\mu}{m} = \frac{1}{\rho}\left(f^\mu + \zeta_E^\mu + \frac{\eta^{\mu\nu}}{c^2}\frac{\partial p_0}{\partial x^\nu}\right) \tag{5}$$

where $\eta^{\mu\nu}$ is the Minkowski metric tensor. In the above argument ζ_E^μ represents the effective force. In our case, it is postulated that $\vec{\zeta}_E$ was applied to the metallic specimens and produced the portion of the deformation not produced by electromagnetic or mechanical forces.

It is apparent from the argument given here that the addition of a new effective stress-energy tensor for teleneural phenomena leads to conservation and force equations in which an interchange can occur between the electromagnetic and teleneural types of interaction. This is appealing because if the normal operation of the neural system of a subject is assumed to be electromagnetic in nature then the teleneural mode of operation might then involve the creation of P_E from S. This raises the question as to whether P_E arises from some special electromagnetic origin such as a new effect due to strong nonlinearities, or from a new type of influence that differs from the usual gravitational, electromagnetic, and nuclear forces, or other new construct.

Field and Information Theory Concepts

We will postulate, following the suggestion of other authors[10] in the field of teleneural phenomena, that a field, Ψ, for teleneural interactions exists and propagates with a velocity that will be assumed to be finite. (We must note, however, that action-at-a-distance is also a possibility to be considered and tested). If the field is characterized by space and time dependence, then $\Psi = \Psi(\vec{r},t)$ where $\vec{r} = \vec{r}_R - \vec{r}_S$ and $t = t_R - t_S$ where R and S denote receiver and source, respectively. We will also postulate that the strength of the field (or number of particles, if the field is quantized) is characterized not only by space and time, but by two subjective quantities — the "psychological factors," ϕ, and the amount of information, H_R, known by the subject about the object or receiver. Then $n = n(\vec{r}_R, t, \phi, H_R)$. The quantity ϕ includes effects of other living systems, climactic factors, geomagnetic disturbances, physiological factors, state of mental consciousness, etc. on the ability of the subject to emit the Ψ field. H_R represents the quantity of information received consciously or subliminally by the subject about the object or receiver with which interaction occurs. Certain aspects of a teleneural field theory can probably be developed following traditional field theories for known interactions. Geometrization of the field might also lead to fruitful results.

Now a general theoretical construct, which applies to fields of any type, namely, information theory, will be considered briefly. One role of information theory in the process of bioinformation transfer has been shown, assuming an electromagnetic model, by Kogan.[23] In terms of bits, a telepathic percipient receives H bits of information for a particular situation in which there are N possibilities to choose from (all of equal probability) and a choice is made n times. This stems from the information theory equation for equal probabilities, which is given by $H = n \ln_2 N$.

The question of whether information theory plays an important role in teleneural interaction with matter arises from a consideration of the information content in a material object and the role of object perception in the interaction. If cognitive or subliminal perception is important in teleneural interaction with matter, then the information in the object may be stored by the subject. We do not consider here the *mechanism* of teleneural interaction with matter; rather, we deal with the object of interaction as a quantity of information. This raises the question of the amount of information stored in an object or a segment of an object. If we consider that a mass of 1 gm has approximately 10^{22} atoms, then we find that the information content for the identification of each atom and nuclear state and for assigning all the degrees of freedom individually is a very large number — greater than 10^{22} bits.[24] If we consider the bit rates that have been measured in bioinformation transfer experiments, we find that it is too large a number for a subject to receive and store in a reasonable time. (Bit rates from 1 to 10^{-3} bit/sec appear to be typical of short- to long-range information transfer.[23,25]) In addition, an upper limit assumed for long-term memory is approximately 10^{20} bits for a person thirty years old, since each neuron transmits approximately ten digital impressions per second, there are about 10^{10} neurons, and thirty years is 10^{9} seconds. Smaller upper limits of $10^{13}-10^{14}$ bits in a lifetime have been estimated; they include effects of various loss mechanisms. Thus, if the information transfer rate in a subject's teleneural perception of matter is similar to that in bioinformation transfer and does not greatly exceed neural information capacities, we can make an important observation regarding teleneural interaction with matter: either the information is not stored by the subject, or the information stored is a *macroscopic* rather than a microscopic description of the object. If it is stored by the subject and the interaction is macroscopic, then the quantity of information about the fracture surfaces in the ring (and needle — see Reference 13) falls within the amount that could be received and stored by a subject in a reasonable amount of time. For example, if a subject is capable of receiving and storing 0.1 bit/sec for ten minutes, this amounts to 60 bits of information, which is more than adequate to describe a simple geometrical object in macroscopic terms. Thus, the storage of information in atomistic detail in macroscopic effects such as fractures appears to be outside the domain of possible teleneural interactions unless a very high degree of symmetry and purity exists in the objects. This observation does not imply, however, that atomistic teleneural events are impossible if the event does not require a prohibitively high bit rate. We should also note that the upper limits on storage capacity of the central nervous system and of the bioinformation transfer rate may be substantially higher than postulated previously.

Electromagnetic Interactions

Bioinformation transfer by electromagnetic radiation has been considered theoretically by Kogan[23] from the standpoint of the information theory. The relationship for the bit rate, C, in terms of the band width, W, and the source and noise powers, P_s and P_n, respectively, is given by

$$C = W \ln \left(\frac{P_s}{P_n} + 1 \right) \qquad (6)$$

The band width is $1/\tau$ where τ is the time required for information transfer per bit. The noise power is assumed to be kT/τ, and the critical signal power required to send a certain critical bit rate, C^*, is given by

$$P^* = \frac{4\pi r^2}{S_A} \frac{kT}{\tau} (2^{C^*\tau} - 1) e^{\alpha r} \left[\frac{h}{2r} S(r - h) + S(h - r) \right] \qquad (7)$$

where r, S_A, T, and α are the distance, antenna area, temperature, and attenuation coefficient, respectively. The wave-guide effects of the ionosphere are accounted for crudely by the square brackets in which h is the height of the ionosphere and $S(r - h)$ is the step function. The requisite biocurrent for generation of P^* is obtained from $P^* = (I^*)^2R$ where R is the antenna resistance. The resulting biocurrents calculated using Equation (7), together with elementary antenna theory, give typical values of 10^{-10} amps or less for distances of a few meters and for typical conditions in bioinformation transfer experiments in which there are a small number of possible choices, N. This theory assumes no power losses except for the attenuation factor $\exp(\alpha r)$, which is very small except for distances greater than a few hundred miles. It represents, therefore, the optimum information transfer conditions, assuming an r^{-2} fall-off for $r < h$ and an r^{-1} decrease of power for $r > h$. If losses are low, the electromagnetic theory seems reasonable for communication for small r and even for large r if τ is also large. However, interference of the signal caused by electronic noise is a very significant factor in interactions with the electromagnetic mechanism and, in addition, living organisms are not known to generate power levels sufficient for intermediate- to long-range communication.

The transfer of information by biological systems through the use of electromagnetic sources and sensors has been studied or considered by many authors.[23,26–33] In recent reviews, Bullock[26] and Hopkins[27] have summarized work on sensory mechanisms for low-frequency electromagnetic radiation in sharks and other fish, certain species of which have thresholds for electric field sensation in water as low as $1 \mu V/m$. Nelson[28] and Callahan[29] have considered direct electromagnetic reception of various frequency ranges by insects. The effects of electromagnetic fields in the radio range on the electroencephalogram of humans has been reported by Presman[30] in a good review of Russian work concerning electromagnetic radiation fields and living systems. Aceto, Tibias, and Silver[31] have recently reviewed the theories of the interaction of electromagnetic radiation and of static magnetic fields with living systems. The biological effects of magnetic fields have been reviewed by Kolin.[34] Changes in reaction time of human beings by exposure to 0.2 Hz magnetic fields of approximately 5–17 gauss have been observed by Friedman, Becker, and Bachman,[35] whereas static and 0.1 Hz fields produced no significant effect. Bawin et al.[36] reported large behavior changes in monkeys exposed to 147 MHz modulated by 0–30 Hz.

The measurement of electric and magnetic fields of and around human bodies have been reported, respectively, by Burr[37] and Cohen.[38] Magnetic fields of 5×10^{-6} and 5×10^{-9} gauss around contracting muscles and cranial regions, respectively, were measured.[38] There are reports of indications that certain people with special capabilities of self-control are able consciously to control and produce magnetic fields of much higher magnitudes.[9] Electric fields were found to be a function of emotional state or state of consciousness in humans.[32,37] A theory of the generation of electromagnetic fields from neuronal activity has been given by Anninos.[39]

The possible mechanisms of interaction of biological systems with electromagnetic radiation include molecular vibration, rotation, and conformation states, and electronic and nuclear states in frequency ranges extending from the upper-microwave to the γ-ray region. At frequencies in the microwave region and less, collective modes of molecular clusters and cellular structures become significant. The possibility of interaction of extremely low frequencies with the Larmor precession frequency of protons in biological materials in the earth's magnetic field has been considered.[40] The Larmor frequency for protons in the earth's field is approximately 2000 Hz. A possibility may also exist for quasi-resonance interactions of extremely low frequencies with antiferromagnetic modes in cell membranes.[41]

The above review of electromagnetic interactions with living systems reveals that bioinformation transfer occurs at frequencies down to less than 1 Hz.[26,36] At extremely low frequencies the attenuation of a Faraday cage is low. In this regard it is interesting to note that Puharich[42] and Puthoff and Targ[9] have done bioinformation transfer experiments with human subjects with the source or receiver in a Faraday cage. Further tests of bioinformation transfer are needed in which bit rates are measured as a function of distance both inside and outside a very good Faraday cage and in a "mu" metal cage.

It is interesting to compare biological communication in the ELF regime with that developed for submarine applications in a program called Project Sanguine.[43–45] Frequencies less than 100 Hz and antenna powers of 1–2 MW were utilized in the Sanguine communication project. The transmitter antenna covers 30–50 square miles, giving about 100 W/acre of power, and the receiving antenna is approximately 100 m long.[45] The bit rate is low; approximately one bit per 60 cycles is evidently possible.[45] The radiated power is less than the antenna power because of radiation resistance, but it is still several orders of magnitude larger than the maximum possible power radiated from a human being in the ELF regime. Historically, it is interesting to note that Nikola Tesla, in 1899, proposed using the ELF regime for a worldwide communication system. His huge spark-gap transmitter drained the power supply of the city of Colorado Springs! The point of these observations is that the power levels and antenna systems required for ELF electromagnetic communication are several orders of magnitude larger than those required for bioinformation transfer between humans. Therefore, it is extremely unlikely that mental telepathy can be propagated at great distances by biosystems in the ELF electromagnetic regime.[46]

Summary and Conclusions

The detailed metallurgical analysis of three fracture surfaces in two metallic specimens broken by, or in the presence of, Mr. Uri Geller revealed two distinct types of fracture-surface microstructure in the SEM photographs. One type appeared quite similar to normal room-temperature ductile failure caused by mechanical loading, except for a viscous appearance at the bottom of a small lateral crack (see Plates 10 and 11).

In the second type of fracture surface, the predominant microstructures were not typical of ductile failure, fatigue, stress-corrosion, or shear failure, nor of room-temperature cleavage. In the platinum specimen, which exemplified the second type of fracture, localized regions of two types were observed on the same fracture surface only 0.02 cm apart. One region looked like ductile failure in an area that had been heated to the point of incipient melting (see Plate 15; the melting point of platinum is 1773° C). The second region looked like low-temperature cleavage, with inclusions or vacancy clusters also appearing in the field of view (see Plates 16 and 17). These observations, which are not typical of SEM fractographs of failures by mechanical loading, indicate that the cause of fracture was not mechanical in nature nor was it a result of usual mechanical methods of fracture. In fact, the possible methods of reconstruction of the fracture surface in the platinum ring by known techniques seem to require procedures such as partial cleavage at liquid nitrogen temperature (−195° C) followed by ductile failure of the noncleaved portion and subsequent exposure of this portion to a small beam from a powerful laser in selected regions and a shear force in other regions. Such a project would not only be difficult to carry out, but could not, in fact, be conducted unless a number of people actually perpetrated fraud. Consequently, it is not considered as a reasonable possibility. In view of the nature of the fracture surfaces, especially those of the platinum ring, it is concluded that the specimens were not broken by techniques known to induce laboratory fractures. The evidence, based on metallurgical analysis of the fracture surfaces, indicates that a paranormal influence must have been operative in the formation of the fractures.

Since the metallurgical analysis of the fractured specimens was completed, a number of reports of other subjects who can bend and/or fracture metal objects have been published. Taylor,[47] in his recent book, has given detailed reports of many children in England as well as people with paranormal teleneural capabilities who could bend and fracture metals. At the international conference on the Physics of Paranormal Phenomena, Taylor, Hasted, Byrd, Owen, and Franklin[48] reported results of metal-bending and fracture studies. These included, in the work of Owen, Price, and Taylor, studies of subjects other than Geller. In addition, there have been many reports in the popular press of metal bending that may or may not have been accomplished by paranormal means. The fork that was filmed during fracture[18] is presently being investigated by the author, as is a 2-mm-thick key fractured by Matthew Manning in the presence of Dr. A. R. G. Owen[49] and two items bent by children in the Akron, Ohio, area. In a historical perspective, it would be interesting to analyze the knife that fractured in the presence of Carl Jung;[50] an attempt is being made to obtain this specimen for metallurgical examination.

Effects, either direct or indirect, or electromagnetic fields of frequencies less than those of the microwave regime have been observed on the central nervous systems of living organisms. It appears, therefore, that there will be a new area of research concerned with the mechanisms of communication of information and biological effects by low-frequency electromagnetic radiation interacting with living organisms. Information transfer has been observed in sharks and other fish[26,27] at frequencies in the range 0.3–30 Hz. Hence, further consideration should be given to low-frequency biocommunication in other living organisms, both animal and plant. It is known that information transfer rates, measured by the bit rate in information theory, are small for low frequencies. Therefore, reasonably long periods of time (in comparison to verbal or telegraphic communication rates, for example) are required for the transfer of low-frequency information. Frequencies in the radio range have been shown to affect electroencephalographs.[30] Also, a magnetic field oscillating at the ELF of 0.2 Hz was found to reduce reaction rates in human subjects.[35] The major portion of the power spectrum of human brain waves lies in the ELF range from 0–30 Hz and most of this power is at less than a few Hz.[51] Also, the peaks of the frequency spectra of contracting muscles usually occur at less than 100 Hz.[38] Higher body frequencies have, however, also been noted.[39] Since the power levels of brain waves and contracting muscles are orders of magnitude less than that required for electromagnetic stimulation of known effects on humans and still less than that required for the weakening or fracture of metal objects, it would seem to be important to consider nonelectromagnetic theories as well as the new aspects of ELF communication.

Whether there exists a channel of bioinformation transfer other than electromagnetic fields and other known channels is an important question, especially when the experimental results with unusual and with normal subjects, which have been reported recently, are considered. In the Geller experiments at SRI the side of a die facing upward inside an opaque container, after being shaken, was guessed or sensed correctly eight times in a row.[9] The transfer of information in this experiment could not have been electromagnetic in nature, assuming known electromagnetic theory (unless some extremely sensitive unknown mechanism exists). In addition to information transfer, which does not appear to be electromagnetic in nature, the apparent change of mass in the dynamic balance experiment at SRI and the unusual fracture surfaces of the metal specimens reported here give evidence that requires further investigation outside known theoretical constructs. Then, too, there is a question regarding the modality of communication in teleneural information transfer between living organisms, especially at large distances.[23] If more than one channel of teleneural interaction exists then it is possible that electromagnetic radiation may either interfere with or enhance the second type of interaction mechanism.

The development of theoretical paradigms that deal constructively with the observations in unexplained teleneural phenomena will demand new insights into the fundamentals of physical laws. Mehra[52] has recently considered the role of the observer in quantum mechanical measurements and the difference between a complete and a quantum mechanical representation. Bohm[53] has also discussed new aspects of the role of the observer and, in addition, the implications of a holographic concept of quantum states. The generality of information theory is appealing for use in teleneural theory since objects can be described as quantities of information regardless of the types of force or influence they are subjected to. The statement of Eigen[54] regarding organization in biological systems — "We need organization in a different 'space,' which one may call *information* space" — may apply, in a broader sense, to teleneural phenomena as well. The recent work of Prigogine[55] regarding the evolutionary origin of the organization in living systems may be significant in its contribution to new methods of treating many phenomena, including those of a teleneural nature, in living systems. It is interesting to compare the questions being asked by paraphysicists and parapsychologists with those being asked in another field in which there seem to be more questions than there are answers: astrophysics. In a recent article the noted astrophysicist John Wheeler[56] questions, "In what way, if any, is the universe, the observed, affected by man, the observer? Is the universe deprived of all meaningful existence in the absence of the mind? . . . In brief, are life and mind irrelevant to the structure of the universe — or are they central to it?" Questions of this nature have been asked recently by physicists who have observed and considered the nature of paranormal events.

REFERENCES

1. Griffith, J. S., *Mathematical Neurobiology* (New York: Academic Press, 1972).
2. Harth, E. M. and S. L. Edgar, *Biophysical Journal*, 7, 689–717, 1967.
3. Harth, E. M., T. J. Csermely, B. Beek, and R. D. Lindsay, *Journal of Theoretical Biology*, *26*, 93–120, 1970.
4. Caianiello, E. R., *Journal of Theoretical Biology*, *1*, 204–35, 1961.
5. Caianiello, E. R., A. DeLuca, and L. M. Ricciardi, *Kybernetic*, 4, 10–18, 1967.
6. Cowan, J. D., in *Towards a Theoretical Biology 4: Essays* (Edinburgh: Edinburgh University Press, 1972).
7. Walker, E. H., *Journal of the Study of the Conscious*, 5, 46–63; 257–77, 1972–73.
8. Delgado, J. M. S., *Physical Control of the Mind* (New York: Harper & Row, 1969).
9. Putoff, H. and R. Targ, Stanford Research Institute news release, March 10, 1973. The initial experiments with Mr. Uri Geller, done in November and December 1972, were reported by SRI in this news release. In addition, a movie of the laboratory experiments with Mr. Geller was made; it has been shown to over 3000 scientists and engineers. Subsequently, results of telepathy and clairvoyance tests

with Geller, Ingo Swann, Patrick Price, and other subjects was reported in *Nature*, 251, 602–607, 1974.

10. The following books, *together with their references,* provide an introduction to the literature of parapsychology: Soal, S. G. and F. Bateman, *Modern Experiments in Telepathy* (London: Faber & Faber, 1954); Rhine, J. B. and J. G. Pratt, *Parapsychology: Frontier Science of the Mind* (Springfield, Illinois: Charles C Thomas, 1957); C. D. Broad, *Lectures on Psychical Research* (New York: The Humanities Press, 1962); C. E. M. Hansel, *ESP: A Scientific Evaluation* (New York: Charles Scribner's Sons, 1966); John White, *Psychic Exploration* (New York: G. P. Putnam's Sons, 1974).
11. Kennedy, J. L., *Proceedings of the American Philosophical Society*, 96, 513–18, 1952.
12. Mr. Uri Geller is an Israeli who was studied in Israel by Dr. Andrija Puharich before he came to the United States in August 1972 and was studied at SRI and other laboratories.
13. Franklin, Wilbur, *New Horizons Journal*, 2, No. 1, 8–13, 1975; Wilbur Franklin and Edgar Mitchell, "SEM Study of Fracture Surfaces Pertaining to the Question of Teleneural Fields From Human Subjects," available on request from Kent State University, Kent, Ohio.
14. Progress in the fields of parapsychology and paraphysics has been severely hindered by the lack of financial support. Unless the scientific community and the government agencies that provide financial resources decide to support high-level research in these fields, the potential usefulness of societal applications will not be developed beyond their present status of parlor curiosities in most scientific circles.
15. SRI financed the SEM study and EDMA, Inc. supported the author during the experiments at SRI with Mr. Geller.
16. The studies of the metal specimens and the conclusions drawn from them are based principally on *metallurgical* evidence. This evidence is much more substantial than merely visual, video-tape, or cinematography evidence of the subject performing the experiment since all of these modes of monitoring may be questionable. For example, hypnotists and magicians can cause metallic objects to appear to bend or, in the case of magicians, actually to bend and fracture. Also, it is well known to metallurgists that small amounts of mercury and other agents can, under certain conditions, cause intergranular fracture when the specimen is exposed to stress-corrosion situations.

17. The results of the investigation of three specimens are reported in Ref. 13 whereas the summary of that work presented in this article includes the results of only two of the three specimens.
18. Vaughan, A., "The phenomena of Uri Geller," *Psychic*, Vol. 4, No. 5, 13, 1973.
19. After a very small deformation, evidently the work-hardening was sufficient to preclude further bending by manual means.
20. The magnification, angle from the vertical, and date taken are recorded in the captions that accompany the photographs of the fracture surfaces.
21. Robertson, H. P. and T. W. Noonan, *Relativity and Cosmology* (Philadelphia: W. B. Saunders, 1968), p. 129.
22. The tensor properties of the stress in a solid can be incorporated but the isotropic fluid model is shown here to keep the model simple.
23. Kogan, I. M., *Telecommunications and Radio Engineering, 21*, 75, 1966; 22, 141, 1967; 23, 122, 1968.
24. A perfect crystal could be constructed with a much lower H utilizing translational and rotational symmetry operators and a distribution of momentums. However, a polycrystalline sample with a typical concentration of impurities, atomic defects, dislocations, and nonhomogeneous strains would have a much higher information content than a perfect cyrstal. Nevertheless, crystals with defects would still have less information content than glasses and plastics, which have little or no rotational or translational symmetry, and might, therefore, be easier for a subject to interact with.
25. The author has done bioinformation transfer experiments with a graduate student up to 380 miles. The bit rates were comparable to those reported by Kogan.[23] However, further work is needed to establish bit rates versus distance with greater reliability.
26. Bullock, T. H., *American Scientist, 61*, 316–25, 1973.
27. Hopkins, C. D., *American Scientist, 62*, 426, 1974.
28. Nelson, S. D., *Transactions of the American Society of Engineers*, 9, 398–405, 1966.
29. Callahan, P. S., *Applied Optics*, 7, 1425–30, 1968.
30. Presman, A. S., *Electromagnetic Fields and Life* (New York: Plenum Press, 1970).
31. Aceto, Jr., H., C. A. Tibias, and I. L. Silver, *IEEE Transactions*, Magnetics *MAG-6*, 368–73, 1970.
32. Ravitz, L. J., *Journal of the American Society of Psychosomatic Dentistry and Medicine*, 17, 119–27, 1970.

33. Mutschall, V., *Foreign Science Bulletin*, *4*, 1–12, 1968.
34. Kolin, A., *Physics Today*, November 1968.
35. Friedman, H., R. O. Becker, and C. H. Bachman, *Nature*, *213*, 949–50, 1967.
36. Bawin, S., R. G. Medici, W. Adey, and L. Kaczmarek, Conference at the New York Academy of Science, Feb. 12–15, 1974.
37. Burr, H. S., *Blueprint for Immortality* (London: Neville Spearman. 1972).
38. Cohen, D., *Science*, *161*, 784–86, 1968; D. Cohen and E. Givler, *Applied Physics*, Letters, *21*, 114–16, 1972.
39. Anninos, P. A., *Journal of Life Sciences*, *3*, 15–18, 1973.
40. Rocard, Y., in *Biological Effects of Magnetic Fields*, edited by M. Barnothy (New York: Plenum Press, 1964), pp. 279–86.
41. Grodsky, I., Conference at the New York Academy of Science, Feb. 12–15, 1974.
42. Puharich, A., *The Sacred Mushroom* (New York: Doubleday, 1959), Appendix 1; *Journal of Neuropsychology*, 2, 474, 1966.
43. Wait, J. R., *Science*, *178*, 272, 1972.
44. Wait, J. R., "The Sanguine Concept," in *Proceedings of the Symposium on Engineering in the Ocean Environment* (New York: IEE, 1972).
45. Ricardi, L. J., Lincoln Laboratories, personal communication.
46. Franklin, W., *Bulletin of the American Physical Society*, *19*, 821, 1974.
47. Taylor, J., *Superminds: An Inquiry into the Paranormal* (New York: Macmillan, 1975).
48. "The Physics of Paranormal Phenomena," International Conference, February 1975, Tarrytown, New York; author's notes are available on request.
49. Owen, A. R. G., *New Horizons Journal*, *1*, No. 4, 172, 1974.
50. Rhine, J. B., personal communication.
51. Vidal, J. J., *Annual Review of Biophysics and Bioengineering*, 2, 157, 1973.
52. Mehra, J., *American Scientist* *61*, 722, 1973.
53. Bohm, D., *Foundations of Physics*, *3*, 139, 1973.
54. Eigen, M., *Naturwiss*. *58*, 465, 1971.
55. Prigogine, I., G. Nicholis, and A. Babloyantz, *Physics Today*, *25*, 23, 1972.
56. Wheeler, J., *American Scientist*, *62*, 683, 1974.

URI'S MAGIC

by Thelma Moss, Ph.D., The Neuropsychiatric Institute,
Center for the Health Sciences,
University of California at Los Angeles.

Thelma Moss is a psychologist and head of parapsychological research at the U.C.L.A. Neuropsychiatric Institute. Her first book, Myself and I, *was a groundbreaker on the use of LSD in psychotherapy, and her most recent book,* The Probability of the Impossible, *surveys current research in parapsychology throughout the world. She is well known for her pioneering work in Kirlian photography, and was among the first American scientists to visit behind the Iron Curtain with Russian parapsychologists.*

The work reported here was conducted in June 1975. Thelma Moss makes it clear in her own introduction to the paper that it was not possible to impose "adequate scientific controls" during the experimentation. Geller visited the UCLA laboratory without giving much advance notice, and Moss had to improvise a good many of the tests that were conducted. Another drawback to the Kirlian photography research presented here, and one made clear by Moss, is that the color photographs had to be taken in a darkroom, making it impossible to absolutely rule out any sleight of hand that may have been attempted by Geller or by a research assistant. Though Moss believes that no such trick occurred, she admits that she cannot offer proof. Her paper appears here as a "subjective description" of the events that took place in her laboratory.

Published for the first time, with the permission of the author.

It becomes increasingly clear that the most significant thing about Uri Geller is not Uri Geller. Rather, it is his influence on various persons around the world. This is the simple fact now being studied by distinguished scientists in England, Japan, Germany, and the United States. Some of these scientists have been fortunate enough to work for weeks or months with Geller — or persons who have learned to emulate the Geller Effect — under controlled laboratory conditions, and can offer splendid scientific data to substantiate their findings. Our UCLA lab cannot. We had only two brief sessions with Geller, in which we seemed to see several paranormal events — all without adequate scientific controls. Therefore, we simply wish to present a subjective description of the events that took place in our lab first on a Saturday afternoon in June 1975, from 3:00 P.M. to 5:30 P.M., and then on the following Monday night from 10:30 P.M. to midnight.

After which report, some observations:

The Events

When we heard, suddenly, that Uri Geller had agreed to visit the lab, we were caught off-guard. Naturally, we were all familiar with his repertoire of Amazing Acts: bending and breaking heavy metals by stroking them, starting watches and appliances that had not functioned for years, sending and receiving telepathic messages, materializing and dematerializing objects, etc. Many magicians had, of course, claimed they could perform these "miracles," which were simply magic tricks. Certainly in conservative scientific circles, Geller was more infamous than famous, and the popular hypothesis was that he represented the Compleat Charlatan. We realized that in one session (which was all that had been promised) it would be impossible to answer the numerous charges of fraud, sleight of hand, and chicanery. We merely hoped to witness one or two of his more celebrated phenomena firsthand. Although we doubted even that possibility. For in our research we have learned that psychics cannot turn their talents on and off on command, and they seem especially impotent in the laboratory, unless there is a trusting, comfortable atmosphere in which success is not demanded. On one occasion, Geller had been unable to perform any of his talents on a national TV program. Why assume he could demonstrate them in our lab, under more rigorous conditions, in a space of two hours?

Nevertheless, we had made arrangements for some controlled studies. We knew Geller claimed to bend, and break, heavy metal objects by stroking them. Could he bend or break them without touching the metal? Barry Taff, in cooperation with the Physics Department, had obtained various metals, which had been encased in glass vials and tightly sealed. They were ready in the lab. Previous experiments by Grad, Smith, Dean, and others[1,2,3] had shown that chemicals could change markedly as the result of psychic healers' "charging" such substances through glass bottles. Since Geller seemed dramatically to change metals, could he also change the chemistry of liquids? John Hubacher had obtained some vials of ethyl alcohol, and they were, too, ready in the lab. Since Geller was famous for mending broken watches, and since we typically obtain best results by starting with a task at which a psychic is most at ease, associates had brought to the lab two wrist watches and two clocks, none of which had functioned in over a year. Also ready to be stroked was a large quantity of heavy stainless steel cutlery.

A major research interest in the lab is Kirlian photography, which requires neither camera nor lens to record its curious pictures; it sends an electrical charge into the object being photographed. Kirlian photography is probably as controversial a research area as Uri Geller, some scientists claiming that the emanations that appear around fingers, leaves, metals (or anything at all) are merely an electrical artifact, or the commonplace "corona discharge." (In our experience we have found that corona discharge is indeed a major component, but does nothing to explain results like the "phantom leaf effect," as illustrated in Plate 19.) We knew that Geller had participated in a few Kirlian experiments; in fact, we had in the lab the slides shown in Plates 20 and 21, taken two years previously by Henry Dakin and James Hickman in San Francisco.[4] Plate 20 shows Geller's fingertip at rest, below Dakin's watch. Plate 21 shows Geller "sending energy" toward the watch. One can see a "spurt" emerging from the fingertip. In the hope that Geller would agree to a similar study, our Kirlian equipment was ready in the isolation booth (which also serves as a photographic studio and darkroom). Also ready in the booth were chemicals for instant development of the film, should Geller agree.

By two-thirty, last-minute details were being set straight, accompanied by scoffing comments to the effect that Geller was notoriously unreliable and would fail to appear. At which time the phone rang. It was a friend of Geller's, announcing that they had just finished lunch at the village drugstore and were unable to find the lab. Immediately two attractive volunteers were sent to bring them. Uri arrived, therefore, not promptly but ahead of time. First surprise.

The second surprise was his enthusiasm and knowledge of our research. The third was his immediate appraisal of the lab. He looked at the array of cutlery and watches on the table and said he was not interested in demonstrating his usual bag of tricks. He wanted, rather, to see if any kind of energy, emanating from him, could be photographed with the Kirlian device. "What kind of controlled study can I do with Kirlian?" he asked. Immediately I flashed on the projector and showed the two Dakin/Hickman slides (Plates 20 and 21). Uri studied the slides, puzzled. "But what are these pictures?" he asked. Apparently, when this study had been done, in Geller's hotel, the film had been taken away to be processed, and Uri had never seen the results. I expressed surprise, but Uri shrugged, explaining that he had done only casual work with Kirlian photography, with "inconclusive results." He was hoping for controlled studies with us.

I was suddenly, oddly, off-guard. Typically we spend thirty minutes making a psychic comfortable. After ten minutes, Uri was suggesting research in an area with which he was unfamiliar (and threatened because, he told us, he had been afraid of electricity ever since, as a child, he had been badly shocked while playing with his mother's electric sewing machine). I suggested a variation of the Dakin/Hickman study: we would bring a broken clock into the booth, place it on film, and Uri would attempt to "heal" it by placing his finger on the film, not touching the clock, but "sending energy" into it. Uri agreed and entered the booth eagerly — but was immediately intimidated by the machinery inside. It took many trials before he was convinced he would not be shocked. When he finally saw that the device was harmless, he asked to begin. Approximately ten observers (chiefly lab associates) crowded into the booth, the door was closed, and all the lights turned out except for the red safe light, which can be on when we use special orthochromatic film.

There began a long series of trials, which were failures. Uri tried to "send energy" into the broken clock. When he felt that the energy was there, he would shout "NOW!!" and I would press the button to take the picture. Then I picked up the clock with one hand, and with the other hand picked up the film and handed it to John, who was developing each piece of film after each trial. We were searching for the "spurt of energy," like the one in Plate 21. It did not appear for twenty-two trials. Perhaps to relieve the mounting frustration, Ruth Williams, who had brought the clock, picked it up and announced, "It's going!" Uri shouted, "NO!!" grabbed the clock from her and held it to his ear, then promptly held it to my ear. I could hear it ticking loudly and steadily. Everyone in the booth took turns listening to its regular ticking, making excited comments.

Here, an interlude to complete the watch phenomenon. That clock kept perfect time for five weeks before it stopped again. What was more peculiar, a second traveling clock, which had been brought into the booth and put aside as unsuitable for the experiment, started going, without ever being touched. Uri also mended two wrist watches that afternoon, one of which had not worked in eight years. But by far the most inexplicable phenomenon happened the following Monday afternoon, when my daughter Pauli and I watched Uri on a local TV program. On the show, Uri asked people in their homes to bring watches or clocks or broken appliances in front of their TV sets, saying that this phenomenon of repair was not his exclusive power, since somehow — he did not know how — people in the TV audience could perform the same "healing." On impulse, I went to my jewel box and brought to the TV set a gold watch that I had been wearing as a pendant for the past sixteen years, since in all that time it had never functioned as a timepiece. I gave the watch to Pauli to hold. She did, but toward the end of the demonstration it was still not working. Pauli handed the watch to me, saying it was very pretty and she would like it as a birthday present. I agreed. She added that she would like me to have it repaired, and I agreed again. Then, as Uri was saying his goodbyes, I absently lifted the watch to my ear. It was ticking steadily. I said to Pauli, "It's going." She said, "Don't be silly." I handed it to her, and she heard it. Startled, she said, "But how could that happen?!" (She is a Harvard student.) I couldn't answer her, of course. The watch has been functioning ever since.

Uri had repaired five watches and clocks taken from our lab alone. Let us freely grant that he may have been performing some legerdemain in the lab. That explanation cannot suffice for the remote TV watch repair, a phenomenon, incidentally, that has been repeated in many cities and countries. (See Appendix.)

In spite of the general excitement, I felt disappointed. I had hoped that whatever energy Uri had used to start that first traveling clock would be recorded in the Kirlian photography. It was not. Uri was similarly dissatisfied, and suggested we continue to try for the Kirlian effect. He felt he could succeed in demonstrating the energy on film, but that it might take one hundred failures before we obtained one success. Would that be all right? Of course. Usually, in psychical research, we achieve at least a dozen failures for each success.

Uri now began working with a key placed at the top of the film; his finger was at the bottom. Again a long series of failures. But eventually John, who had been developing each piece of film as I handed it to him, suddenly said quietly, "It's there." Uri shouted his characteristic "NO!!" And reached to see the film. But the red light in the booth is dim, and he could not make out what was on the film. I suggested a break, so that we could go into the light and study the picture. But Uri, with his swift impatience, rejected the idea. He felt he might now have a handle on the "energy," and he proposed a series of trials, three of which would be control pictures (for which he would not attempt to send energy), and three experimental pictures (for which he would try to achieve the effect). On each of the "energy" pictures the effect appeared, to a greater or lesser degree, and nothing unusual was observed in the control pictures. The best of this series is printed here in Plate 22; and Plate 23 gives a close-up of Uri's finger pad, with energy spurt.

It should be strongly emphasized that the red dimness in the booth makes sleight of hand easy indeed. There is no way, therefore, that we can rule out fraud in these Kirlian pictures.

We left the booth to examine the negatives in the light. Uri was delighted with what he saw and asked me to explain the phenomenon. I laughed and asked him to explain what he had done. He shook his head and laughed, too. Stimulated by the success, he said he would like to try a telepathy experiment. We had made plans for such an experiment, should the opportunity for it arise. Three students — Judy Orloff, Kerry Gaynor, and Ruth Brady — were to go to my office, five floors below the lab. There, when they received my phone call, they were to draw on a piece of paper a number between one and ten (chosen randomly, of course). Uri would try to receive the number in the isolation booth, where he would remain with me. During this time, Uri agreed to keep his finger on a Kirlian device that we use to take moving pictures. (It was hoped that the number, should Uri receive it, would appear in the emanations around his fingertip. We obtained good movies of his finger — which looked no different from a normal, healthy fingertip in Kirlian cinematography.)

After the telephone signal was given, Uri reported seeing the Star of David, and after a few more minutes said that the only other impression he received was the infinity sign (∞). Finally he said he had failed in the experiment, for he had received no other impressions. He asked me to call down to the office to find out what the number was. When Judy answered the phone, I said, "Uri didn't get a number. His only impressions were the Star of David and the infinity sign." Judy laughed. "We all said he'd get the infinity sign! The number was eight — and as we looked at it, we said it looked like the infinity sign."

Success? We like to think so — even though the telepathic impression had arrived, as it frequently does, with primary process distortion. We felt more secure about the success when the students brought to the lab the piece of paper on which the eight had been written. It looked very similar to the infinity sign Uri had written in the booth.

Collusion? Possible, certainly. Scientific research — and, recently, parapsychological research — has been plagued with a few dishonest scientists. Another possibility, widely hypothesized, is that Geller wears a miniature transistor radio in his teeth and can hear what is occurring in remote places. More plausible, perhaps, is that Geller was employing a magic trick. Magicians claim this is an effect they can easily duplicate. This was the best controlled of our studies that day — and one can see how easily the controls can be shot down.

The "infinity sign" success had charged the lab with excitement. But suddenly the sweet sounds of success were drowned by friction. It was discovered that an observer in the lab, a professional photographer from a magazine that had published exposés on Geller, had been taking pictures of the day's events. Geller was angry that the photographer had been allowed in the lab. (I had agreed that he come, with the proviso that he take no pictures.) During this fracas, Uri and the photographer went into the hall. While I was wondering what to do, they reappeared. Uri was now holding the photographer's key chain, saying he would bend whichever key the photographer selected. (Barry Taff quickly turned on the video tape to record the event, should it occur. It did.) The photographer, delighted, chose a key, which Uri stroked gently. Barry exclaimed, "I can see it bending!" Uri replied quietly, focusing on the key, "No, no. No one can see it bend." Eventually, we could all easily see that the key had been deformed to an angle of approximately forty degrees. The photographer was so enchanted that he surrendered the roll of film he had shot.

Another collusion? Between Uri and the photographer, a "stooge"? Why not? Their violent argument could have been contrived so that they would disappear into the hall, where Uri could rub chemicals on the key (another frequently offered hypothesis). Once again, we had no adequate controls for this example of psychokinesis.

After all this excitement, Uri had developed a headache. I suggested that one of our lab members, a medical doctor doing research on the "laying on of hands," give Uri a healing. Uri went into the isolation booth with the doctor, who emerged in less than a minute, smiling and saying, "Uri's pain is gone." Uri came to the door of the booth, a bemused expression on his face. "How does he do that?" he asked.

A highpoint: Uri Geller asking how someone else can do something . . .

More than two hours had passed and I had to leave for an evening lecture. Uri was exhilarated, and stood in the hall with John and Barry, talking about the possibility of returning for further experiments. (Neither Barry's metals encased in glass nor John's chemicals had been touched.) I left them chatting and missed a dramatic episode:

Early in the day a physics student, Jim, had brought to the lab a sophisticated electronic device in the hope that Geller would be able to distort the 100-cps sine wave it had been programmed to produce. This sine wave was shown to me on an oscilloscope; it could also be printed on a chart recorder. I agreed, after trying vainly to distort the sine wave on the oscilloscope, that it would be an excellent test for PK, but that we had already too crowded and busy a schedule. Also, the device was too large to fit into our small lab and must be left in the hall (with someone standing guard over it). Naturally, Geller saw it right away and knew what would be expected of him. But he dismissed the idea, saying he had never been able to affect electronic instruments voluntarily — only spontaneously. (Reports from Harold Puthoff and Russell Targ from the Stanford Research Institute confirm this lack of voluntary control in Geller, although they admit to several spontaneous occurrences in which electronic devices went berserk in Geller's presence.)

While John and Barry chatted with Uri in the hall, Jim surreptitiously turned on the machine and chart recorder. No one was aware that he had done so, or that anything unusual occurred. But a very excited Jim arrived on Monday morning, bringing with him the chart of the 100-cps sine wave, which had accelerated to 4,000,000 cps, going through four modifications in shape, and ending in a triangular wave, at which point the machine suddenly stopped working. Jim had gone to his professor with this fascinating data, only to be told that sophisticated electronic gear will quite often suddenly malfunction, and that it was merely a coincidence that Geller was standing near it when the malfunction occurred.

Uri telephoned the next afternoon (Sunday), saying he was so intrigued by the Kirlian pictures, he would like to return for another session, this time to obtain color pictures. The only satisfactory time proved to be 10:30 P.M. on Monday night.

And Monday night Uri arrived, again a little ahead of time. For this session, Uri and I remained alone in the isolation booth, while John Hubacher stayed outside, trying to send telepathic messages. Our goal was to obtain, on color film, any impressions Uri might receive and channel through his fingertip. Since we were working with color film, which cannot be processed immediately, Uri knew he had to leave Los Angeles before learning the results. Nevertheless, he worked very hard, insisting that for every experimental trial (to channel his telepathic impression on film), there would be a control picture (when he was inactive).

Once more it must be stressed that for color film, *no light at all is possible.* Uri and I worked in the booth in total darkness. Therefore, some kind of chicanery was conceivable.

There were many trials in which Uri tried to receive a number, or a geometric figure, or a letter of the alphabet. He was never successful. On one occasion he reported feeling an "electric sensation" traveling up from the film into his arm. On that trial he had been trying to receive a number, but had felt unsure and did not say the number aloud — although he wrote it on a box top, in the dark, and showed it to me after John told us the number was five. Uri did not claim success for the telepathy, but felt something might appear on the film. Several times after that Uri felt an "electric sensation," and I made notes of those trials. In three of them, unusual effects did appear. They are shown here in Plates 24, 25, and 26.

And, of course, all of these effects could be tricks, easily performed in the dark. The result of manipulating a fine wire, for example. Attempting to duplicate the effect, one of our lab associates obtained the picture in Plate 27 by plucking a hair from his head and holding it under the tip of his finger. The effect is as interesting as the Geller pictures.

On the other hand, on rare occasions in the lab, we have obtained pictures, which look similar to the Geller Effect, from ordinary subjects doing routine experiments. We have labeled these "Kirlian anomalies," and two of them are shown here in Plates 28 and 29, depicting what we call "unexplained eruptions."

Toward midnight Uri was tired, as indeed were we. But John was not quite satisfied. He asked if Uri would mind trying to send energy into the vials of ethyl alcohol he had placed in the booth. Uri obliged, commenting that he did not know the purpose of the experiment and did not care to find out. While he held his hands above the vials, I quickly left the booth and snipped a leaf from a plant. I handed the leaf to John, who grinned and cut off a small section of the leaf, and then asked Uri if he would mind one last Kirlian study. Uri sighed and nodded. When John asked him to send energy into the cut leaf, Uri did as requested, remarking that he had never tried to energize a leaf. As soon as the picture was taken, Uri left, without waiting to see the result of that final black-and-white leaf picture. But John and I were quick to develop it — and we found a "phantom leaf effect." As one can see in Plate 30, it is not a vivid or exciting "phantom" effect, but it is there. As I write this, I realize Uri was never told about the purpose of this last study — nor about his success.

*

OK. What had come of those two Uri Geller sessions? Five mended watches, one bent key, one successful telepathic experiment at a distance, several very interesting Kirlian photographs, including one "phantom leaf," an oscilloscope that went berserk and broke — and, finally, a chemical analysis that showed striking changes in the composition of the ethyl alcohol (changes that were not conclusive, because the chemicals had not been adequately analyzed before the experiment). And, of course, without rigorous controls, as we have said, we can offer no scientific evidence that any one of these effects was genuine.

*

Observations

But scientific evidence is not the theme of our paper. The essential theme is this:

Since Geller's appearance in Los Angeles, our lab has been visited by several persons who claim that they, too, can bend metals by stroking them. And they have successfully demonstrated their ability. The most remarkable episode of this kind, in our experience, occurred in August, when a young woman named Cindy visited us and succeeded in dramatically distorting a heavy fork. It took her two hours to complete the job, during which time two high school boys came into the lab and watched the proceedings. I suggested they try to bend something, too, since the talent seems to transfer to others who watch. The boys took out keys and began stroking them. At the end of the session, the fork had gone through several transformations. Plate 31 shows the fork at the end of an hour; Plate 32 shows it after one and a half hours; and Plate 33 at the end of two hours. In addition, one of the boys had made a small bend in the key. He felt rather sheepish about his accomplishment, compared to Cindy's. I suggested he look at the key later on, since sometimes the object continues to bend after the stroking. He called a few hours later to tell us excitedly that when he took the key out of his pocket to look at it, it had bent double. And the next morning he called, aghast, to say that when he woke up and looked at the key, he saw it break in two pieces. (I believe he was frightened by this episode, because when I phoned to ask him to bring the key in, his mother promised to have him return the call. He never did.)

Here is an interesting chain reaction. Geller had performed on Los Angeles TV. A sixteen-year-old, Colleen, saw him and discovered she could bend metal. Cindy saw Colleen (never Geller) and found out that she could do the same thing. A high school student watched Cindy and found out he could do it, too. We saw it in our lab.

Other scientists in other countries have seen it in their labs. And they have documented their findings with many persons (usually, but not always, between the ages of ten and twenty). In particular, Professor John Taylor, in his book *Superminds*,[5] gives excellent hard data on the mysterious qualities found in the metals deformed by these subjects.

What is it that these subjects do? No one knows. Not even the subjects themselves. (Not even Uri Geller, who asked me very seriously, "What does all this mean?")

This faculty — bending and/or breaking metals by gentle manipulation — is considered by many to be nothing but a parlor trick. In my opinion, it might be likened to the inane game, played in Ancient Greece, in which people would amuse themselves by rubbing amber and then picking up light objects with the amber, sometimes to the accompaniment of little sparks and crackles.

Amber, in Greek, is called *elektron*. From which root word we have derived our words *electron* and *electricity*. Although it took eighteen hundred years to proceed from the game of rubbing amber to pick up objects all the way to the creation of the huge dynamos that serve today's complex technology.

It is conceivable that this foolish TV entertainment of metal bending is the emergence into our awareness of another powerful energy, an energy emitted by the human body, an energy that thus far science has overlooked. Physicists are puzzled by the deformed metals they have analyzed. For, to obtain such twists and turns in metal, intense heat (hundreds, if not thousands, of degrees) would seem to be required. But nothing more than body heat has been recorded.

Can so powerful an energy be emitted effortlessly by the human body? Is there a bioenergy capable of so much work? Properly understood and harnessed, an energy like this could offer vast new areas of exploration in medicine, metallurgy, and biology — not to mention psychokinesis, which has generally been ignored by science until now.

These are powerful implications. And it is just because of these implications that Uri Geller's magic may prove to be quite marvelous.

APPENDIX

Of the numerous anecdotes reported to our lab about broken watches, clocks, and other appliances repaired in front of a TV set when Uri Geller was performing, this report — a letter received from Mrs. Pauline Figer of San Francisco — is the most remarkable:

Dear Dr. Moss,

I have been reading about your tests with Uri Geller. And your findings are amazing. But I think my experience concerning Mr. Geller is even more amazing. He was on TV Channel 2 in Oakland, Calif., not so long ago. During the interview all of us at home were asked to get out our watches that needed repairing. I had a bunch of old watches I have had for years. Six began to run for me. Out of the six, five are still running. However, the most amazing experience is as follows: I had forgotten all about my grandfather's watch that hasn't worked for years and years. My dad kept it in a glass container on a table in his living room as just a keepsake from his dad who died when I was 13 years old. I am now 55. When my dad died the watch was given to me. The watch was in my dresser drawer, and I couldn't have told you just exactly where! After watching Mr. Geller I turned off the TV and decided to go to bed. I knelt down and said my prayers as usual. Then as I started to pull back the covers on my side of the bed, something fell to the floor. (The lights were off.) I picked up the object and took it to the light to see what it was. It was my grandfather's watch and it was running!!! It had *been transported some way* from the drawer to the bed while I was in the living room! The watch is still running. I wrote to Mr. Geller because I thought he would like to know.

However perhaps you also can relate the experience to him for I thought he would be pleased to know it.

It is a delight to relate this experience for Mrs. Figer.

REFERENCES

1. Dr. Grad's research has been published in various scientific journals. The *Journal of the American Society for Psychical Research, 61*, 286–305, 1967, article contains a good bibliography.
2. Sister Justa Smith's research with enzymes is published in the *Proceedings of the Dimensions of Healing Symposium*, Academy of Parapsychology and Medicine, Los Altos, California, 1972.
3. Douglas Dean and Ed Beame's paper, "Physical Changes in Water by the Laying on of Hands," is published in the *Proceedings of the Second International Psychotronics Conference*, Monaco, 1975.
4. Dakin, H. S. *High-Voltage Photography*. The quotation may be found on page 30. This monograph, published in San Francisco, 1975, may be purchased from the Edmund Scientific Company, Barrington, New Jersey, 08007.
5. Taylor, John. *Superminds: An Inquiry into the Paranormal* (New York: Macmillan, 1975). This book contains the best experimentation yet published on the Geller Effect, performed by a well-known physicist.

MAGNETIC PATTERN ERASURE: A PROPOSED METHOD OF SCIENTIFIC STUDY

by Ronald S. Hawke, Lawrence Livermore Laboratory, Livermore, California.

Ronald S. Hawke received a B.S.E.E. degree from the University of California at Berkeley in 1961, and did graduate work in electromagnetics and solid state physics. A scientist at the Lawrence Livermore Laboratory of the University of California since 1961, he has published more than a dozen articles in several fields, including plasma physics, microwaves, Raman spectroscopy, and high pressure physics. Hawke spent a year on sabbatical leave at the Max Planck Institute. He is currently doing research on metallic hydrogen at the Lawrence Livermore Laboratory.

Hawke's paper serves two functions. First, it presents a series of events that occurred during a visit by Geller to the Lawrence Livermore Laboratory in late 1974, events that, Hawke says, might be suggestive of paranormal happenings, but cannot be offered as unequivocal proof. In the second part of the paper, Hawke gives a detailed outline of some tightly designed experiments to which he feels Geller should be subjected.

Hawke's observations presented here involve Geller's influence on magnetic program cards. Such cards typically contain information that is to be fed to a computer. The information is not printed in ink on each card, but is contained on the surface of the card in the form of certain magnetic patterns; each pattern conveys a different piece of information. A layer of plastic covers all of the patterns on a given card. Rubbing a magnetic program card with one's fingers, as Geller did, will not alter its pattern. However, an extraneous magnetic field can change a program.

Published for the first time, with the permission of the author.

Abstract

This paper summarizes a meeting with Uri Geller, during which the magnetic pattern stored in the iron oxide layer of a magnetic program card was erased. In order to determine the mechanism of the erasure, a detailed outline for a possible experiment is given. The method is based on the known properties of iron oxide and would ultimately lead to a fundamental understanding of *what* is happening, whether it be normal or paranormal.

Introduction

There has been a considerable amount of effort spent in validating paranormal phenomena,[1] not to mention what has been spent in disproving it. There has been much less work done to determine exactly what happens at a macroscopic, microscopic, molecular, atomic, or nuclear level during a psychokinetic (PK) event. Ultimately, greater understanding would not only reduce the mystery surrounding these events, but also would make it possible to develop useful scientific theories and/or practical applications, as there has been profit from studying seriously other originally mysterious phenomena, such as magnetism, electricity, radioactivity, etc. Basically, unstudied phenomena remain mysterious and debatable, but studied phenomena enhance understanding and usefulness. This paper gives an example of a proposed method for the detailed investigation of a single phenomenon that might or might not be paranormal.

The first part of the paper is a brief summary of a meeting with Uri Geller at which we began to observe a class of possible PK phenomena that seems to be unusually susceptible to quantitative scientific study. We present the results of preliminary tests; then we outline a systematic method that would lead to an understanding of what kind of phenomena causes the particular result of a test without assuming or precluding the existence of a paranormal or anomalous nature.

Nature of the Phenomenon

The particular phenomenon chosen for this discussion results from a meeting of a few colleagues and myself with Uri Geller in late 1974. Additional study is warranted by the following event, which should not be construed as a conclusive demonstration of a paranormal phenomenon, but rather as a suggestion for an interesting area to investigate more thoroughly.

An attempt was made to erase or at least alter the highly ordered magnetic pattern corresponding to a specific routine encoded on a magnetic program card normally used with a Hewlett Packard Model 65 pocket calculator. The cards consist of a .0004-inch-thick layer of iron oxide bonded to a .008-inch-thick plastic base. Plate 35 is a photograph of a typical card and Plate 36 shows the magnetic pattern stored in the iron oxide layer. The magnetic pattern is made visible by a magnetic viewer,[2] which utilizes a colloidal suspension of fine iron oxide particles. The stored magnetic field in the card penetrates the colloidal solution and condenses the particles along the lines of force, causing the formation of a dark region, which can be photographed.

During the meeting with Geller, the erasure of three cards and the change of one card were attempted. The first card (Card 1) given to Geller for erasure was sealed in a glass bottle with its plastic top glued in place. The bottle was opened and the card, inspected after the meeting, was found to be unchanged.

The second and third cards (Cards 2 and 3) were directly rubbed by Geller with his fingers. After each attempt the card was inserted into an HP 65 calculator, which will reject the program if the pattern is ambiguous. Both Cards 2 and 3 were accepted prior to

Geller's attempts and rejected afterward. Subsequent inspection with a magnetic viewer after the meeting with Geller revealed that the magnetic patterns had been altered, as shown in Plates 37 and 38. (Of course, mere rubbing normally has no effect on the magnetic pattern.)

The fourth card (Card 4) was lightly touched, but not rubbed, by Geller; his intention was to "change" the program rather than erase it. It remained operable in the calculator and subsequent inspection did not indicate any change had occurred.

The first point to determine is whether the magnetic program cards responded to an applied magnetic field, and/or other applied forms of energy, or if their behavior was anomalous. If it is found that there is a sufficient causal magnetic field present during the cards' alteration, then the next step is to determine the source of the field. If, on the other hand, a magnetic field of sufficient intensity is not present during an alteration, then the next step is to study other known possible causes. If all known causes are excluded, then research at the molecular and atomic level is indicated. Below is a summary of what is already known about the magnetic, thermal, electric, and ultrasonic properties of the program cards.

Properties of the Magnetic Program Cards[3]

Magnetic

Normally the magnetic field intensity required to erase the magnetic pattern is about 265 oersteds (Oe). A slight altering of the pattern can occur at an intensity as low as 150 Oe. For comparison, the earth's magnetic field intensity at the surface is of the order of 0.5 Oe. Common permanent magnets have field intensities of about 1000 to 20,000 Oe at the surface of the poles.

The minimum duration of the applied magnetic field needed to alter the magnetic pattern is about 50 nanoseconds (ns).

Thermal

Temperatures above the Curie temperature can cause a randomization of the magnetic pattern. For iron oxide the Curie temperature is about 450° C. The base material is plastic, which permanently distorts at about 100° C., much lower than the Curie temperature; hence distortion of the base would accompany a thermally induced erasure.

Ultrasonic

Ultrasonic waves do not erase or alter the magnetic pattern without eroding the iron oxide layer. Again, inspection of the card would indicate damage.

Electrical Conductivity

The cards are fabricated completely of high-resistance materials, so small voltages would not be able to cause sufficient currents to generate magnetic fields intense enough to alter the magnetic pattern.

Electrostatic

Electrostatic fields up to the point of breakdown in air ($\approx$ 10 kV/cm) do not cause any observable changes in the magnetic pattern. If the voltage gradient is high enough for the air to break down, an electric arc will occur. An arc is capable of producing a magnetic field intense enough to alter the magnetic pattern. A sufficiently intense arc would probably be audible and would leave a charred area. A record of electric field intensity, however, would be advisable.

✲

Proposed Experimental Setup

For the purpose of answering the question, "Is the alteration of the magnetic pattern caused by a magnetic field?" the following setup or its equivalent would be suggested.

Magnetometers

At least two magnetometers should be placed with their sensitive axes aligned with the plane of the iron oxide layer and orthogonal to each other, as shown in Figure 1. If possible, a third magnetometer should be aligned orthogonally to the plane of the card. The magnetometers should be set at a sensitivity such that they can detect a very concentrated magnetic field at a distance much greater than that at which the magnetic pattern can be altered.[4]

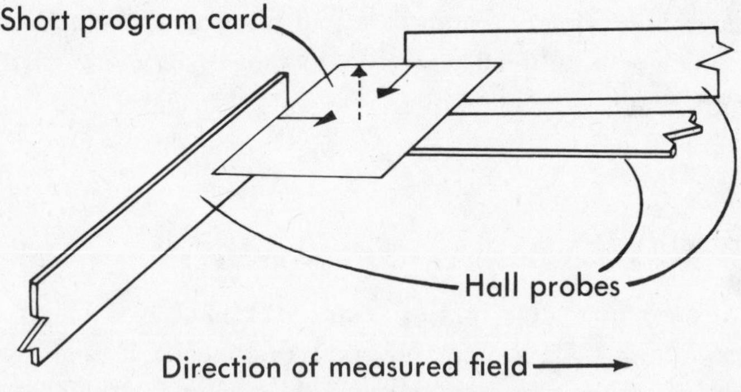

Fig. 1. Magnetometer setup

Inductive Pickup Coils

Magnetometers respond slowly, compared to the switching time of the program cards. They alone, therefore, are not adequate.

Inductive pickup coils can be used to detect more rapid changes of a magnetic field. Such coils develop a voltage output that is proportional to the number of turns in the coil, the cross-sectional area, and the time rate of change of the magnetic field. Figure 2 shows the frequency regions covered by magnetometers (Hall-type) and two types of coils with few and many turns.[5] The coil with a few turns should have inductance low enough to respond to pulses 50 ns or shorter. The coil with many turns is to provide larger signals at the lower frequencies. The inductive pickup coils should also be more sensitive than the program cards; they can be tested with pulsed magnetic fields produced by a pulsed current, of variable duration, applied to a low-inductance coil. Sensitivity can be established for a variety of pulse lengths and applied field orientations.

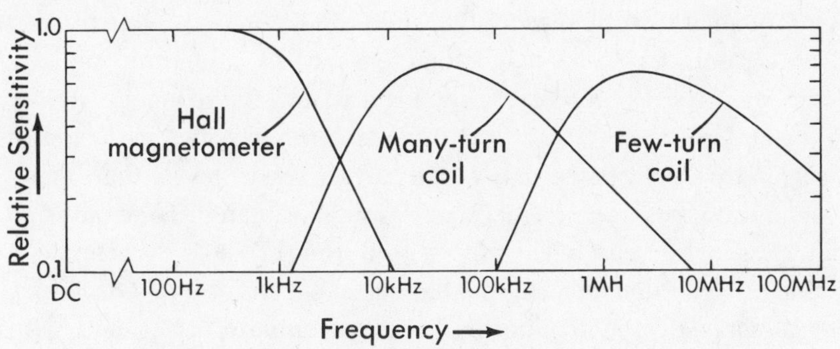

Fig. 2. Frequency response of Hall magnetometers and inductive pickup coils

Electrostatic Field Detectors

Two sets of parallel wires along the sides of the card, as shown in Figure 3 (page 130), should be used to detect electrostatic fields and arcs.

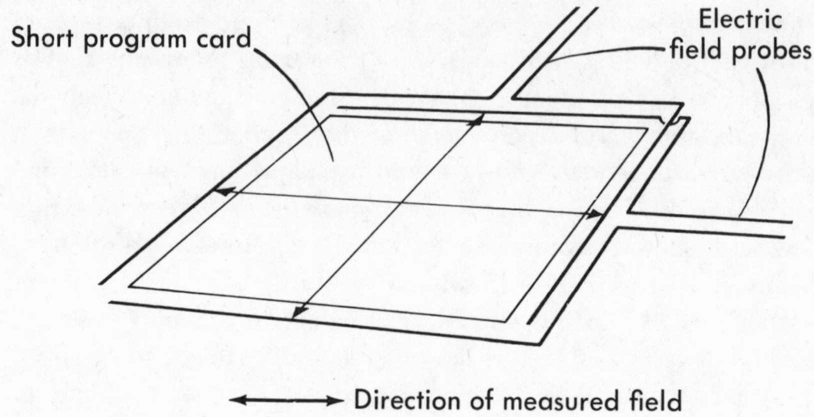

Fig. 3. Electric field probes

Recording Instrumentation

One of many possible recording methods is briefly outlined here. The outputs from the magnetometers can be monitored directly with strip chart recorders. The outputs from the magnetic pickup coils and electrostatic field detectors can be amplified and used to trigger threshold detectors, which are preset to levels that correspond to signals from magnetic pulses smaller than those required to alter a program card. The output from the threshold detectors can then be recorded on a multichannel event recorder. Of course, more sophisticated monitoring of all potentially fast signals with video-tape techniques would be an added asset. Naturally, other factors are also necessary, such as continuous video-taping of the region around the magnetic program card, including its inspection before and after its placement in the instrumented region.

Summary

A brief description of what might be an unusual erasure of a magnetic program card has been given. On the supposition that an anomalous phenomenon could be the causal mechanism, a possible *basic* experiment is described: The experiment would ascertain if an erasure is caused by normal mechanisms or not. If known mechanisms are not the cause of erasure, then the anomalous behavior of the magnetic iron oxide film certainly requires further study. If, on the other hand, the erasure is caused by a known mechanism, such as a magnetic field, then its source must be studied.

The same style of pursuit would be scientifically useful in other types of PK study; for example, acoustic emission studies *during* the bending of metals, and photoelastic analysis *during* the bending of plastics.

At the time of this writing plans are under discussion for Geller to undergo a series of experiments devised by Ronald Hawke. The first of these tests, if they come about, will be an attempt by Geller to alter or erase information stored on magnetic program cards in the manner outlined in the above paper. If significant results are obtained, then Hawke would like to try two other PK experiments, which he briefly mentions in the closing paragraph of his paper. In one experiment Hawke wants to run sound waves through a metal object Geller is trying to bend. Any deformations in the metal will alter the pattern and intensity of the waves. By studying the differences between the input and output sound waves, Hawke hopes to understand better the mechanism that produces the deformations. He would then like to perform the same general type of experiment while Geller tries to bend plastics; the difference here would be that light waves rather than sound waves would be used as the investigative probe. Geller has consented to participate in such tests, but no definite date has yet been set.

REFERENCES

1. A good summary of several areas of PK research with extensive references can be found in *Psychic Exploration: A Challenge for*

Science, E. D. Mitchell, ed. by John White (New York: G. P. Putnam's, 1974).

2. Product of 3M Company, St. Paul, Minnesota.
3. "Magnetic Tape Erasure — How Serious Is the Threat?" M-CL-237(322)R (Jan. 1972), *Product Communications*, 3M Company, St. Paul, Minnesota.
4. A concentrated magnetic field can be obtained for testing by using a very small chip from a magnet.
5. The exact number of turns in each coil would depend on many factors but a typical number would be about 100 for the few-turn coil and 10,000 for the many-turn coil.

FILMED AND NONFILMED EVENTS: ON URI GELLER'S VISIT TO WESTERN KENTUCKY UNIVERSITY

by Thomas P. Coohill, Ph.D., Physics Department,
Western Kentucky University, Bowling Green, Kentucky.

Thomas P. Coohill received an undergraduate degree in physics and a doctorate in biophysics from Pennsylvania State University. He has held research positions at the VA Hospital in Pittsburgh, Pennsylvania, and at the schools of medicine and dentistry of the University of Pittsburgh before becoming an associate professor of biophysics and Chairman of the Biophysics Committee at Western Kentucky University. He is the author of numerous articles on the interactions of natural and artificial light on living matter.

During a one-day visit to Western Kentucky University (February 19, 1974), Uri Geller participated in a series of informal tests under the direction of Dr. Coohill. Geller had been invited to the school as a lecturer and not as a scientific subject, but he consented to Coohill's request to "try some tests." The tests reported in the following pages were not executed with the rigor essential for a scientific investigation. They are presented here as anecdotes because Dr. Coohill, a respected scientist, believes that the events he and his colleagues witnessed that day — and two days after Geller's visit — were paranormal in nature.

Published for the first time, with the permission of the author.

Filmed Events

The following events were video-taped in the physics laboratory at Western Kentucky University (W.K.U.). Present were Drs. T. P.

Coohill, J. E. Parks, N. F. Six, R. Hackney, A. Wawrukiewicz, E. Dorman, and D. L. Humphrey of the Physics Department, W.K.U., and Drs. R. Miller and R. Mendel of the Psychology Department, W.K.U. Dr. F. Brown of the Psychology Department at Centre College was also present, as were numerous students. As shown on the film, Uri Geller chooses one of six opaque double envelopes, each containing a drawing by Mrs. Jo Six. Mrs. Six was not present at the filming nor did she know if Uri would be asked to try this test. She had drawn all six pictures the previous day. No one in the room was aware of what was in any of the envelopes. Geller chose one envelope and began drawing figures on a pad. This initial attempt included the following sequence: a set of points, some interesting lines, two triangles, and the eventual union of the two triangles to form a Star of David. Geller's final drawing was a Star of David of the same size as the one in the envelope. (See Plate 39.) His remarks while making the drawing included: "It's difficult, you know," "Look, if I'm wrong, I'm wrong," "I feel very strongly about this," "I'm getting it very correct," "If I didn't feel it I would pass," "Psychologically, I'm being pulled away from it because I'm from Israel and this is my Star of David," and "The lines are very mathematical, precise."

Later Geller tried to influence the reading of a Bell 240 Incremental Magnetometer with a Hall Effect probe. He had been able to change the reading on a similar instrument at Stanford. He worked very hard for a period of twenty minutes with no success. He was clenching his fists, holding his breath, waving his hands, and visibly straining himself. His comments included: "Are you sure it's working?" "When I go like this, you must want it to go. You must all want it to go," "I know it's coming," "Want me to make currents running through the circuits?" "Are you sure it's not broken?" The probe was tested by one of the physicists present and found to be nonfunctional. It was further shown that the probe was indeed broken. No working probe was available to continue the experiment. Uri wasted a lot of energy on this attempt.

Also on film are a small (10%) deflection of a magnetic compass and a small (10%) deflection of a gaussmeter. The film is available for viewing from Western Kentucky University, Department of Physics.

Nonfilmed Events

The following events occurred at the home of Dr. and Mrs. Thomas P. Coohill on February 19, 1974. Present at the time were Dr. and Mrs. Coohill, Mrs. Sally Beal, Mr. and Mrs. Bob Williamson, Dr. N. Frank Six (Chairman of the Physics Department at Western Kentucky University), Dr. Ed Dorman (a physicist at W.K.U.), Uri Geller, and his friend Shippie.

We did not ask Geller to bend anything for us at lunch, nor did he suggest that he do so. However, after we had eaten Geller and I went into my living room and began talking about caving (spelunking). After about a minute we both heard a metallic "clink"; it sounded as though something metallic was dropped on a solid floor. Looking around, I saw a spoon lying behind my desk. It was bent in this manner:

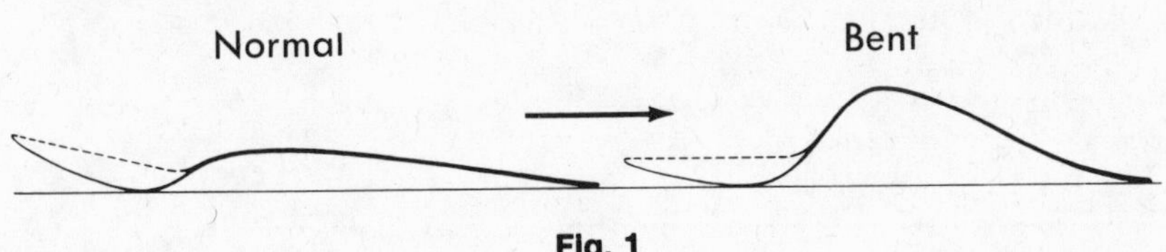

Fig. 1

As I held it in my hand and called the other people into the room, the spoon suddenly began to bend in another plane (at a right angle to the handle; see p. 136). It seemed as if the spoon were observed by all present. (For photographs of the spoon see Plate 40.) This incident further amazed me since the floor of my living room is thickly carpeted. Where the "clink" came from I cannot imagine.

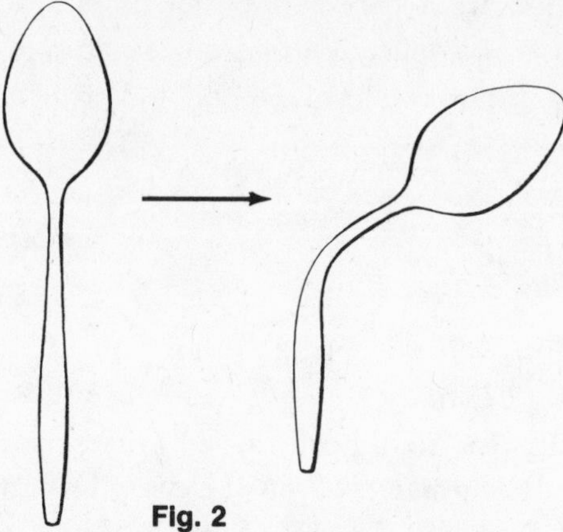

Fig. 2

In another incident Geller asked my wife, Patricia, to place her hands about 5 cm above a long teaspoon. He then waved his hands slightly above hers and asked her to remove her hands. The spoon was broken into two. Dr. Six says he heard a distinct "pop" occur while my wife's hands were over the spoon. At no time did Geller touch the spoon. Reconstruction of the long teaspoon, achieved simply by holding the two fragments together, shows that the spoon's shape had changed as a result of its being broken: its curvature is missing. (For photograph of the spoon see Plate 40.)

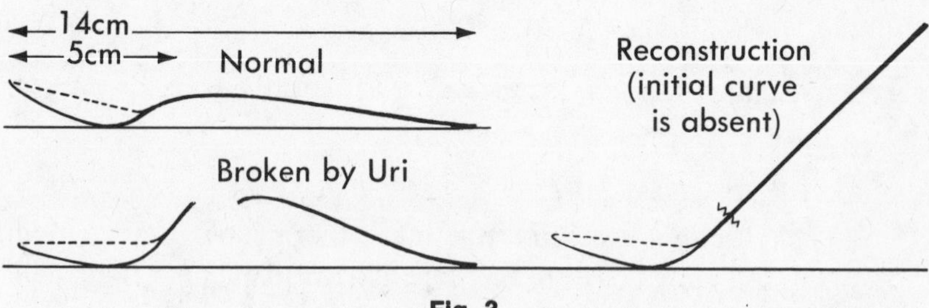

Fig. 3

For me, the most convincing event occurred two days after Geller left our home. I was about to put some sugar in my coffee when suddenly I noticed that the sugar spoon was bent. Since my wife and I had carefully checked all of our silverware after Geller's departure and found none of it damaged, we were alarmed. But even more alarming was the fact that the spoon continued to bend slightly (as measured later by a ruler) for about the next fifteen minutes. (For a photograph of the spoon see Plate 41.)

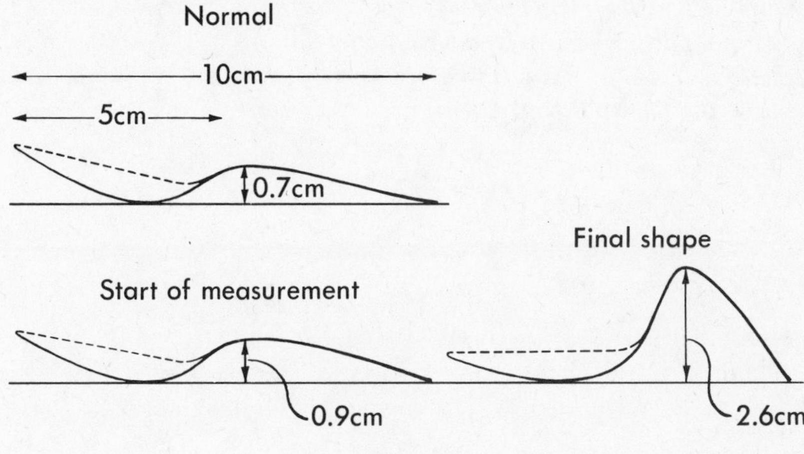

Fig. 4

Dr. Coohill does not know what to make of the fact that the magnetometer Geller tried to influence was broken. It may be nothing more than a coincidence, he says, but Coohill also feels that it may have been due to Geller's presence in the laboratory. Harold Puthoff and Russell Targ demonstrated that Geller was able to influence laboratory equipment during his visits to Stanford Research Institute. Exactly how Geller influenced particular pieces of equipment was never predictable: an electronic balance scale, for example, underwent both positive and negative random fluctuations when Geller held his hands above the glass bell jar housing the scale. Dr. Coohill thinks that if Geller could alter the normal behavior of a device, he probably can also cause a malfunction. But Coohill has no proof that the magnetometer was inoperative because of Geller's presence.

Dr. Coohill is less uncertain about the event that happened two days after Geller's visit to his home. He is convinced that the sugar spoon bent before his eyes and in his hand, and that it was a genuinely paranormal event. Coohill's personal experience does not stand alone. It must be taken in the context of the observations of Drs. Thelma Moss, John Taylor, John Hasted, and E. Alan Price, all of whom report cases of psychokinetic phenomena occurring to individuals after they have seen or heard of Geller's talents. Dr. Price's report, which is the last paper in this book, is the most extensive field study of the phenomenon that scientists are now calling the Geller Effect.

A PRELIMINARY SCRUTINY OF URI GELLER

by William E. Cox, The Institute for Parapsychology, Foundation for Research on the Nature of Man, Durham, North Carolina.

William E. Cox is a research associate at the Institute for Parapsychology, Durham, North Carolina, and a specialist in psychokinesis. He is also a semiprofessional magician, an associate of the Society of American Magicians, and formerly a member of the International Brotherhood of Magicians. He is a Fellow of both the American and British Societies for Psychical Research. Mr. Cox has been active in the fields of both magic and parapsychology for over forty years, and is the author of numerous parapsychological research papers, as well as an advisory booklet for magicians on ESP. He has organized a committee within the Society of American Magicians to investigate false claims of ESP.

The following investigation of Geller took place on April 24, 1974, at Geller's New York City apartment. Cox's paper is the first of three reports by magicians. It has been suggested that the design of many parapsychological experiments can be tightened and enhanced through consultation with magicians, for a magician brings his own rigorous standards to testing procedures — standards that can help rule out any form of trickery or deception. Thus the reports by magicians in this book are of particular interest. Where several of the scientists whose papers appear here state that they cannot guarantee that sleight of hand did not occur under their eyes, all four magicians (William Cox, Artur Zorka and Abb Dickson, and Leo Leslie) are convinced that Geller did not use any magic tricks to accomplish the events they witnessed. In fact, the statements made by the magicians in their respective papers are among some of the most positive and forceful claims to the genuineness of Geller's talents. However, not all magicians are convinced by the affirmative words of their colleagues. In talking with several conjurers who have not had the opportunity to work with Geller, it has become clear that each magician wants to see for himself what Geller can do before he will draw any conclusions. Theoretically this is commendable. It is, however, an impracticable procedure. It has been suggested, therefore, that a committee of magicians be formed to test Geller, and that their collective report be taken as the "final word." At the time of this writing, such a committee has not been convened.

Published for the first time, with the permission of the author. A shorter version of this paper was published in the Journal of Parapsychology, *Vol. 38, Dec. 1974, pp. 408–11.*

THROUGH THE GOOD OFFICES of Mrs. Judith Skutch, President of the Foundation for the Investigation of Parasensory Phenomena, I was able to spend an hour with Uri Geller in the early evening of April 24, 1974. This is a report of my findings, in some detail. A full description often is essential when an effort is made to arrive at a definitive conclusion (if I may call it that) about a personal demonstration of one or more of the strong paranormal claims made by reputed or alleged sensitives.

Although there still is the unfulfilled need for standardized PK-testing with Geller, I felt that my first objective should be a further certification of his chief claims. I already had considered what approach to take. To be too demanding, I reasoned, or equipped with too many arbitrary rules, would not be any wiser than to be extremely lax, since quite likely little or no phenomenal effects would ensue. To give Geller as much freedom as he liked — for a limited portion of the session — was, I felt, the best course. This is not to imply that I had come to any judgment in the matter of his being a genuine psychic or a fraud. It shows mainly the advantage of having some specific objectives. My technique was first to let him in on a novel idea or two concerning proposed test procedures, during a preliminary telephone conversation, and thereby heighten his interest in undergoing semiformal study by a PK research specialist.

One idea was the use of a ten-sided die, both openly and under glass, which he might make roll about in specified directions, or until specified numbers were uppermost (visibly and then blindly). Six-sided dice seemed less appropriate, as well as less novel, nor had Geller been known to have any affinity for throwing dice in the manner of standardized test procedures.

Another static PK novelty was related to his favorite public practice of starting defective watches. I would propose that he start a watch whose internal speed regulator had been adjusted too far to one extreme to allow any continuous function, with the novel objective of letting him get it running and then ask for the back to be opened up to confirm that he had indeed caused the regulator arm to change its position.

I was admitted to Geller's midtown Manhattan apartment by Mr. Yasha Katz, his associate, who introduced me to another on his staff, Mr. Werner Schmidt, and then to Geller. A fairly large living room was the scene of operations. Geller and I were alone, on either side of a glass-topped coffee table.

1. After a few preliminary remarks, Geller asked if I had a key. I handed him one that looked new; simply a flat, blank key, neither grooved nor toothed. He examined it and asked if I did not have a *personal* key he could use. I said I did not (though I did), and he agreed to try something with the one I had given him. He directed me in what to do, and within a minute he had bent the key to an angle of 12¼ degrees. I was seated at a corner of the table; Geller stood on the other side.

Before describing the event in detail, I should describe the key. It is made of steel, with an overall length of 2¼ inches. It was of a commercial quality and was unyielding to efforts at bending it by hand. It is extremely unlikely that such a plain and blank duplicate key of this kind would have been in Geller's possession. The key was of the safe-deposit box type.

Geller returned the key to me and asked me to place it near the edge of the coffee table, and to put my finger on its larger end. My motive in letting him handle the key was deliberately to allow opportunity for trickery, in the event that Geller had contemplated attempting such means. Being a magician myself (which I did not allow Geller to learn), I was impressed with his general attitude and his lack of interest in details.

The key was flat upon the glass table, touching along its length. My right forefinger pressed upon one end of the key with only a normal force, and Geller's right forefinger gently stroked the rest of the key as he stood bending over the coffee table.

I took advantage of the table's transparency to gain a view of the underpart of the key with the aid of a mirror I held in my left hand. Light from a window, at 6:15 P.M. EDT, enabled a relatively clear view. The top of the key, of course, could be seen directly, with Geller's finger touching it. After making several strokes, he said it was bending, then raised his hand and pressed his end of the key so as to rock it approximately one eighth of an inch. He slid the key from under my finger and again rocked it, expressing some pleasure. I resumed control of my end of the key, bringing the mirror into use at this point. Geller then resumed stroking the key until it bent to an angle of about 12¼ degrees. The entire event, I would judge, took less than a minute.

The temperature of the part of the key under my finger did not appear to change. What is more important is that the position of my end of the key did not change, except when Geller first rocked the key. The distance between my eyes and the key throughout the test was no more than one and a half feet. Intentionally, I had exerted no strong pressure on the key, nor did the normal downward pressure of my finger vary more than it might have if Geller had met with complete failure.

Other tests followed the key bending event.

2. From my briefcase I took a plastic ten-sided object, roughly the size of a three-inch diameter ball. Its faces were numbered in ink from 1 to 10. I proposed that Geller attempt to make this object roll about, and stop with a desired number uppermost. He reacted by saying that he did not like numbers. I replied that he could keep the die and perhaps try it at some later time. The die remained on the coffee table.

3. I had brought with me two other keys, of the skeleton key variety. They were of zinc alloy, and could be bent by hand if enough pressure was applied. When Geller again asked if I had another key, I produced one of these from a previously unopened plastic container within the confines of my briefcase so as not to give the appearance that the key was a recent purchase, for Geller expressed a preference for a "used" key. The key was secured in the same manner as before, except that I held my finger upon the toothed end. A bend soon began to appear, but this time it took place an inch closer to the opposite end instead of right at my finger. The movement was conspicuous, moderately slow, and continuous, until the key was bent to an angle of about thirty-six degrees. Why the bend was located at a relatively isolated spot an inch from my finger is a question in itself. An ordinary upward force at the end of a projection would produce a bend at the fulcrum instead of an inch away. (See Plate 42.)

My angle of vision was about forty-five degrees (for both key events), plus the angles gained by the mirror held in the background. The second key then was laid to one side of the table in order to leave it in view without its being near the hand of either of us. (The first key also was on the table.) This was because Geller and I had discussed his talent for causing silverware, etc., to continue bending after it had been laid down. We both had mused about seeing this happen to the first key, as I recall, and also to the extra skeleton key in my briefcase (which I mentioned but did not use, and which was later found not to have bent). A second reason for thus protecting this key was because it was *relatively* easy to bend by hand. I also was aware that such a key was easily obtainable by a trickster, but I preferred not to make identification marks on them.*

4. Three GESP** effects made up the next test, which Geller himself suggested. He asked, in his usual lively manner, if I would draw something on a piece of paper. "I'll go out of the room while you write," he said. Then he added, "No. Will it be all right if I just turn my head to the wall?" He did the latter, and I did not ask for any further safeguards. This was an objectionably weak precaution against his peeking; but I was not there to test his ESP, which already had been satisfactorily tested at the Stanford Research Institute. Since I had a continuing interest in detecting any signs of deception, I intentionally allowed the upper part of my pencil to be exposed as I wrote on the inside surface of a small envelope, but Geller's head remained turned completely away (toward a wall). He asked, while trying to perceive the diagram, for me to look at him (rather than at the coffee table), and after a pause he said, "I can't get it. I think you are thinking of a word. What did you write?" I then showed him figures representing the Greek letters *psi* and *kappa*. "Let's do it again," he replied, "and please write a geometric figure this time." The same procedure was repeated. I drew a circle with two lines inside it, and Geller responded, after looking at me a moment, by quickly drawing two diagrams, each containing a circle and lines. His comments were, "I think you drew either this," as he drew the larger of the two responses, "or a triangle and a circle like this," as he completed the second with equal speed and an air of certitude. We agreed that the second showed a very good degree of success.

* This account, written two days after the experience, was followed by a metallurgical examination of both keys and of two "control keys." The examination revealed no abnormalities, since the deformations due to bending were insignificant in comparison with the effects the metals had undergone during manufacture. A detailed report of metallurgical findings is available from the Institute for Parapsychology, Durham, N.C.

** GESP means General Extrasensory Perception, that is, ESP that could be telepathy or clairvoyance or both.

5. A cheap digital counter was used for the next test. I asked Geller to see if he could guess its three exposed numbers. He asked that I change them. I punched all three buttons several times, stopping on the combination 402. His incorrect guess was 332.

6. I next withdrew from my briefcase five colored dice and told Geller of their usefulness in testing for PK among other subjects. He was asked to think of numbers and then I tossed the dice against the wall. But his thoughts had no effect on which sides of the dice landed face up.

7. I spoke to Geller about his claims for making obects leave a closed room, or a container, and pass through other matter to reappear suddenly in another location. Then I showed him two leather rings, which I had made years earlier for just such an occasion as this. They were oval, about four inches in the greater diameter, having been cut from flat sheets of leather of two different thicknesses. "If these should ever become linked in your hand," I said, "it would be a most exceptional accomplishment." He took an interest in the idea, which was quite novel to him, and gladly retained them for the purpose. To my knowledge, nothing since has happened to the rings.

8. The most impressive experiment came next. It involved my own 17-jewel Hamilton pocket watch. Before I list any subsequent actions, a description of the watch itself, and how it was prepared, is in order.

Advance preparation of the watch: Plate 43 shows how the inside of the watch appeared when I gave it to Geller. It was intentionally placed in his hands without any instructions. The back has two covers, both hinged to the case. The outer one is very easy to open. The inner one is very difficult to open without a knife.

A deliberate obstruction — a piece of aluminum foil — projected into the balance wheel and prevented normal operation of the watch. The strip of foil was about 3/32 of an inch wide and an inch long. It had been laid flat upon the balance wheel bridge and beneath the regulator arm. This regulator was set slightly beyond the letter *F* (for Fast), on the left side of its range of movement when the watch is held with the stem downward. Projecting directly to the left of this arm, and extending over the balance wheel, was a $3/16$-inch strip of foil. The remaining foil projected down and to the left, having been folded over upon the mainspring barrel plate, though not fully touching it, to form a figure 7.

Installation was done by me at a jewelry shop in my hotel (the Commodore) during the afternoon. To prevent damage to the foil, a folded paper containing the foil was first inserted beneath the regulator arm and then removed. The source of the foil was a candy wrapper, whose thin layer of wax paper was allowed to remain on one side of the narrow strip. The strip had been cut approximately one third of an inch wide and then folded along its length. This was done somewhat off-center, which allowed the white waxed surface to make up nearly half of the underside. The short end projected over the balance wheel, but did not touch it at this time.

At 5:50 P.M., ten minutes before arriving at Geller's apartment, I had opened the back of the watch and depressed the short projecting foil strip in between the spokes of the balance wheel. (The regulator already was at *F*.) Apparently no amount of shaking would dislodge the foil obstruction.

I told Geller that I had fixed the watch so that it would not work, but I did not mention having employed a foreign obstruction. The watch and chain were placed in Geller's hands, even though he has claimed to repair watches without having to touch them. He held it to his ear, shook it gently, and discovered that the outer back could easily be opened. He made no move to start the watch by any ordinary twisting of it — nor would it have worked if he had. The watch was never out of my sight, nor was it even partly concealed by Geller's fingers.

Geller's only remark was that he did not know if he could make it work, since he often fails. He already knew that I had pushed the speed regulator to an extreme. Within half a minute, he held the watch to his ear for the second time and exclaimed, "It's ticking, it's ticking!" He handed the watch to me, I confirmed the ticking, and promptly opened the back of the watch; I encountered some difficulty with the inner lid.

I discovered the *F—S* regulator had moved completely to the S side of the gauge and beyond (to the right when the watch is held stem down). The 3/16-inch piece of foil that had been positioned between the balance wheel spokes had also moved. This was not all that occurred within the watch, for the remainder of the narrow foil strip, that is, the 3/4-inch length, which had been folded by me to form a figure 7, had been severed and was now lodged with its nearer end half an inch away from the *F* position, at an angle of approximately ninety degrees from its original position. (See Plate 44.) The end looked as if it had been "pulled" from the remainder. It adhered to the plate surface of the works when gently lifted part way with my fingernail. A knife was used to complete the removal, care being taken to detect to what degree the waxed foil was stuck upon the plate. It was not loose, but appeared to adhere slightly. This I tentatively attributed to some sort of gum upon the plate (unlikely), to gum upon the wax-paper underside of the foil strip (almost as unlikely), or to softened or melted wax. Tests for the latter were later made upon a similar foil wrapper and resulted in a similar adherence to a metal surface.

Subsequent Notes

It would appear that Geller personally appreciates a challenge, if my experience is any criterion. He is aware, to be sure, that if he is not interested in someone's proposed experiment he will not be likely to succeed in it. Since success is what he earnestly desires, at this stage of what I would suppose to be a search for identity, he apparently can rely on his paranormal proclivities to achieve it. Further research should help to answer this question, if it is designed toward that objective. Equally as important, certainly, is the necessity of measuring the extent to which he can effect PK through conventional techniques.

As for my opinion on the question of paranormality in the events I observed, I so far have failed to find any support for hypotheses of fraud and deception of any variety. Of the three major types of effects I have seen (GESP with drawings, key bendings, and starting a watch) the one that was most impressive was the last, and the next most impressive was that of the keys.

There is no doubt in my mind concerning the events I observed when Geller was under my close scrutiny. I do not consider the absence of an assistant or coexperimenter to be sufficient reason to invalidate the accuracy of my observations of the key phenomena at this stage, inasmuch as they were limited to uncomplicated movements at fairly close range, in good light, upon a clear glass table surface, and with the aid of a mirror. Furthermore, the chance of Geller's having had his own untoothed safe-deposit box key is most remote. If there had been such a bent key available to Geller, his substituting it under the procedural conditions outlined would have been quite out of the question, as the bending I saw occurred in two distinct steps. The force that normally would be required for the first and more difficult of my two keys is nearly 40 pounds upward at Geller's end, and some 100 pounds downward at my fulcrum end. This is two or three times the force that an ordinary Corbin-type key would require. In this problematical issue, Geller's lack of interest (which would have been unthinkable to a deceptionist) was obvious.

Concerning the watch, there are particulars that would appear to support strongly my contention that the effect was no more dubious than were the key phenomena; it was the result of static PK alone:

1. In subsequent test efforts, as well as in previous experiments, the balance wheel spokes could not be caused to disturb a similar piece of foil, inserted downward as before, if the watch was shaken in any manner. The spoke-striking force thereby produced was decidedly insufficient.

2. Even so, the implications of this scientific finding (1) are obviously weaker than those drawn from the positive movement of the regulator itself from the *F* to S position, against the confirmed normal tightness of the arm. The distance was slightly in excess of the lettered and gauged area, for a total of forty degrees counterclockwise. Its exceeding the normal limits was the result of my set-screws' having been permanently removed.

3. The impossibility of Geller's opening the inner back cover has already been described.

4. The transference of the superficial ¾-inch long extension of the narrow foil strip to a secured position ½ inch farther away and at an angle of nearly ninety degrees from the original (which had been on a line from balance wheel to stem) was unmistakable.

If this record is read by others, some discount for what might appear to be a prejudicial view on my part in the above, or in this accounting of it, could hardly surprise me, for it clearly would appear that I am reporting occurrences that are "manifestly impossible." Confirmation of the effects I have observed with Geller will, of course, be necessary by other experimenters.

ON THE ISSUE OF URI GELLER AND HIS CLAIMS

by William E. Cox, The Institute for Parapsychology, Foundation for Research on the Nature of Man, Durham, North Carolina.

This paper is a follow-up to the previous article by the same author. In it, Cox presents a more detailed and thoughtful discussion of Geller's talents and personality; Cox also suggests fruitful routes for future research. Can Geller, for instance, heal wounds that have been intentionally inflicted on laboratory mice? Can Geller affect the growth rate of plants? (Researchers working with other subjects have reported such phenomena. See Bernard Grad, "Some biological effects of the 'laying on of hands': A review of experiments with animals and plants," Journal of the American Society for Psychical Research, *Vol. 50, 1965, 95–127.) And can Geller, by his mere presence, transmit a temporary paranormal ability to a person physically near him — a phenomenon, if it exists, that parapsychologists call telergy?*

Published for the first time, with the permission of the author.

When one considers the effects reportedly produced by Uri Geller, there are a number of factors, both pro and con, that seem to stand out. It may be helpful for any future study if these are brought together in brief outline.

First, there is the fact that in GESP, just as in his PK efforts at metal bending, etc., Geller appears quite gifted. His clairvoyant drawings have been demonstrated to about the same high degree of significance as has been shown in past experience with selected psychic sensitives. This parallel excellence in both physical and mental psi domains supports the view that favors the existence of a basic relation, and interaction, between these two traditionally distinct divisions. It is interesting to note that a number of other sensitives have also displayed both mental and physical psi phenomena.

Some Proposals

One thing that is needed now is a study to determine the limiting factors in Geller's psi capacities. The scope of his ability should be examined, using not only metals (as has been done), but film and the possible movement or levitation of selected objects, and by investigating other effects that Geller has not yet displayed (such as healing, which, for example, could be tried out on laboratory mice).

One effect Geller does claim to have, but one that occurs so infrequently that no bounds of credibility can be established,* is the acceleration of plant growth and plant withering.

The only effect of Geller's that is quite novel in the history of psi phenomena appears to be his bending of metal. (In the case of a steel key bent by Geller while the key was under my direct control, it was later determined that a pressure of forty pounds at the point of the bend was required to cause such a deformation; or 100 pounds beneath my finger, that is, near the actual key-end fulcrum, could have caused the bend. But I felt *no* increase in upward pressure throughout the test.)**

Another important route that should be pursued with Geller, both in ESP and PK, is "telergy," that is, the telepathic transmitting of a psi percept to other persons — such as clairvoyant card-hitting suddenly manifesting itself in the investigator. Unlike some practitioners discussed in the literature, Geller may not know if he can do this except during television performances. The latter example,

* The nature of these bounds is a question to be pursued, granted one gains Geller's cooperation and understanding.

** See the previous paper by W. E. Cox for a full description of the test.

Plate 1. Graphic material consisting of target pictures and responses drawn by Uri Geller under shielded conditions.

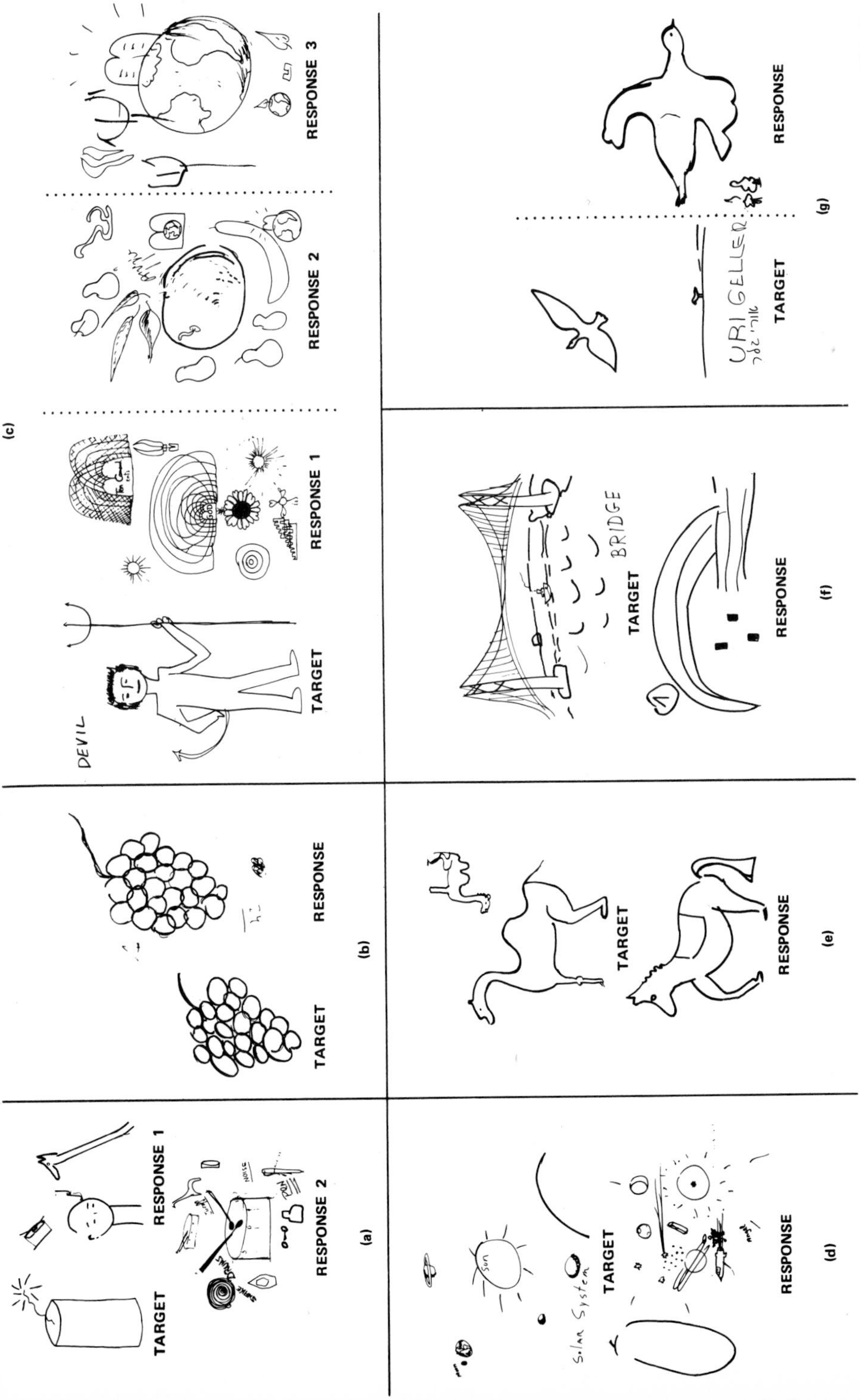

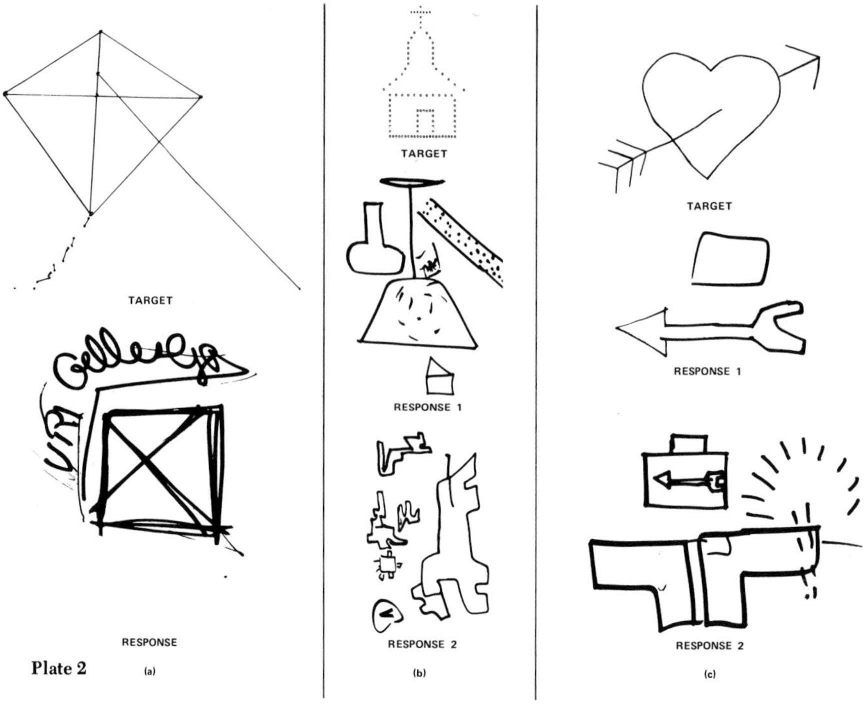

TARGET
RESPONSE
(a)
TARGET
RESPONSE 1
RESPONSE 2
(b)
TARGET
RESPONSE 1
RESPONSE 2
(c)

Plate 2

Plate 2. Graphic material from computer drawing experiments with Uri Geller. (a) Picture stored on video display. (b) Picture stored in computer memory only. (c) Picture stored on video display with zero intensity.

Plate 3. Occipital EEG spectra, 0–20 Hz, for one subject (H. H.) acting as receiver, showing amplitude changes in the 9–11 Hz band as a function of strobe frequency. Three cases: 0, 6, and 16 flashes per second. (12 trial averages).

Potential (arbitrary units)
0
6
16
5 Hz
10 Hz
15 Hz

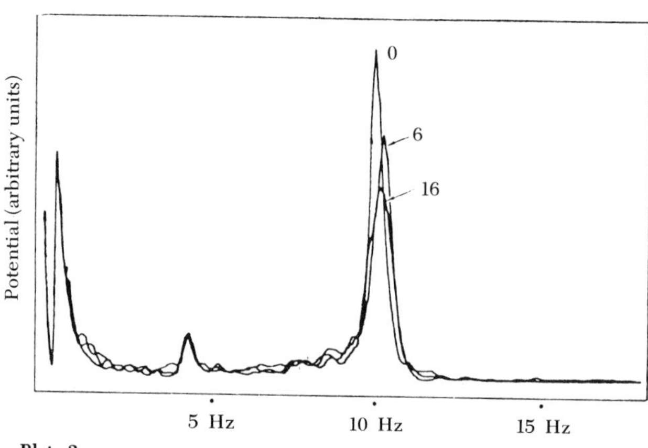

Plate 3

Plate 4. Two pieces of nitinol wire. Upper: The straight, normal shape of the wire before Uri Geller rubbed it gently with his fingers. Lower: The shape of the wire after Uri Geller rubbed it, and after it had been heated in the laboratory to restore its original, straight configuration. The wire is now permanently deformed. **Plate 5.** A shadowgraph of one of the pieces of nitinol bent by Uri Geller. The radius of curvature of the bend was found to be less than one mm. **Plate 6.** This piece of nitinol wire rubbed gently by Uri Geller developed multiple *two-dimensional* bends which are permanent. **Plate 7.** Uri Geller's influence on this piece of nitinol induced a *three-dimensional*, permanent bend. After Geller's rubbing, the wire took the shape of an ellipse. The only known technique by which one can bring about this result is twisting the wire into an ellipse, constraining it so that it cannot move, and then heating it to a temperature of about 500°C.

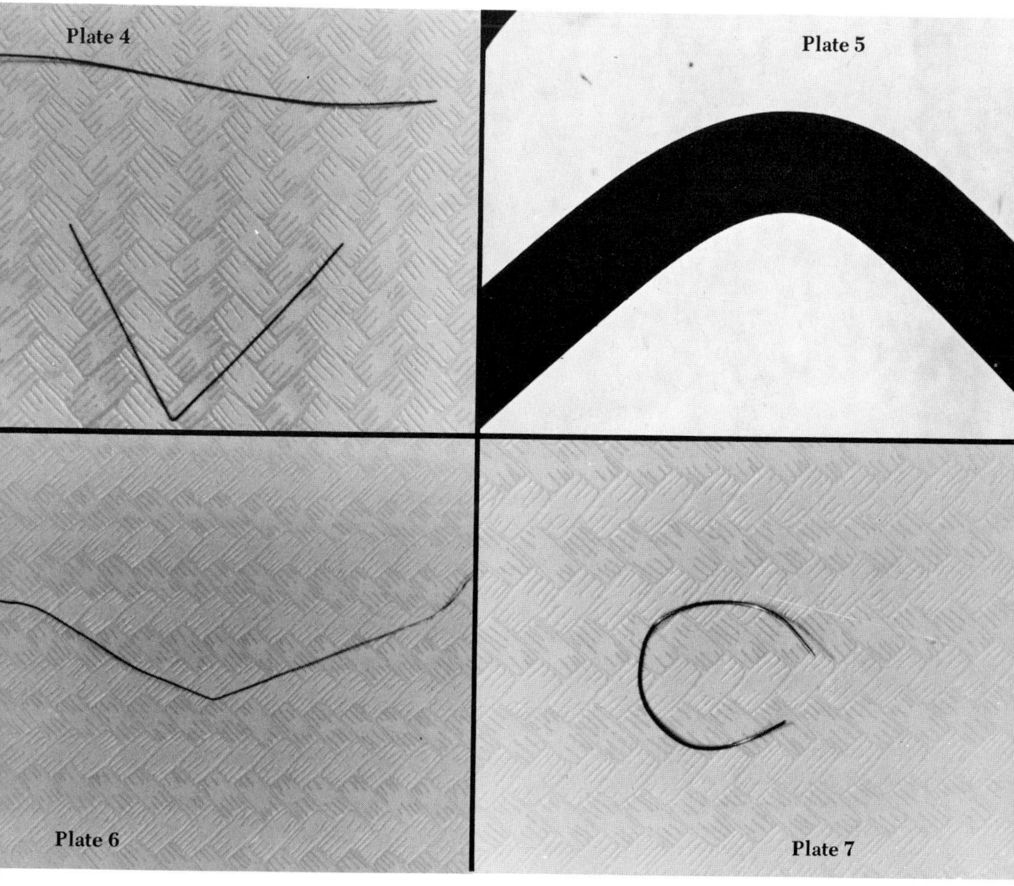

Plate 8
Plate 9
Plate 10
Plate 11
Plate 12
Plate 13
Plate 14
Plate 15

Plate 8. Scanning electron microscope (SEM) photograph at a magnification of 570X of the surface of the Geller fracture in the stainless steel spoon. The dimpled pattern with a lacy white filigree is typical of ductile failure. The angle from the vertical, which affects the image characteristics, was forty-five degrees. **Plate 9.** Laboratory fracture surface at 660X and thirty degrees. Plates 8 and 9 are typical of the Geller and lab fracture surfaces, respectively. The differences between the Geller and lab fracture surfaces, as shown in Plates 8 and 9, do not appear to have significance. **Plate 10.** A crack in the shank of the spoon adjacent to the Geller fracture is shown in the center of the figure. **Plate 11.** The crack shown in the previous figure at ten times higher magnification (220X). The unusual viscous appearance in this and the next figure is not typical of room-temperature fracture. **Plate 12.** Bottom of the crack at 1100X. The microstructure is typical of high-temperature rather than room-temperature shear. **Plate 13.** Fracture surface in a platinum ring broken by Geller. **Plate 14.** Lower right quarter of the fracture surface of the platinum ring. This quarter contained regions that resembled low-temperature cleavage and incipient melting. Magnification 210X at an angle of thirty degrees. **Plate 15.** Upper left region of the field of view of Plate 14 showing small protuberances and a depression. This region is suggestive of localized incipient melting. Magnification 1115X, angle thirty degrees. **Plate 16** Lower right region of the field of view of Plate 14 showing a flat terraced structure with small geometrical shapes. The former is characteristic of low-temperature cleavage. Magnification 2300X, angle thirty degrees. **Plate 17.** Central region of Plate 10 at the higher magnification of 12,000X and an angle of thirty degrees. The geometric shapes reflect the face-centered-cubic structure of platinum and are probably inclusions or vacancy clusters.

Plate 16

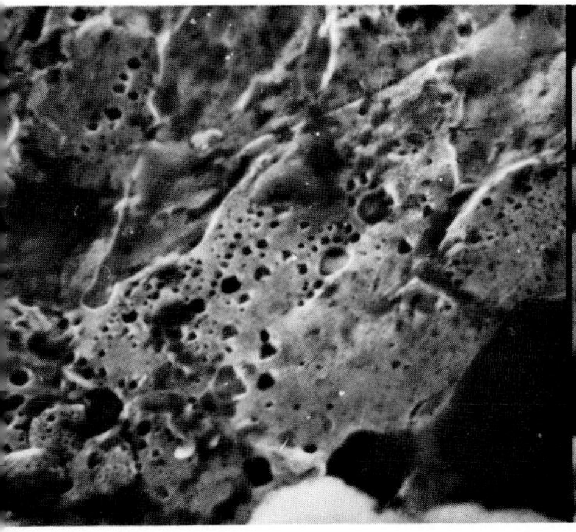

Plate 17

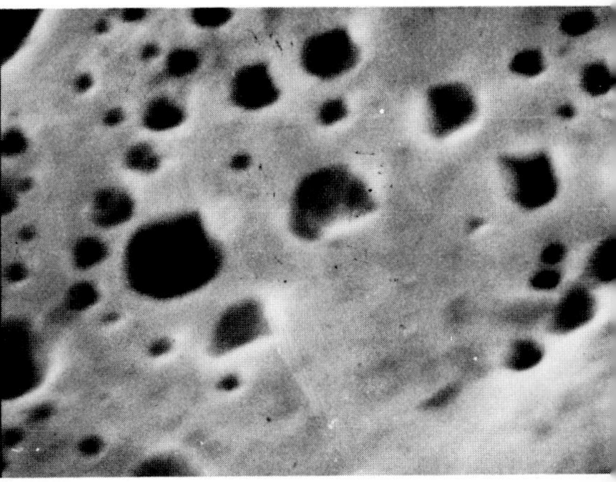

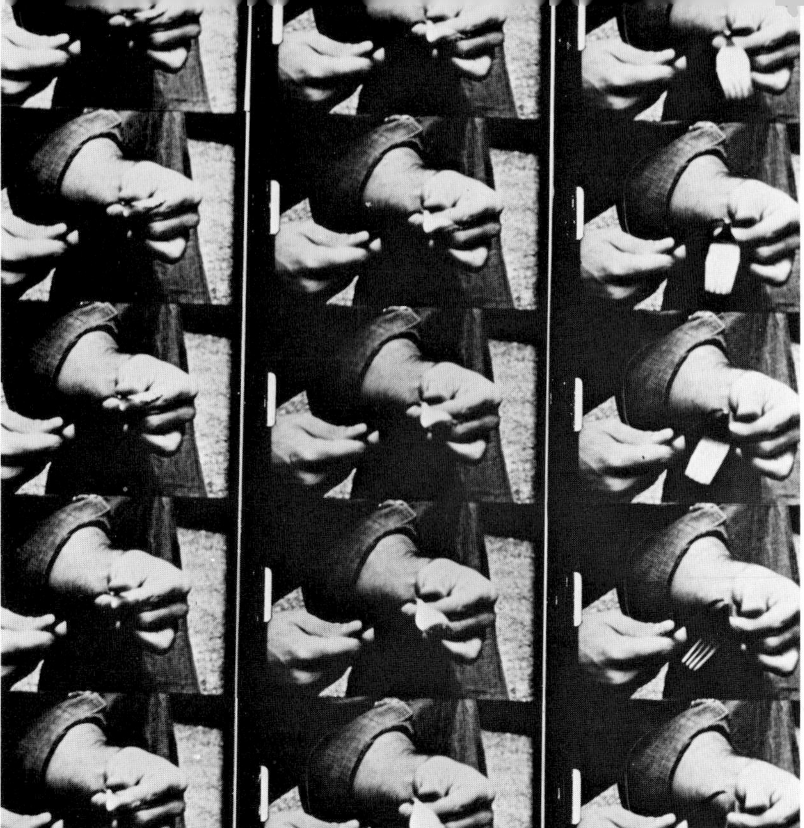

Plate 18

Plate 18. *(Courtesy of* Psychic *magazine)* This sequence of photos from a Super 8 movie film taken by James Bolen, editor and publisher of *Psychic* magazine, shows Uri Geller breaking a dinner fork in two by rubbing it gently. The fork, which Bolen personally verified as being intact before the demonstration, gradually becomes pliable at its midsection as Geller rolls his thumb and index finger over it. The fork finally breaks apart, the prong part clinging slightly to the handle just before it drops away, suggesting that the stainless steel momentarily became plasticlike. To verify that no deception occurred in the developing and printing of the film, Bolen secured the following affidavit from the photo lab.

> This is to certify that I, Ralph Elliott of Ramell, a photoprocessing laboratory of professional standards at 650 Howard Street, San Francisco, California, did receive from James Grayson Bolen three rolls of Super 8 movie film on May 7, 1973, and had them processed for Mr. Bolen. I hereby state that Mr. Bolen did not have access to the film at any time during the processing thereof and that I released the film to him—two full rolls developed and one undeveloped because it was unexposed—on this the eighth day of May, 1973. I hereby place my hand in signature to state that the foregoing is factual and correct.
>
> Signed *Ralph Elliott*

Plate 19. "Phantom leaf effect" in Kirlian photography. The right portion of the leaf was cut away before the leaf was placed on the film. Apparently the "energy field" of the cut portion of the leaf has been photographed using the Kirlian technique. **Plate 20.** (*From* High-Voltage Photography *by H. S. Dakin. Courtesy of the author.*) Prints of simultaneous exposures of a Seiko wrist watch at top and subject's finger at bottom. Streak of light in **Plate 21** occurred when subject attempted to transfer mental energy from his finger to the watch during the high-voltage exposure. **Plate 22.** "Spurts" of energy emerging from Geller's fingertip as he tried to influence the key at the top of the film. **Plate 23.** Detail from Plate 22, showing "energy spurt" from Geller's fingertip. **Plate 24.** Geller's fingertip as he tried to visualize the number "5" transmitted to him telepathically. He did not receive a telepathic impression but felt an "electric sensation." (Kodak Ektachrome film).

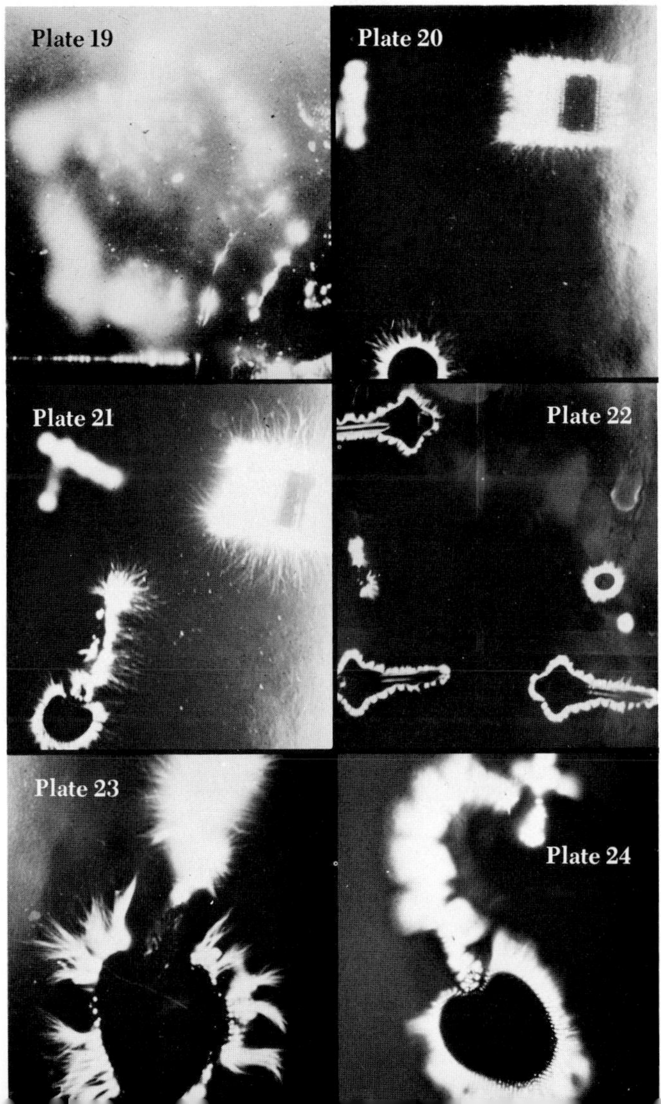

Plate 25. Again Geller described an "electrical sensation," but without receiving the geometric form being sent to him telepathically. (Kodak Ektachrome film). **Plate 26.** Once more Geller denied receiving a telepathic impression when the letter Z was sent to him, but this emanation appeared on the Ektachrome film. **Plate 27.** An attempt to duplicate the Geller "energy spurt" by deliberate manipulation: holding a rubber band under the tip of the finger. **Plate 28.** An "unexplained eruption" from a subject's finger pad, under presumably normal conditions.

Plate 25

Plate 26

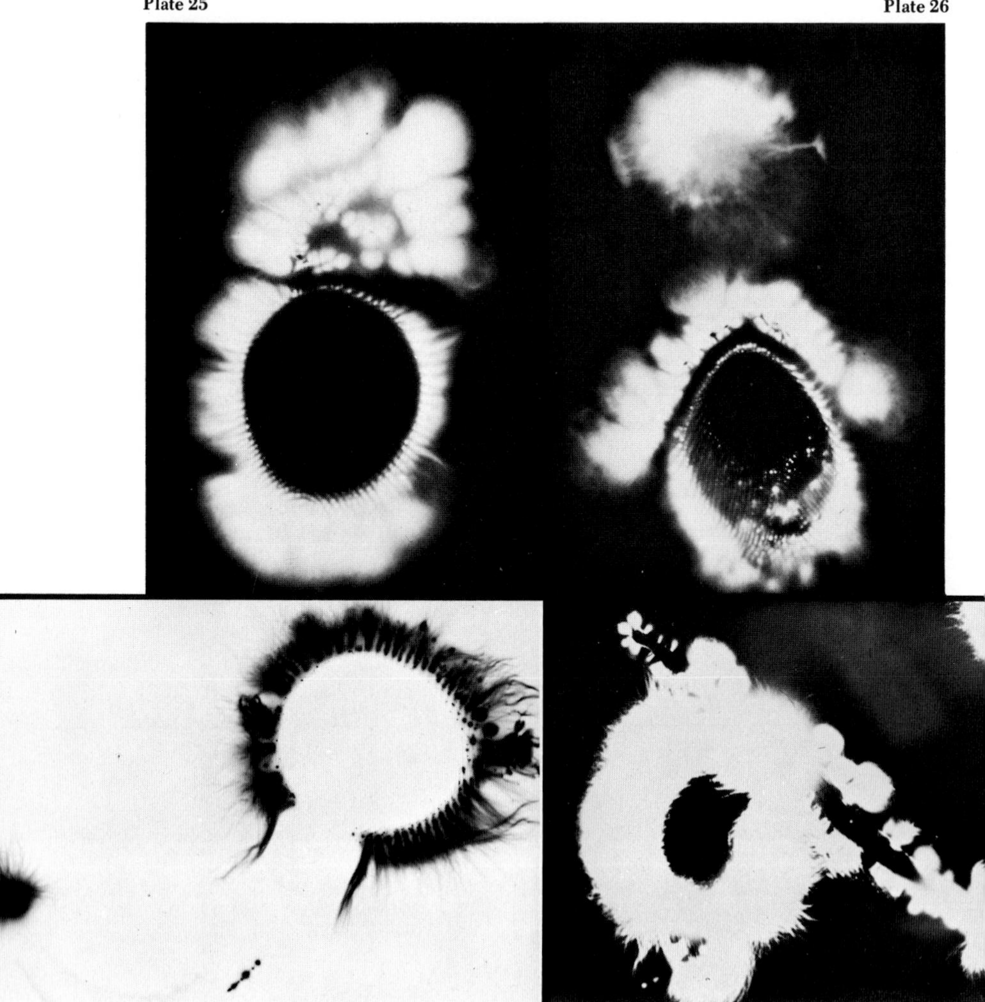

Plate 27

Plate 28

Plate 29. An "energy spurt" in red emerging from the subject on the left, visualizing sticking a needle into the other subject, who suffers from a needle phobia. The phobic subject's finger pad seems to be retreating from the fantasied needle. **Plate 30.** "Phantom leaf effect" obtained by Geller, who was not informed of the nature of the experiment. **Plate 31.** Cindy's fork after one hour of manipulation. **Plate 32.** The same fork, after an hour and a half of manipulation. **Plate 33.** The same fork, at the end of two hours.

Plate 29

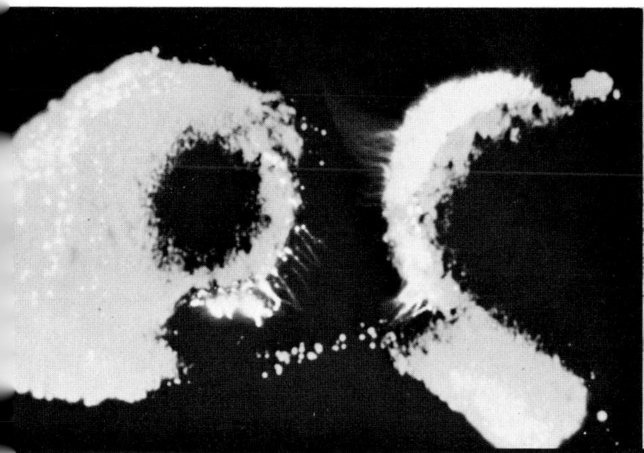

Plate 30

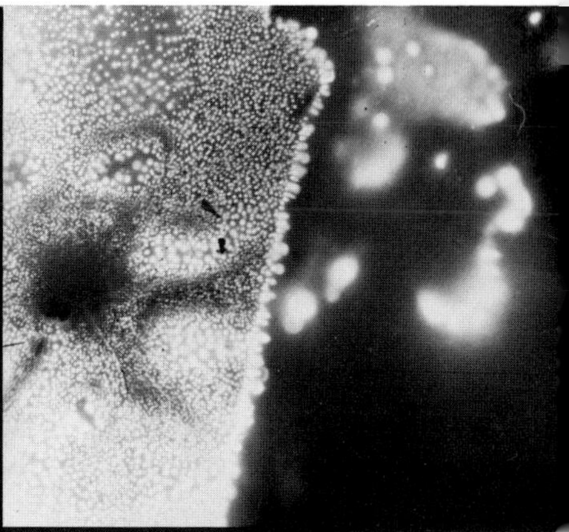

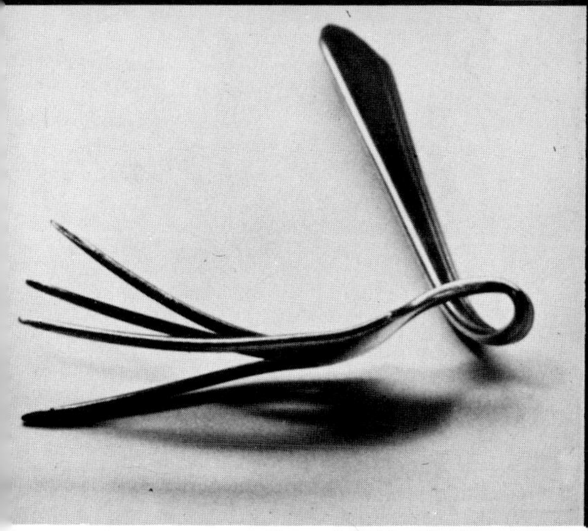

Plate 31

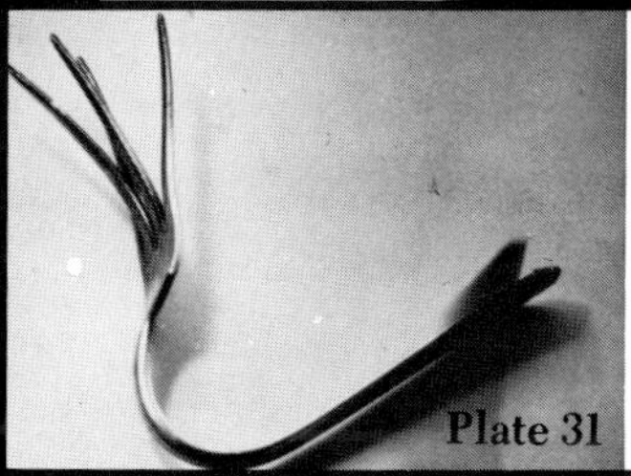

Plate 32

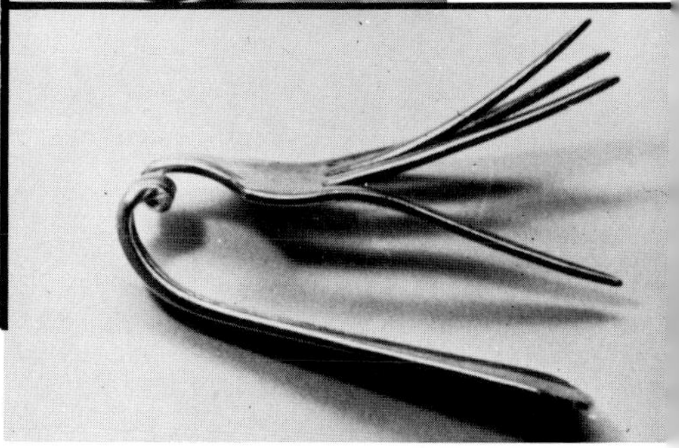

Plate 33

Plate 35. A photograph of a typical magnetic program card consisting of a .0004-inch-thick layer of iron oxide bonded to a .008-inch-thick plastic base. (HP 65 magnetic program card.) **Plate 36.** The normal magnetic pattern stored in the iron oxide layer is seen at the top of the picture. It is made visible by a magnetic viewer, which is a colloidal suspension of fine iron oxide particles. The stored magnetic field in the card penetrates the colloidal solution and condenses the particles along the lines of force causing a dark region to form. **Plate 37.** Card 2: This card had been rubbed by Geller's fingers, and subsequently rejected from a program calculator. A study of the card revealed that the magnetic patterns had been altered. Mere rubbing of a card normally has no effect on its magnetic program. **Plate 38.** Card 3: The magnetic program on this card was also found to be altered after the card had been rubbed by Geller. **Plate 39.** In a double-blind experiment performed at Western Kentucky University, Uri Geller correctly determined the target figure, a Star of David. His final attempt is the drawing on the right. **Plate 40.** Spoons influenced by Uri Geller at the home of Dr. Thomas P. Coohill. The spoon on the far left, which mysteriously dropped onto a carpeted floor, made a metallic "clink"; on examination it was found to be bent. Dr. Coohill picked up the spoon and as he held it in his hand it began to bend in another plane—at a right angle to the original bend (middle spoon). The long teaspoon on the far right was broken when Uri Geller merely passed his hands over it while it was held between the palms of Mrs. Thomas Coohill's hands.

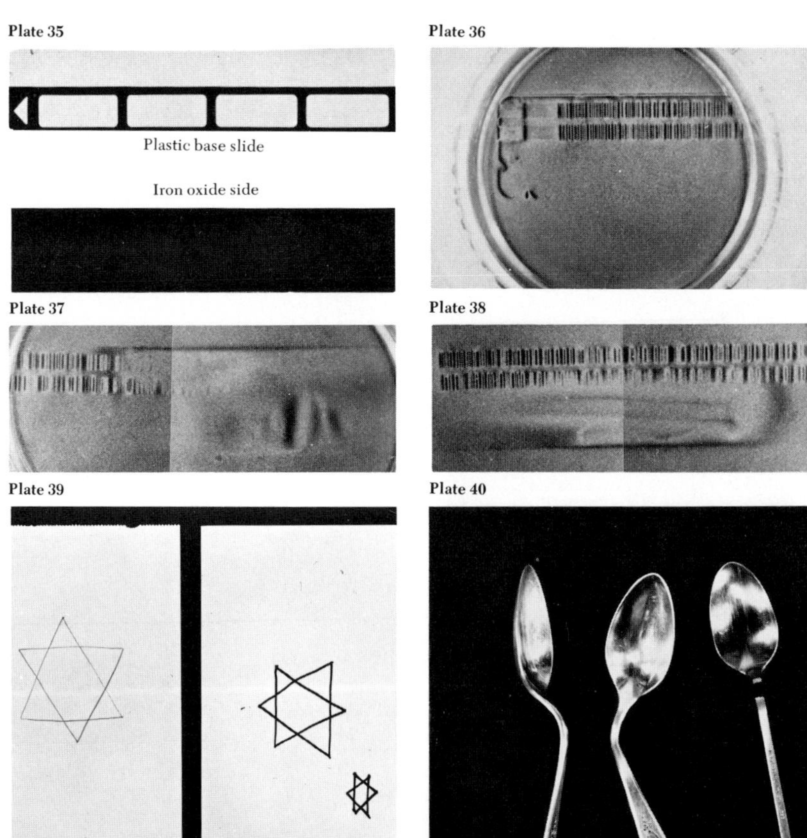

Plate 41

42

Plate 43

Plate 44

Plate 41. *(Courtesy of Guy Briggs)* Mrs. Thomas Coohill examines a spoon that was observed to bend two days *after* Uri Geller's visit to her home. **Plate 42.** Simulation of a key-bending event: Uri Geller bent an ordinary three-inch skeleton key while psychic researcher and magician William Cox held his forefinger against one end of the key. The key bent to an angle of thirty-six degrees. Cox held a mirror in the background to provide him a greater viewing range of the subject's motions. (Simulation by William Cox and a member of the Foundation for Research on the Nature of Man, Durham, North Carolina. The key is the one that was actually bent by Geller.) **Plate 43.** A Hamilton pocket watch belonging to William Cox. Before testing Geller for his ability to repair damaged watches, researcher Cox inserted a piece of aluminum foil over the watch's internal regulator arm, which was set in the *F* (Fast) position. The obstruction prevented the watch from running properly. **Plate 44.** Geller knew nothing about the foil obstruction in the watch, but after he held it in his hand (the watch had a double-backed case), it began to tick. On examination Cox found that the foil had shifted ninety degrees and pulled out of the balance arm; the regulator arm had moved a total of forty degrees (its extreme limit) to the *S* (Slow) position.

Plate 45

Plate 45. *(Courtesy of Bernard Gotfryd)* A fork made of forged steel with a nylon-reinforced handle shattered in Uri Geller's hand, sending fragments across the room. The fork had been handed to Geller by professional magician Artur Zorka. Zorka and fellow magician Abb Dickson detected no sign of trickery on Geller's part. **Plate 46.** Target drawings made by Artur Zorka and Abb Dickson, with Geller's responses. The last two images, those of a dog and of a twice-bisected circle, were not drawn on paper, but only thought of by Artur Zorka. Adjacent to them are Geller's impressions of Zorka's thoughts.

Plate 46

TARGET	RESPONSE	TARGET	RESPONSE
			None
			None
			None
(THOUGHT-NOT DRAWN)		(THOUGHT-NOT DRAWN)	

Plate 47

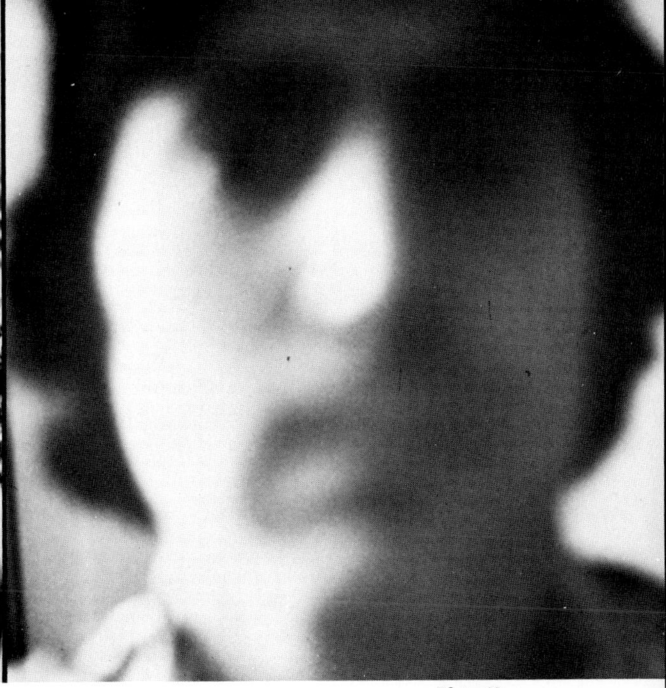

Plate 48

Plate 49

Plate 50

Plate 51

Plate 47. *(Courtesy of Lawrence Fried)* Uri Geller attempts to photograph himself through the covered lens of a camera. The lens cap was tightly secured by generous amounts of two-inch-wide, clothlike tape. Geller "exposed" an entire roll of 35-mm film in his try at "thought photography."
Plate 48. *(Courtesy of Lawrence Fried)* Frame number 10, the only one on the roll of film that contained an image, shows Geller, somewhat blurred and out of focus, seated at the exact location where he had taken the "thought" picture. **Plate 49.** *(Courtesy of Robin Owen)* A key bent by Uri Geller without his touching it. The bending process was photographed by a close-up television camera and viewed by a large audience.
Plate 50. *(Courtesy of Robin Owen)* The same key displayed to show the angle of the bend. **Plate 51.** *(Courtesy of Robin Owen)* Rare items bent or broken by Uri Geller before Dr. A. R. G. Owen of the New Horizons Research Foundation, Toronto, Ontario, and members of a television audience.

Plate 52. A vanadium carbide crystal had been encapsulated in a plastic pharmaceutical capsule (drawn here). One scientist at Birkbeck College held his hand over the capsule and Geller held his hand above the scientist's. After a few moments the capsule jumped a slight distance. On examination it was found that about half the vanadium carbide crystal was missing. **Plate 53.** A disc of molybdenum crystal bent by Uri Geller without his touching it. Geller's hands were held above those of one of the researchers, whose hands in turn were above the disc. At the time the disc bent the researcher felt a tingling sensation in his hands. **Plate 54.** Geiger counter circuit and chart recorder trace. Uri Geller held the screen of a Geiger counter in his hand continuously for about fifty minutes. During that time eight count-rate pulses, of approximately a second each in duration, were recorded (a, b, c, d, e, f, g, h).

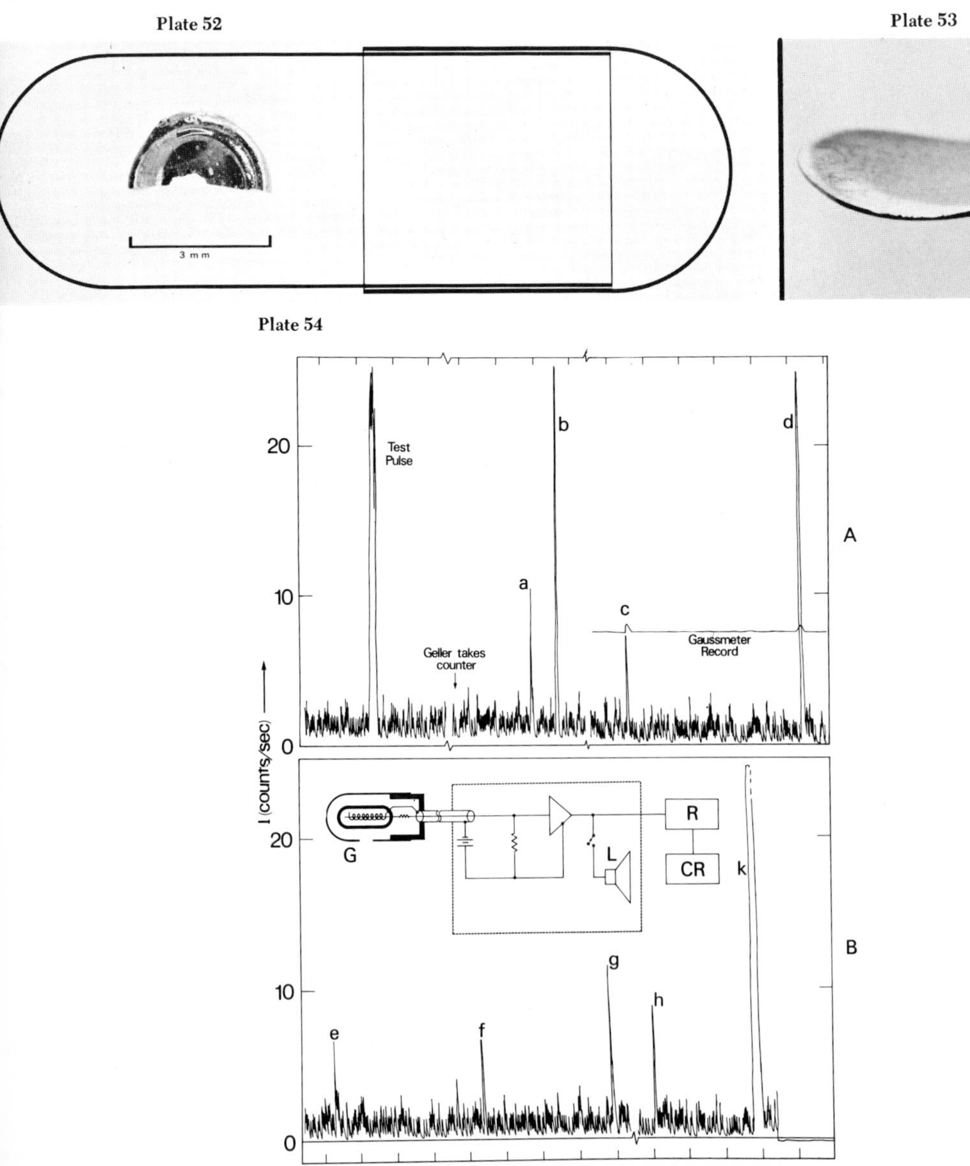

Plate 55

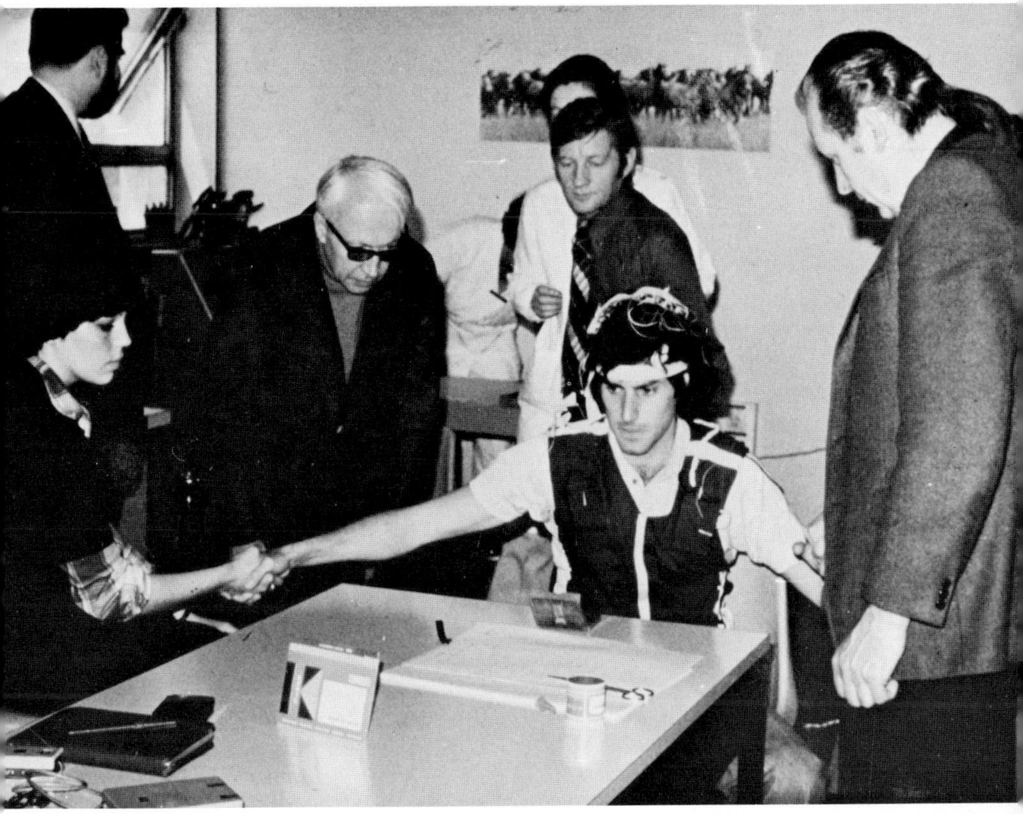

Plate 56

Plate 55. Uri Geller is wired with electrodes to measure his brain-wave response during telepathy experiments and during his attempts at producing psychokinetic phenomena. **Plate 56.** *(Courtesy of G. Delrey)* Geller attempts to deflect the needle of a compass. After achieving only a slight deflection, Geller asked that the scientists and technicians gather around him. His subsequent attempt was considerably more successful.

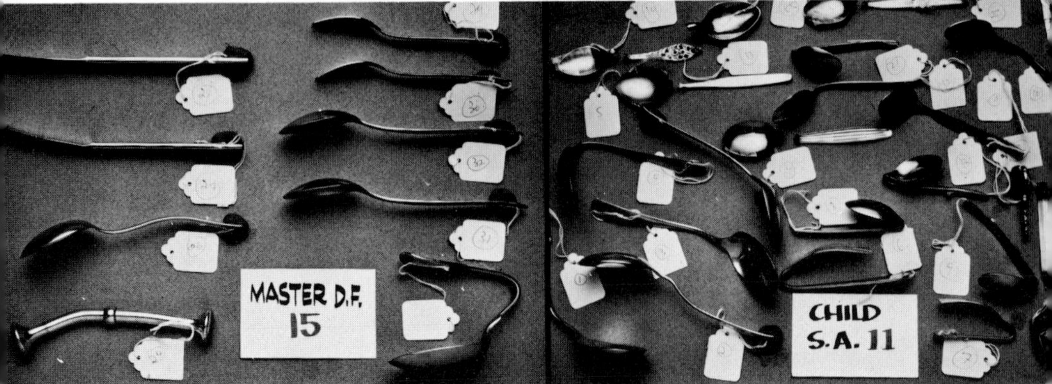

Plate 57

Plate 58

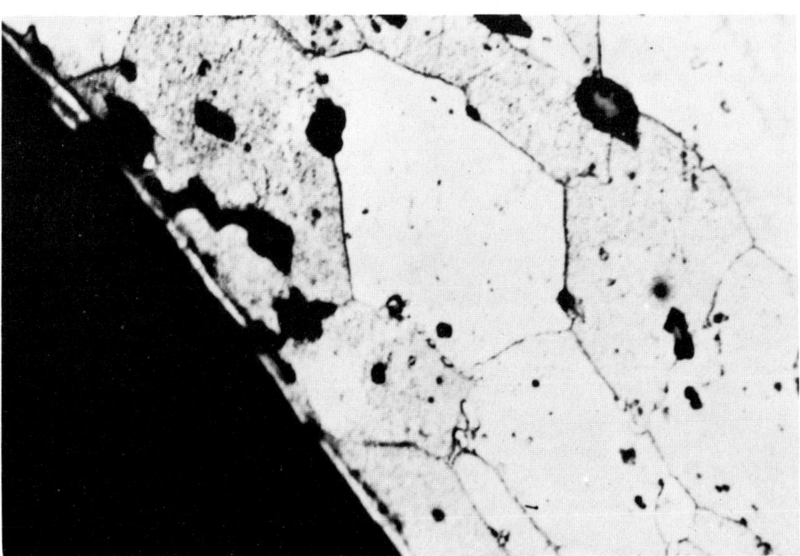
Plate 59

Plate 57. Some of the metal objects bent by D. F. (aged sixteen). **Plate 58.** Some of the metal objects bent by a "mini-Geller," a little girl of eleven. **Plate 59.** Microscopic examination showing metallographic structure of a key at the location where it was bent by Uri Geller. No evidence of recrystallization or any softening could be found. The brittle chromium plating was cracked.

assuming that some of the reports concerning it are reliable, is itself another Geller innovation because it involves PK rather than GESP.

Fraud

Perusal of available literature on the scientific study of Geller has shown that investigators confined their attention mainly to the question of how fraud conceivably might have been employed, and presumed it on slight evidence (some quite absurd), excluding much analytical scrutiny. Perhaps this is because physics researchers, teachers, and writers seem, to date, to have taken a greater interest in Geller than have parapsychologists. It also may be one of the reasons why he has been both disillusioned and, in my opinion, underinvestigated.

A helpful means of partially settling the question of fraud and deception would be a study of the video-tape records that have been made of the efforts of skilled magicians in competition with Geller on television — provided Geller's performance, which a magician replicates, is included in the sequence (inserted from earlier films or, preferably, conducted on the same occasion). The chief value of video sequences, I believe, is not just certification, nor is it the providing of means for subsequent scrutiny, by skeptics, of Geller's every move and manipulation. Its value is that it would allow for a comparison of manipulations. Superiority of one over others is not difficult to detect if they are seen together.

To the question, "Will there be a distinct difference in the outward appearance if Geller uses psi and a magician uses sleights?" the answer is exceedingly likely to be yes. Take ESP drawings, for example: if only ESP is involved, Geller here could (and he does) draw his design in advance of the opening of a sealed target design, and be carefully filmed as he does so. The magician seen replicating that specific effect a few moments later cannot allow actual film coverage of his own drawing (unless he bribes the investigator and camera technicians), and would be forced to conceal from others and from camera the face of his drawing board until shortly after the hidden target has been exposed for checkup. (Note: There *are* means of invisibly copying a target. If there were not, he would fail to score a hit at all.)

When the magician, alone, has used the technique of concealing the drawing board, it may be deemed impressive evidence against Geller's claims "to do the same thing" paranormally. When, however, both performers are seen, the fraudulent means of the magician probably will differ so distinctly from Geller's as to be easily distinguished as inferior; nor, in this situation, is any training in sleight of hand very necessary to spot the differences.

In the several competitive TV demonstrations I have watched, the magician was excelled by Geller. The demonstrations included metal bendings. Here the most significant of several differences, which seemed implicit to me, was that the magician was more concerned than Geller about knowing (probably in advance) exactly what was to be bent.

Another good example of a conspicuous difference between the "skill" of Geller and that of magicians happens to lie in the abnormal movements of watch hands. I have seen magicians Kreskin and the Amazing Randi on television hold a borrowed watch, point to the time, turn it over, return it to the owner while making some patter, then successfully "command" the hands to move. In both cases there was clear opportunity for them surreptitiously to twist the winding crown and push it back in from the setting position to which it could have been pulled at the moment they received it. This is so crude, since it is patently the only practical means, that almost any viewer could figure how it was done; and accordingly the trick has literally died aborning among Geller's imitators.

If, however, at Geller's hands, this "trick" has become a classic (and he has, as often as not, refrained from touching watches), then there obviously are very good odds that this is not simply because he is a more adroit magician.

It is not possible to answer the question of whether Geller has ever resorted to trickery. There are precedents for this among known psi sensitives in the past. My own negative opinion is only deductive: why would he use such sleights for unique effects that are *not* easy to palm off without skill — a skill he is not reliably known to have learned, accusations to the contrary notwithstanding. Even if rumors to this effect, which stem from early stage appearances, were substantiated, they would have no specific bearing on whether he did or did not use deceit on a given occasion. If it should develop that on some occasion he is indeed caught doing so, one need only recall that there are various precedents; such human tendencies exist, however unfortunately. Hence, "Once a fraud, always a fraud" may be inaccurate and a wasteful theory.

Magicians in particular can be as rigidly prejudiced against ESP and PK, and just as unwilling to refrain from holding any opinion, as were the clergy when, for example, Galileo tried to convince them that the sun was the real center of our universe. There are two attitudes strongly held by an inordinate number of magicians, as I have said in a paper on the subject.* One is expressed in their derisive reaction — "What's the gimmick?" — when a paranormal claim (such as Geller's) is called to their attention. The other, a fairly pervasive attitude (though often concealed) manifests itself in the "I can, you can't" syndrome. Perhaps, however, the second of the two is also held by most ESP sensitives as well, including Geller.

Other Observations

There still remain some dichotomies, and one cited here may be useful. If Geller is competent at ESP and PK, and therein certified to the degrees claimed, why is there so seldom any evidence for his claim of the passage of matter through matter? Enough of this has

* "Parapsychology and Magicians," W. E. Cox, *Parapsychology Review*, Vol. 5, No. 3, May–June, 1974.

been reported by Geller to be tantalizing,* but it has been done so, nearly always, unexpectedly or informally and cannot, therefore, be considered as adequately and reliably witnessed. Furthermore, Geller now has the pair of unlinked rings, made of unseamed leathers, that he gladly accepted from me nearly a year ago. He conceded that the value of linking them permanently, without damage, would exceed that of any other matter-through-matter effect; but to date I have heard nothing more about the rings.

The psychological requirements for the production of psi effects are known to be very delicate, and particularly so for the production of comparatively strong psi evidence. Accordingly, there is no element of surprise in the fact that Uri Geller is relatively ineffective in the presence of magicians, if they are known to him to be such. At times, too, he has been very hesitant about honoring requests from organized or *ad hoc* research groups, being naturally concerned about the possibility of failure and its imagined effects. On the occasion when I myself examined his physical claims in a private demonstration, Geller had not been told that I was either an amateur magician or associated with the Institute for Parapsychology, but only that I had a special interest in the physical branch of psychical research; and he gave no reason to think he suspected either of my associations (notwithstanding his apparent mind-reading abilities).

In due time, the suggestions in this paper will perhaps be added to those of other investigators, and the necessary arrangements made for a more intensive study of this exceptionally gifted individual, Uri Geller. If he is not, in fact, possessed of inordinate psi capacities, then he is unquestionably more expert a magician than any professional twice his age — if my experience during four decades in the fields of both magic and parapsychology is any criterion.

* "A Brief Outline of the Psi Phenomena Reportedly Effected by Uri Geller," W. E. Cox, Feb. 1974. Unpublished. Case Nos. 29, 34, and 36.

OFFICIAL REPORT: SOCIETY OF AMERICAN MAGICIANS, ASSEMBLY 30, ATLANTA CHAPTER

by The Occult Investigations Committee,
Artur Zorka, Chairman.

Artur Zorka is a professional magician and member of the Society of American Magicians. He is founder of the Junior Magic Club of Atlanta, past Vice-President of a division of the International Brotherhood of Magicians, and Chairman of the Atlanta Occult Investigations Committee. He was voted by his Atlanta peers the Magician of the Year in 1974.

When the report by Zorka was made public, and material from it picked up by the press, Zorka and fellow magician Abb Dickson came under critical attack by many members of the Society of American Magicians. They argued, among other things, that the report was not "official" because it did not go through the appropriate internal channels of the magicians' fraternity, and that both Zorka and Dickson were "relatively inexperienced investigators." Following Zorka's report here are four letters that shed light directly and peripherally on the investigation and on the attitudes of some magicians toward Uri Geller.

The first letter is addressed to Geller and is signed by Frank Bullock, President of the Atlanta Society of Magicians, and by five of the society's members. The letter denounces the "official" nature of the Zorka report and claims that "the findings were totally inconclusive, being merely opinions of relatively inexperienced investigators." Concerning this latter contention, Zorka's biographical credentials speak for themselves — he is an experienced, competent magician, a fact that is ironically reinforced in Bullock's own letter, in which he states that Zorka is the Chairman of the Atlanta Society's Occult Committee. Mr. Bullock, in personal communications of November 1975, stated that Zorka is indeed a competent magician and a specialist in occultlike magic, and regretted the derogatory statement the society had earlier made against Zorka and Dickson.

The second letter is from Zorka to the National President of the Society of American Magicians, William P. Dunbaugh. Zorka states what he feels was the real focus of the attacks on him and Mr. Dickson: "I sincerely believe," he writes, "that had Mr. Dickson and I discovered Mr. Geller at some sort of trickery, and released that information, there would have been no concern." His letter is followed by Dunbaugh's reply.

The fourth and final letter is from Zorka to Milbourne Christopher, a magician, and the National Chairman of the Occult Investigations Committee of the Society of American Magicians. It is of interest because of the experimental details it adds to Zorka's Official Report. Where the report summarizes the results of the investigation of Geller, the letter to Christopher gives a sequential account of the tests that Zorka and Dickson tried with Geller, including Geller's failures as well as his successes. All of the experiments were done on June 2, 1975.

The following material is published for the first time, with the permission of Artur Zorka and Abb Dickson.

As CHAIRMAN of the Occult Investigations Committee of this society, I hereby submit the findings of this committee regarding its investigation of Uri Geller.

On June 2, 1975, I, Artur Zorka, and several fellow magicians witnessed a taping of a television program in which Mr. Geller was interviewed as a guest. Unknown to Mr. Geller, five magicians were seated at various locations in the audience for the purpose of detecting the methods by which he claims to be able to produce his "phenomena." Although we were impressed by his ability as an entertainer, conditions were less than ideal for making any final judgment.

Following the taping, however, Mr. Abb Dickson,* a member of this committee, and I were able to meet with Uri Geller privately for a personal interview and some *controlled* experiments. I italicize controlled because the type of control put on by a magician is different from that of any other investigator. It is a control designed specifically, by those who are trained for a profession in the art of deception, to prevent fraud.

Being a specialist in that particular area of magic which deals in the psychic, I took special care to set up tests under conditions that, I believe, could not produce results through trickery.

The tests took place in a room that contained no mirrors, no windows, and one door, by which we entered. The door was locked behind us. Mr. Dickson, Mr. Geller, and I sat facing each other. No one else was present or in the near vicinity of the testing area.

The first test involved Uri Geller's attempt to bend a fork that I provided. The fork was made of forged steel, with a nylon-reinforced handle. I specifically selected this fork because of its extreme resistance to physical stress. I placed the fork in Mr. Geller's outstretched left hand. His fingers curled around it, and in moments, without the fork's leaving my sight for even an instant, it literally exploded, sending fragments of the handle across the room. (See Plate 45.)

For the tests of Uri Geller's telepathic abilities, he was asked to turn his back while members of the committee, in turn, made simple drawings. The object was for Mr. Geller to duplicate the drawings without having seen them. After a few false starts, Geller was able to make remarkably accurate facsimiles of the target drawings. The target drawings were made on plain sheets of white paper, and when the drawings were finished they were covered. While each target drawing was being made, Geller was being

* Abb Dickson is a professional magician who was selected master of ceremonies and performing magician for a State Department-sponsored tour of eleven European countries in 1966. He has published several articles on magic in publications of the International Brotherhood of Magicians and the Society of American Magicians, and served as a consultant for the popular New York City production of *The Magic Show*.

carefully watched by the other member of the committee to make sure that there was no way for him to see the drawing. The person making the drawing was extremely careful as to what paper was used and how the pen was held; he kept hand and arm movements to a minimum. In later tests, Geller was able to duplicate on paper target designs of which I merely *thought*. No drawings, in these later tests, were made by me. (See Plate 46.)

In another test, I watched, from a distance of no more than five feet, as a key bent beneath Geller's touch. I was able to see, under these controlled conditions, the bending process actually taking place.

Therefore, it is the unanimous finding of this committee that although we, as magicians, can duplicate each of these test results using methods known by us, under the proper conditions . . . there is no way, based on our present collective knowledge, that any method of trickery could have been used to produce these effects under the conditions to which Uri Geller was subjected.

Letters

August 14, 1975

Dear Mr. Geller:

It has come to our attention that you received a copy of a series of tests placed on you by the chairman of our local Occult Committee, Mr. Arthur Glick (a.k.a. Artur Zorka). As a copy of this report was received by you before the original was presented to the Atlanta Society of Magicians, it is an unauthorized copy of the findings and in no way represents the opinion of our Society.

The report was presented to the Society in an Executive Committee meeting where it was determined that the findings were totally inconclusive, being merely opinions of relatively inexperienced investigators.

Considering the above findings of the Executive Committee, the Atlanta Society of Magicians respectfully requests that you do not use the report in any of your publicity.

Mr. Glick does not have the official authority to commit the Atlanta Society of Magicians.

Sincerely,
(signed) Frank Bullock, President
Atlanta Society of Magicians
Julian V. Boehm, Assembly #30

(signed)
Harold R. Martin, Vice-President
Joe T. Gattis, Secretary
Walter J. Harris, Treasurer
John W. White, Sgt.-at-Arms
Calvin W. Tooles (Past President)

*

August 13, 1975

Dear Mr. President [William P. Dunbaugh],

I have been asked by the Board of Director of Assembly 30 to respond to a recent inquiry of yours concerning my report on Uri Geller.

It was the decision of the Board of Directors that the only wrong done by me was to release an official report without the consent of the Society. If, indeed, it was wrong to give Mr. Geller a copy of a report concerning him, then I indeed apologize, and stand corrected.

However, I sincerely believe that had Mr. Dickson and I discovered Mr. Geller at some sort of trickery, and released that information, there would have been no concern. If this is so, then I'm afraid there is a contradiction here.

Be that as it may, if I have caused the Society any embarrassment, I am truly sorry. I only ask that your opinion of the content of the report not disguise the real issue.

I am enclosing a copy of a letter to Milbourne Christopher. It may answer some of your questions also.

Yours in magic,
(signed) Artur Zorka

*

August 19, 1975

Dear Mr. Zorka:

Thank you for your kind and courteous letter regarding the Uri Geller incident, but would like to point out the only reason I got into the picture was through a telephone call from *Reader's Digest* as to whether you were speaking as the National Occult Chairman of the Society of American Magicians. This led me to make two inquiries of your Assembly's Secretary and National Deputy, as I, personally, could not express an honest opinion regarding any action you took pertaining to your belief in Mr. Geller.

They informed me you were not speaking for the National Office of the S.A.M. and it was an internal or local problem. I so informed the *Reader's Digest* that your opinion was not that of the Society of American Magicians and if any report you submitted implied that you were speaking for this organization, it certainly was in error. This was the extent of my contact with the people from *Reader's Digest.*

You have not, in any way, caused the Society any embarrassment and inasmuch as you were thoughtful enough to inform Milbourne Christopher of your experience with Uri Geller, and your recognition that any report submitted by members of the S.A.M. for public consumption should not be submitted in the name of our Society without National Council approval should close this incident. Mr. Christopher, I might add, is the National Chairman of our Occult Committee.

I certainly do appreciate your concern in the matter, the respectful manner in which you outlined the entire situation to me and your compliance in the future with our regulations. In conclusion I must say that in no way am I questioning your personal opinion in this matter as we are all certainly entitled to that without criticism.

Sincerely,
(signed) William P. Dunbaugh
National President
The Society of American Magicians

✲

Dear Milbourne,

Forgive me for taking so long to answer your letter. I have been on the road performing and have had very little time to keep up with correspondence. This incident with Geller has caused many people to write to me and I found a mountain of mail waiting for me when I returned home.

I really don't know what I can add to what was written in the report. I do know that talking with you and reading your latest book was a great help in setting up conditions for the tests. I was prepared to nail the guy, but as Abb Dickson can testify, the results were quite another story.

To begin with, I was present during a taping of a TV program for educational television, to be aired this fall. When I heard that Geller was to be at the station, where there would be a live audience, I contacted as many local magicians as I could and asked them to be in the audience. I am quite friendly with the people out at the Georgia ETV network and was able to do this. I was even asked to help make up the questions the narrator was to ask Geller. The majority of them were questions you posed in your book.

The magi were seated at various locations throughout the audience. Most of them, unfortunately, were novices and probably could have been fooled by even a mediocre sleight-of-hand man and so most of what they had to say must be taken with a mountain of salt.

However, prior to the taping, Geller walked through the audience collecting key rings. With the lighted stage behind him, and him standing in the shadows, there would have been ample opportunity for him to do most anything with the keys he collected on his way back to the set. For this reason, all results occurring during the program must be discounted due to lack of control.

Following the taping, Geller was surrounded by members of the audience asking him to bend one of their keys for them. I was able to make my way next to him, and between demonstrations I was able to tell him that I needed to talk to him in private and that it was very important. He asked where we could go to talk. Abb Dickson and I escorted him to the office of one of the directors, and I closed the door behind us.

I had been hoping to get Geller alone, so I had come prepared. I handed him a fork and asked him if he could bend it for me. He looked puzzled, as if wondering why we needed to be alone. Why couldn't I have given him the fork out in the hallway? I told him I would explain in a moment. The fork was part of the table service we used when you had dinner with us. It has a black nylon-reinforced handle, and is stamped "forged stainless — Japan" on the back. I tested a similar fork the day before. I could not bend it by hand. When I put the fork in a vise and tried again, the handle cracked, as it did with Geller, but with one significant difference. The metal rod which extends from the tongs of the fork and is inserted into the nylon handle was not affected. The handle cracked before the metal could give. With the fork Geller used, the handle cracked and the metal rod inside the handle was bent.

The sound that came from Geller's hand after he closed his fingers around the handle was not unlike the sound ice makes as it cracks in warm water. The hand, with the ends of the fork protruding from either side, was in sight at all times.

It was at this point that I told Geller that I am a magician. I told him that I am very interested in what he is doing. His first reaction was to accuse me of doing something to the fork to make the handle crack. I told him that I am a mentalist, that while on stage I have had many experiences I am unable to explain, and that for this reason I am not close-minded when it comes to the existence of psychic phenomena. I told him that I am the chairman of the Atlanta Society of Magicians' Occult Investigations Committee, S.A.M. Assembly 30, and in that capacity, along with committee member Abb Dickson, would like to give him some tests. I told him that I was not out to get him, that Mr. Dickson and I would be honest and fair with him. I told him that if, after the tests, we were unable to detect any trickery, I would give him a copy of the report I would be submitting to the Assembly. He agreed. He told me the reason why he decided to agree was that in the past every magician who ever approached him for testing had been hostile. He knew that they would be uncooperative. He said that there was a big difference between being a skeptic and being hostile. And for this reason, and because he believed me when I said I would be honest with him, he agreed to the tests.

I asked him what sort of accuracy he had been having with telepathy. He said he'd like to try some tests. There were three chairs in the room, so we formed the chairs into a circle and each sat down. I asked Geller to turn his head, and while he did, with his hands acting as blinders on either side of his eyes, Abb watched him closely. We made sure he was wearing no rings and had nothing in his hand which could act as a shiner. I picked up a book I had with me and made a drawing on the inside back cover. I held the book upright, just in case he might have had some method of seeing behind him. After I closed the book, Geller turned back to face me.

Following some time of concentration, he guessed. He was wrong. We repeated the experiment. Wrong again. Another try; again no results. Finally he told me not to write anything. Just think of some object. Some time passed as I concentrated on one of my dogs at home. He made some drawing on a pad I had given him, then became unsure of what he had drawn and discarded the paper. He said he was not getting anything definite. He suggested we go back to the original method of my drawing the object I was "sending." I drew a picture of a dog bone. Then Geller turned around and told me to think. I did. Nothing. He told me that I should stare at his forehead as I thought. I did. Nothing. Then he held up the pad I had given him earlier. He told me to imagine the object was drawn on it. Again nothing. Next he drew what looked like the outline of a TV screen on the paper. He told me to imagine that the object was inside the screen. After a short while, he drew four dots on the paper, forming the four corners of a rectangle. Another few moments passed and he connected the two upper dots with a horizontal line. I said, "Good." He told me not to say anything, and then connected the two lower dots, making two horizontal parallel lines on the paper. He said that if this looked anything like what I had been thinking of, that I should complete the drawing in my mind. I thought of two opposing threes at the ends of the lines. He drew the threes. They were a little out of alignment for a perfect bone, but close enough to indicate to me that that is what it was. Afterward, when I showed him my drawing, he made some sketches on his paper describing what had gone through his mind.

In making my original drawing of the bone, I kept in mind the various methods of trickery, i.e., pencil reading, impressions, etc., making sure to take the necessary precautions, even though his back was turned. We made several other tests of a similar nature, with the same results.

We then tried some metal bending with no success. It was getting late and I had a dinner engagement. Abb offered to drive me to my appointment, and Geller asked for a ride to his hotel, since his party had left long before. They had been waiting, with the security guard, in the lobby of the TV network, and when it looked as if Geller would be some time, they went ahead to the hotel.

As I was straightening up the office before we left, I picked up the paper Geller had discarded in one of the first tests. The one where I had not drawn the "target." On it was a rough drawing of what looked like a dog. I had merely thought of that dog. I had not mentioned to him, at any time, that I had been thinking of my dog or that I even had a dog. I was careful not to show him any of the misses. I only told him that he was incorrect.

On the way to the Regency Hyatt House, where I was to meet my father for dinner, I showed Geller some sleight-of-hand magic. He seemed impressed. Upon arriving at the hotel, Geller got out of the car with me to say goodbye. I asked him to try, one more time, to bend a key for me. I gave him a very short key which I chose because its length might make it difficult to get a good grip on. He didn't even take it from me. He told me to hold it between my thumb and forefinger. As I did, he stroked it with his finger and it started to bend. I placed the key into my palm and watched as it continued to bend. I cannot explain it.

We shook hands, said goodbye, and Abb drove Geller to his hotel. I kept my promise and had a copy of my report in the mail to him within several days.

That's all I can tell you of what happened. I have never claimed that Geller was authentic, or that the Society had any opinion as to Geller's authenticity. I only said that I know of no way that he could have used trickery to do these things. That is a fact.

I don't believe I was fooled. The only way I will change my

thoughts about this matter is when some magician comes along and duplicates what I saw Geller do, under the same rigid conditions.

I'm sorry that there had not been any more magicians present for the tests. I really tried to get as many as possible. I called all over the city, inviting everyone I could reach to come. Only Abb and a few novices showed up. It's too bad.

I hope I have answered your questions. I really only regret that such a disturbance has been caused. However, at no time did I say anything to indicate that it was the opinion of the Society that Geller is authentic. Only that, if trickery was used, neither Abb nor I were familiar with the method.

In any case, if there is anything more you would like to know, please contact me.

Yours truly,
(signed) Artur Zorka

THOUGHT PHOTOGRAPHY: A PHOTOGRAPHER'S ACCOUNT

by Lawrence Fried, President of the American Society of Media Photographers, The Society of Photographers in Communications.

Lawrence Fried's photographs have appeared in such publications as the Saturday Evening Post, Life, Look, Woman's Day, Paris Match, Vogue, Holiday, *and* Newsweek, *and Fried is the recipient of the Overseas Press Club Photography Award and seven different awards from* Popular Photography *magazine. He is Director of Photography for the Image Bank, Inc., New York, New York.*

Because of the impromptu nature of the "thought photography" session between Lawrence Fried and Uri Geller, the following report cannot be taken as positive proof of the occurrence of a paranormal event. Fried's account of what he and his two colleagues witnessed in Geller's Manhattan apartment on a day in mid-1973 is an anecdote at best. Fried, an experienced photographer, is convinced that Geller could not have removed the lens cap from the camera to take the "thought" image that appeared on the developed film. The lens cap had been tightly taped on; Fried (and his two assistants) had watched Geller throughout the session, photographing him with another camera, and when Geller returned the camera he had been using, it showed no signs of having been tampered with. The circumstances under which the film was developed also convinced Fried that Geller could not have used trickery at the developing stage of the photograph. Fried recounts all of these things in his brief report, which is included in this book because of Fried's unimpeachable professionalism and expertise with a camera.

Published for the first time, with the permission of the author.

In mid-1973, I received a photographic assignment from *Human Behavior* magazine to photograph the Israeli psychic Uri Geller. I had not met Mr. Geller before this meeting took place, and, in fact, was not familiar with his psychic abilities. At one point during our photographic session, Geller mentioned, casually, that he had once or twice before been able to project his own image on film through a completely closed camera. He was eager to try to do it again.

I suggested that I put the lens cap on one of my lenses and cover it with tape to make it entirely light-tight and then have Geller attempt to take his own photograph. He agreed to make the attempt. He said he had never done it with color film before, so I put color in the camera. I fastened the lens cap very securely onto a 50-mm Nikkor lens and then, using generous amounts of photographer's gaffer tape (a two-inch-wide, silvery, clothlike tape), I put two complete layers of said tape across the lens cap, overlapping at least an inch onto the barrel of the lens. I then wound another long piece of tape around the lens barrel itself, covering the ends of the first two layers that had gone across the lens cap. I immediately handed the Nikon camera to Geller and with another Nikon proceeded to photograph him.

Geller held the camera at arm's length, pointing it at his head and tripping the shutter. (See Plate 47.) He repeated this at various distances from his head until he had the camera pressed directly against his forehead. He did this many times until the entire roll of 35-mm exposures had been "exposed." All the time Geller was tripping the shutter, I was photographing him. My two assistants, Hank Gans and Laurel Gallagher, were present, standing on either side of me and never taking their eyes off Geller. In addition, there was also a reporter from the New York *Post* in the room at the time. No one else was present.

I took the camera from Geller's hands upon completion of the experiment and personally removed the roll of film. I marked it to keep it separate from the rest of the exposed film and put the roll in an inside pocket of my jacket. We packed our equipment and left

Geller's apartment. At no time after I loaded the camera before the start of the experiment was I separated from that camera. It was never out of my hands until the second I handed it to Geller, from which time I never took my eyes off it and was never more than three to five feet away from it. This can be corroborated by my two assistants.

The film (high-speed Ektachrome) was sent to Berkey–K&L Laboratory, in New York, for processing, with instructions that the processor not cut the roll or mount any slides if there were any pictures on the film. Mr. Geller, incidentally, was never advised as to where my film was to be processed.

The next morning I received the processed roll from the lab and opposite frame marker number 10, on the edge of the roll, was an image of Geller. It was somewhat out of focus and slightly underexposed, but unmistakably a photograph of Geller taken at the exact spot where the experiment had been conducted. (See Plate 48.) When I finally removed the tape from the lens that Geller had used, there was absolutely no indication that it had been disturbed in any manner whatsoever.

URI GELLER'S METAL PHENOMENA: AN EYEWITNESS ACCOUNT

by A. R. G. Owen, Ph.D., Executive Director,
New Horizons Research Foundation, Toronto, Ontario.

A. R. G. Owen has been a lecturer in mathematics at the University of Bristol, England, and Head of the Department of Genetics at Cambridge University, England. He has published more than twenty papers on mathematics, genetics, and parapsychological research. Currently, Dr. Owen is Vice-President and Executive Director of the New Horizons Research Foundation in Canada, an organization that performs parapsychological research.

The reader will understand, from this paper, that Dr. Owen's observations of Geller were obtained under less than desirable conditions: in a television studio before a live audience. This is not to say that Owen was deceived or that Geller accomplished his feats through legerdemain. Rather, these words of caution are given only to make it clear that Owen's report on Geller does not constitute proof of paranormal happenings. As is true of the other informal reports contained in this book, Owen's paper appears here because he is a respected scientist who is completely convinced of the genuineness of Geller's talents.

Published in New Horizons Journal, *vol. 1, No. 4, July 1974.*

Introduction

The purpose of this paper is to report observations of Mr. Uri Geller's metal-bending and -breaking phenomena made by myself and others on the afternoon of Friday, March 8, 1974. The conditions in which these phenomena occurred were such as to convince the audience that these phenomena were paranormal and totally genuine. This, by itself, is well worth putting on record. However, there are certain additional circumstances, which, so far as I and my wife (Iris Owen) were concerned, had the effect of making Uri's presentation not merely a convincing demonstration, but also an experiment with a considerable degree of control. To put the matter simply: in the event, out of the large number of metal objects present in the room, it so happened that the objects — a fork and two keys — that were bent or divided were ones that my wife and I had brought to the studio. As will be explained, we knew their condition right up to the moment when Uri's presentation commenced. The nature of the objects was also so highly individual that there was no possibility of anyone's having substituted like, but prepared, objects for them without the substitution having been subsequently detected. Thus, from the viewpoint of my wife and myself the presentation constituted an experiment in which beyond reasonable doubt Mr. Geller's metal phenomena were genuine and paranormal. Having reached this conclusion, we feel it to be our duty to say so, both in fairness to Mr. Geller and because what we have to say may be of value to those serious students of paranormal phenomena who will place some reliance on our opinion. The progress of parapsychology has, I believe, often been retarded by the failure of responsible investigators sometimes to report what they have found.

The Background to the Presentation

Mr. Geller arrived in Toronto about Tuesday, March 5. It had been previously agreed with Miss Joan Schafer, producer of several programs for CITY-TV (Channel 79), that, if possible, he would record an interview that would be broadcast in due course. In the event, Uri's schedule in Toronto proved to be a heavy one. Finally, however, he agreed to the interview, provided that there was only a small audience, which should include the "Philip" group,* of whose work in producing physical phenomena (see Owen and Sparrow, 1974) he had learned, and in which he expressed great interest. It had further been agreed by Joan Schafer that the Toronto Society for Psychical Research should advise on how the interview and any experiment or demonstration should be set up.

I should explain that prior to this I had seen no demonstrations of metal-bending phenomena by Uri either alive or recorded except the bending of a spoon shown in a film made at the Stanford Research Institute. However, I had formed an estimate of Uri based on informative articles such as those of Alan Vaughan (1974), the direct testimony of investigators who had experienced his phenomena at very close quarters, and finally from a television interview by Miss Pat Murphy of Toronto CTV, broadcast live on the morning of March 7. Though I had not yet met him in person, I gained the impression that Uri is an honest and sincere person, and that his phenomena were quite likely to be paranormal and genuine. Indeed, the oddities and vagaries of some of the phenomena and the way in which they were manifested were in themselves exceptionally convincing, as these peculiarities entirely fitted the general picture of paranormal phenomena that I had built up over the years.

In a discussion with Joan Schafer and Pat Murphy (who was to conduct the interview) I therefore impressed on them my conviction that Uri's phenomena might well be totally genuine. It was agreed, therefore, that the presentation should be conducted entirely as a sympathetic interview, without overtly expressed hostility (and, so far as could be managed, without suppressed hostility, because, as I pointed out, Uri could possibly sense our thoughts!). The aim would be primarily to let Uri talk about his phenomena and how they seemed to him both in their mode of occurrence and in their possible significance. This alone would be

* The "Philip" group is a collection of eight people who have trained themselves over a number of years jointly to produce psychokinetic phenomena. In 1975, after hearing of the exploits of Uri Geller, they added metal-bending to their PK repertoire. For further information see: *New Horizons Journal*, Vol. 1, No. 3, Jan. 1974; Vol. 2, No. 1, Apr. 1975.

thoroughly worthwhile. However, we also thought it likely that in a genuinely friendly atmosphere Uri might well successfully demonstrate some of his phenomena. It was agreed that members of the audience should bring their *own* metal objects and that during the interview these should lie on a low table in front of Uri and Pat Murphy, in full view of the audience.

The Experimental Material

About 3:00 P.M. on Friday, March 8, my wife and I and five members of the Philip group, with two other members of the Toronto S.P.R., convened at CITY-TV studio. The audience was otherwise made up of some friends of Uri and some friends of Joan Schafer. On arrival I met Uri in the corridor and introduced myself briefly to him. He asked me to collect together plenty of "stuff" for him to work on, and to ask the audience to be actively "willing" for things to happen so that good phenomena would result. I looked through my own pockets and found some extra keys, while Uri went down to the make-up room. He passed through the basement café where the audience was congregated, and briefly said hello to them, and again asked them to actively "will" him to succeed.

The objects I had collected previously had been handed to Miss Valerie Elia of CITY-TV, who had put them with the other material brought by the audience on a bronze tray, which was resting on a low glass-topped table on the dais in front of the two chairs in which Uri and Pat Murphy would be seated during the interview. I deposited the extra keys on it; there were already about twenty metal articles and a few watches. The metal objects were some nails and large screws, spoons and knives, forks, car keys and door keys. I verified that all the objects I had brought (which will be specified later) were there. Also, I spent a few moments handling every object and verified that, so far as could be disclosed by visual inspection and application of moderate manual pressure, each object was a normal one of its type, not made of especially soft metal. It seemed clear to me that none of them had been prepared by cutting and rejoining with soft metal, glue, or pliable material.

Though I was not continuously in the studio thereafter I did, in fact, visit it several times while the studio was being made ready and the lights and cameras positioned. (Needless to say, during this period technical crews were in the studio all the time, and the focus of attention was the dais — so it would have been impossible for anyone to do anything to the objects on the tray without being observed.) Each time I came in I went to the tray and verified by a *coup d'oeil* that the objects were the same ones I had last seen. Finally, about two minutes before Uri and Pat Murphy took their places on the dais, I made a last inspection, confirming the objects were the same ones I had looked at originally. Meanwhile, Mrs. Adrienne Henwood had talked to Uri, who asked her to get still more material. She went to the basement and commandeered a further batch of house and car keys from the Philip group. Returning to the studio, she dropped this material on the tray and took her place in the studio audience only a matter of seconds before recording started. Uri and Pat had taken their places on the platform only a short time before. The tray on its table was at all times in the full view of the audience (and also of the TV cameras when they were on wide angle). After my final inspection I had kept the tray under continuous observation and saw that none of the objects had subsequently been handled by Uri or Pat or anyone else.

The Phenomena

Until the first commercial break, the interview concerned itself with mental phenomena (telepathy, clairvoyance, etc.). It included an illustration of Uri's ESP ability, which Uri stressed was only an illustration, not a rigorous experiment.

During the first commercial, matters began to take a different turn. My wife, who was sitting with Mrs. Sparrow and Bernice Mandryk on the top row of the set of wooden terraces provided for the accommodation of the audience, opened her purse and inspected her bunch of six keys of various kinds. Previously they had all been inspected by herself, Mrs. Henwood, Mrs. Sparrow, and Bernice Mandryk, and declared normal; this was in the basement after Uri had gone up to the studio. Though my wife and Uri might have passed one another in the studio while he and the audience were getting to their respective stations, there was certainly no further conversation or physical contact between them. She did not open her purse until the first break. To her surprise one of the six keys was noticeably bent at a point about a quarter of an inch from the haft. This key was of the Yale type and was stamped "Reilly's Lock Corp. Ltd. Toronto." The angle of bending appeared to me to be about twenty-five degrees of arc. The key (which was not removed from the bunch) was inspected by myself, Iris, Mrs. Sparrow, and Bernice. We called out to Uri, who asked that it be brought down to him. He looked at it, held it in front of the cameras, then tossed the whole bunch of keys to a point on the carpeted floor about four feet away from him, and said, "Let's look at it again later." It should be reiterated that this was the only occasion on which he had touched or even seen this key.

When the interview was resumed, Uri discussed his ability to rehabilitate broken watches. He picked out two "fob," or "turnip," watches (which Pat confirmed were not working), placed them on the table top, and made about two passes over them with his hands. Pat testified to the fact that they immediately started ticking. I mention this for interest only, as the matter was not investigated in depth.

Uri next talked about his metal-bending ability. He casually picked up and replaced several of the spoons and forks on the tray. Finally, he selected a fork about seven inches in length. He asked Pat to hold it in such a way that the whole of the stem would be visible to the audience and cameras. This was achieved by Pat's holding the blade part of the fork between her thumb and forefinger, these digits being in contact with the outermost prongs of the fork. The blade was thus broadside to these fingers. The fork was oriented broadside to the audience. Then Uri, using the tips of the thumb and forefinger of his right hand, gently "massaged" a section of the stem of the fork, the traverse of his fingertips being about three quarters of an inch. The portion of the stem that he stroked was situated just below the blade. It was the part narrowest in width. However (as we ascertained later), the *thickness* was the same as that of the rest of the stem, which in this respect was uniform throughout its length. Uri first said that he thought nothing was going to happen. Then he smiled and nodded and said, "It's going" (or words to that effect). With the thumb and finger of his right hand he held the bottom of the stem and gently waggled it. The stem moved relative to the blade (which Pat kept immobile), thus showing the audience that the section he was stroking had lost its rigidity. So that this could be seen more clearly Uri asked Pat to present the profile of the fork to the audience. Then, holding the narrow portion of the stem in the thumb and finger of his right hand and the end of the stem with his left thumb and finger, with what appeared to be minimal effort he waggled the stem to and fro, the blade being kept immobile. The total angle traversed between extreme positions appeared to me to exceed forty degrees. After five or six wagglings he released the bottom of the stem and pushed it lightly with his fingertip. The stem suddenly parted at a point in the portion that Uri had stroked, and fell to the floor of the dais. Uri picked it up and handed the two parts to Pat Murphy. When the applause had subsided she read the inscription on the stem; it said "Koba, Stainless, Japan." It was at this stage that I realized the fork was one that I myself had brought from home.

The day previous to the interview I had taken this fork, together with two others (of dull gray metal not matching the first one and stamped "1847 Rogers Bros., I.S.") from the kitchen cutlery, also two old spoons. I supplemented this collection of expendable material with a couple of long steel screws and some derelict watches. Oddly enough, I did not notice that among the forks of various vintages we had a second "Koba" fork — the exact mate of the one that Uri had divided. I discovered this only on returning home with my material, which I had recovered from the tray the moment that the recording ceased. I was pleased that the divided fork had a mate because it affords a good comparison of the "before and after" states of the object. I need hardly point out that the "Koba" forks are somewhat out of date and so are relatively individual objects. Even if, for the sake of argument, it were supposed that despite the considerable evidence to the contrary Uri had substituted a prepared "Koba" fork for the one on the tray, the odds against his selecting one by chance for this purpose are astronomically large. A severe critic might argue that conceivably Uri knew by extrasensory perception that a "Koba" fork would be there and obtained one by teleportation; but this would be a rather self-defeating criticism.

After his success with the fork, Uri noticed two keys on the tray. These I immediately recognized because they were not on a key ring but were tied by string to a buff-colored cardboard label. These keys were, in fact, unique. They were both of the long variety stamped "YALE, The Yale and Towne Mfg. Co., Made in England." One of them was stamped "RKC 25A 13." It was a Fellow's key of Trinity College, Cambridge, issued to me many years before. The number 13 was its own individual number and is registered as issued to me personally. The other key is also a unique object. It formerly opened a door in the Department of Genetics, Cambridge, and bore the individual number 6 as well as a type number, 8150. The label bore an annotation in my handwriting done in (now rather faded) blue ink: "T.C.C. Gen. Cambridge U.K." Remarking that these seemed an interesting pair of keys, Uri picked them up by the label without touching the keys themselves. It was then noticed that the Genetics Department key was in process of bending. This was actually seen by the audience and by the TV cameras in close-up. Uri supported this key with a finger of his other hand. It continued to bend and finally stopped at about fifteen degrees of arc. (See Plates 49 and 50.)

By now we had reached the second commercial break. Uri suggested that the bunch of keys, including the bent Reilly key, be put, together with other material that the audience still had in its pockets, in a pile at the back of the audience. This was done; the pile was made on the back seat between Mrs. Sparrow and me. Uri then answered three questions put by members of the audience. Then he suggested that the pile be looked at. It was discovered that only the top half of the Reilly key was still attached to the bunch. The blade had separated from it, the metal being divided at a point close to the original bend, an operation that normally would require either a hacksaw or a cold chisel and mallet. The blade was found among the other keys in the pile.

Remarks

When the fork and the Reilly key were examined, it was noted that they were divided at their narrowest points, which suggests that the paranormal forces responsible tend to be applied in conformity with a principle of least effort.

The selection of our own fork can doubtless be put down to chance. The pair of Cambridge keys were eye-catching and it may well be that Uri picked them out just because they looked interesting. It is just conceivable that Uri chose these objects intuitively. I was certainly concerned that the interview should constitute what, for me, would be a good experiment.

After the recording Uri talked to various members of the audience. He said to Iris that it was she who had (paranormally) bent and broken the Reilly key. This is indeed possible, though mysterious, because similar events, reported from England, suggest that Uri can temporarily endow other people with the metal-bending ability. Among the items on the tray was an old-fashioned teaspoon contributed by Mrs. Sparrow. It was of a very standard design and previously had nested in perfect congruity with a spoon of similar vintage. When Mrs. Sparrow retrieved it, it appeared normal, but back at home, after a period of an hour or so, it was visibly bent. When inspected later it was still more curved. When the process terminated there was a gap of half an inch between the middle of this spoon and its mate when they were in juxtaposition. (See Plate 51.)

REFERENCES

Owen, Iris M. and Margaret H. Sparrow, "Generation of paranormal physical phenomena in connection with an imaginary communicator," *New Horizons Journal,* *1*, No. 3, 6–18, 1974.

Vaughan, Alan, "The phenomena of Uri Geller," *Psychic,* *4*, No. 5, June, 13–18, 1973.

EXPERIMENTS ON PSYCHOKINETIC PHENOMENA

by John B. Hasted, Ph.D., Department of Physics,
Birkbeck College, University of London.
David Bohm, Ph.D., Department of Physics,
Birkbeck College, University of London.
Edward W. Bastin, Ph.D., Language Research Unit,
Cambridge University.
Brendan O'Regan, M.S., Institute of Noetic Sciences,
Palo Alto, California.

John B. Hasted is Professor of Experimental Physics and Head of the Physics Department at Birkbeck College, University of London. He began his professional training as a chemist and moved into physics at the Clarendon Laboratory, Oxford, during wartime work on radar. He did pioneering work in opening up the microwave region of the electromagnetic spectrum in communications, was reader in physics at the University College of London, and has published books on atomic collisions and on dielectrics.

David Bohm has been professor of theoretical physics at Birkbeck College since 1961. He obtained his Ph.D. at the University of California, Berkeley, and was the last student to study under the atomic bomb-pioneering physicist J. Robert Oppenheimer. Professor Bohm has worked in the field of plasma physics, extending the concepts of this field to the many-body system, and he spent several years at the Institute of Advanced Study at Princeton, New Jersey, during which time he worked with Albert Einstein. Partly through his discussions with Einstein, Professor Bohm was led to challenge the orthodox views on quantum mechanics, which he has continued to expand and refine to this day. He has published books on quantum theory, relativity, and on the role of causality and chance in modern physics.

Edward W. Bastin holds doctorate degrees in both physics and mathematics. He won an Isaac Newton studentship to Cambridge University, and for a time was Visiting Fellow at Stanford University, California. Dr. Bastin's current interests are in physics, mathematics, and parapsychology.

Brendan O'Regan is a member of the Institute of Noetic Sciences, Palo Alto, California, and a consultant to R. Buckminster Fuller's Design Science Institute in Philadelphia. He has performed work in biochemistry and brain research and has written on acupuncture, Kirlian photography, and various areas of psychic research.

The experiments presented in the following three papers were designed to investigate Geller's ability to bend metal, deform crystals, and activate a Geiger counter. The first paper here presents a summary of the events that took place between Geller and the Birkbeck team on four different occasions: February 5, June 21 and 22, and September 10, 1974. The authors' focus is on the results of their experiments and not necessarily on the laboratory circumstances that surrounded their research. These circumstances are, of course, of crucial importance in determining the overall validity of the information reported in the first paper. This paper, therefore, is followed by two pertinent excerpts from John Hasted's unpublished manuscript: "My Geller Notebooks," which present a fuller description of the Birkbeck investigation.

The first part of this paper, which gives experimental results, is published for the first time, with the permission of the authors. The second part of the paper, an essay on the nature of paranormal talents, was first published in Nature, *Vol. 254, April 10, 1975.*

REPORTS of psychokinetic events produced by Uri Geller at the Stanford Research Institute (see pages 35–66) have prompted us to investigate the authenticity of such phenomena.

The phenomena fall under the following headings;

1. Bends produced in polycrystalline metal specimens, i.e., spoons and Yale keys, by gentle handling.

2. Plasticity, similarly produced, in which a part of the metal specimen becomes soft, and easily fractures.

3. Brittle fractures of metal and cleavages of single crystals, similarly produced.

4. "Dematerialization," or apparent vanishing of part of a single crystal of metal.

5. Electromagnetic phenomena.

Table 1 summarizes phenomena of types 1,2,4 recorded by us, mostly under supervised conditions, at sessions 1–4. Specimens were previously prepared and in most cases numbered and weighed to within ± 0.2 mg. "Supervised conditions," under which the majority of phenomena were observed, signifies that the gentle handling of weighed specimens by Mr. Geller was carried out on a tabletop under the close scrutiny of a small number of seated witnesses,* with subsequent reweighing of the specimens; written and sometimes sound records were taken, but there was no video-recording. The other phenomena were witnessed, but not so closely that the conditions could be described as supervised. The "gentle handling" of the specimens consisted of a stroking action by forefinger and thumb of either hand, or sometimes by forefinger alone, with the specimen resting on the table and steadied by the thumb. A phenomenon generally took several minutes to complete. The bends in the Yale keys occurred gradually, sometimes continuing after the stroking had ceased; the specimen would then rest on the table with one end appearing to rise very slowly. Being made of rolled metal, the keys are probably under internal stress.

It is not improbable that manual forces play a part in assisting some alleged psychokinetic bending phenomena, since it is not always easy to ensure that these forces are negligible. However, we are confident that they can be neglected in phenomena 1, 2, 3, 7, and 8.

The mean grain size and grain orientation at the bent Yale key

* Witnesses at sessions 2 and 3 included the authors and Dr. K. Birkinshaw, Dr. J. A. Sarfatti, Messrs. Arthur Koestler, Arthur C. Clarke, K. A. Appiah, and N. Nikola; at session 1 only the authors; at session 4 only the authors and Mr. N. Nikola.

surfaces has been compared with those in mechanically bent parts of the same specimens, using x-ray reflection; no significant differences were noted. Thus the hypothesis that the grains coalesce and produce internal stress is untenable, so far as the relatively small (ten- to thirty-degree) bends in these keys are concerned.

The plasticization, by handling, of about 2 cm of the neck of a stainless steel teaspoon (phenomenon 7) took place in the course of informal conversation around a desk. The teaspoon, which had previously been handled and bent through about thirty degrees by a child who also displays PK ability, was taken by Mr. Geller for a few seconds, when the center became floppy. A witness was able to take from Mr. Geller the two ends of the spoon in either hand while the center was still plastic. It was then handled very much as a heated glass tube is when it is bent to a desired angle in the laboratory. In this way the plasticity could be clearly verified by movement of the hands of the witness. The witness attempted to set the spoon at an acute angle, and to put it down on the table; it retained itself in one piece on the table for a few minutes, but due, presumably, to thinning of the neck by the flow of metal, its strength was so small that a slight disturbance fractured it. The weight loss of the fractured spoon was almost within the estimated experimental error. Electron micrographs of this fracture are under preparation; the procedures used are similar to those used in another study of a similar fracture obtained in the experiments of Professor J. G. Taylor. (See pages 213–217.)

No conventional physical or chemical explanation of the bending and plasticization phenomena is readily apparent. Chemical corrosion is ruled out by the constancy of weight, and by the absence of change of appearance of the metal surfaces; neutron activation and electron-probe microanalysis are in progress as an additional check.

Similar phenomena were observed by one author (J. B. H.) in the course of work carried out on several children by a larger group of researchers. These phenomena included a .0001 axis cleavage of a

7.0 cm x 0.635 cm diameter cylindrical crystal of zinc that was being gently handled by a child under supervised conditions. Such a crystal requires symmetrical three-point loading with a weight of $\simeq$ 4 kg to produce a cleavage at laboratory temperature 20° C so that it might be broken by hand by exercise of strength. One advantage of using an expensive crystal is that the unexpected cleavage could reveal, as the usual gradual bending does not, the presence of excessive manual forces; their presence was not noted in the observation of the cleavage phenomenon.

The important "dematerialization" event 8 was observed by us in session 4 with Mr. Geller. Two encapsulated vanadium carbide V_6C_5 electron microscope foils had been provided by Dr. A. Lee; these are single crystal discs about 2.0 mm in diameter and 0.4 mm thick, with central orifices surrounded by thinned sections. They had been examined by electron microscope. Each had been placed by Dr. Lee in a plastic pharmaceutical capsule about 1 cm long; the capsules were not opened by us until they were returned to Dr. Lee; the discs were not weighed. Vanadium carbide is a very hard material, but a fracture of these discs by hand, with a tool, would be possible, although it would require dexterity. A number of metal objects of various sizes were then placed randomly on a metal surface plate, some encapsulated and some not; the vanadium carbide crystals were among the former. Under scrutiny of three witnesses, one witness covered the group of objects lightly with his open hand, on which Mr. Geller's hand rested for a few seconds. Mr. Geller then clasped both hands together above the witness's hand. One capsule was seen to move by a few millimeters, rather like a jumping bean.

On examination, about one half of the vanadium carbide disc was seen to be missing. (See Plate 52.) Next day the capsule was unsealed and examined by Dr. Lee, who identified the disc and confirmed that half of it was missing; electron micrographs showed that the missing part included most of the thinned section. A brittle fracture, with a small amount of conchoidal fracture, had taken place in the 100 plane; a very low density of dislocations was found, which is typical of mechanical failure. A search for vanadium in the surroundings of the experiments is in progress. (Ed.'s note: See Excerpt Two from "My Geller Notebooks," by Dr. J. B. Hasted, which follows this report.)

The bending of the disc of molybdenum crystal, also provided by Dr. Lee, occurred, following very much the same procedure, at session 2. A sudden bend, possibly accompanied by slight movement, took place. (See Plate 53.) Mild physical sensations were experienced in the hands of both witnesses.

The disc was of 1 cm diameter and 0.22 mm thickness, so it could just about be bent by hand. Such crystals are unusual in that they become more brittle with increasing temperature; our laboratory temperature was 20° C. The bend induced apparently psychokinetically was through an angle of twenty-one degrees.

At sessions 2 and 3 Mr. Geller attempted to produce counts on a nuclear radiation monitor held in his hands. The monitor consists of a Geiger counter partly surrounded by a stainless steel screen, which acts as return path for the electrical circuit. It is sensitive to γ radiation, for which the background count rate in the laboratory was about 0.5 counts per second.

The counter is connected by screened cable to an amplifier, whose output was fed to a Harwell 2000 series ratemeter and chart recorder. During a total period of about fifty minutes, eight count-rate pulses of duration of the order of a second were recorded, some of them of magnitudes corresponding to more than fifty counts/sec. (See Plate 54.) However, the radiation monitor loudspeaker clicking, which was recorded on magnetic tape, did not always accelerate during the chart-recorded pulses, nor did a second radiation monitor record clicks consistently. Moreover, two of the largest chart-recorded pulses corresponded in time to recorded pulses of a magnetic field ($\approx$ 1 mG) at a fluxgate magnetometer about 1 m distant from the counter.*

* In another experiment Mr. Geller was able to deflect a compass needle held in his hand, at the same time producing a chart-recorded pulse of magnetic field at the magnetometer head. However, magnetic field experiments are notoriously sensitive to bodily movements.

Mr. Geller held the Geiger counter screen continuously in his hands during the recordings; the recorded count-rate pulses were not associated with any appreciable bodily movement, nor, of course, could pulses be produced by witnesses. Although Mr. Geller has informally indicated that there has been some learning in producing psychokinetic phenomena, attempts to use the chart recorder readings as biological feedback were unsuccessful in this case.

The least unorthodox hypothesis with which these Geiger counter

Table 1

Session number	*Phenomenon number*	*Specimen*	*Phenomenon type*	*Conditions*	*Number of Witnesses*	*Weight difference (mg)*
1	1	2 Yale keys simultaneous)	1	Supervised	4	−0.1 ± 0.2 −0.1 ,
2	2	Molybdenum single crystal	1	Supervised	8	Unknown
2	3	Yale key	1	Supervised	8	−1.1 ± 1.0
2	4	Stainless steel paper knife	1	Not supervised	2	Unknown
2	5	Yale key	1	Not supervised	3	Unknown
3	6	Yale key	1	Supervised	4	Unknown
4	7	Stainless steel spoon	2	Supervised	3	+0.4 ± 0.2
4	8	Vanadium carbide single crystal disc	4	Supervised	4	Unknown

observations are consistent is that Mr. Geller produced through his hands occasional unpredictable pulses of electromotive force across metal conductors. These pulses are apparently much larger than normal body static electricity. The particular model of radiation monitor used will respond in a similar manner when a 90-volt battery is shorted along the stainless steel screen that surrounds the Geiger counter and forms the return path of the electrical circuit. A current of several amps will then flow through the screen, whose resistance is $\approx 3\Omega$. It appears that a Geiger counter connected in this way is a sensitive detector of voltage transients, since they force it off the plateau of its characteristic.

The Approach to Experimentation

We have come to realize that in certain ways the traditional ideal of the completely impersonal approach of the natural sciences to experimentation will not be adequate in this domain. Rather, there is a personal aspect that has to be taken into account in a way that is somewhat similar to that needed in the disciplines of psychology and medicine. This does not mean, of course, that it is not possible to establish facts on which we can count securely. Rather, it means that we have to be sensitive and observant, to discover what is a right approach, which will properly allow for the subjective element and yet permit us to draw reliable inferences.

One of the first things that reveals itself as one observes is that psychokinetic phenomena cannot in general be produced unless *all* who participate are in a relaxed state. A feeling of tension, fear, or hostility on the part of any of those present generally communicates itself to the whole group. The entire process goes most easily when all those present actively want things to work well. In addition, matters seem to be greatly facilitated when the experimental arrangement is aesthetically or imaginatively appealing to the person with apparent psychokinetic powers.

We have found also that it is generally difficult to produce a predetermined set of phenomena. Although this may sometimes be done, what happens is often surprising and unexpected. We have observed that the attempt to concentrate strongly in order to obtain a desired result (e.g., the bending of a piece of metal) tends to interfere with the relaxed state of mind needed to produce such phenomena. It appears that what is actually done is mainly an unconscious function of the mind, and that once the intention to do something has been firmly established, the conscious functions of the mind, insofar as they have bearing on the goal, tend to become more of a hindrance than a help. Indeed, we have sometimes found it useful at this stage to talk of, or think about, something not closely related to what is happening, so as to decrease the tendency to excessive conscious concentration on the intended aim of the experiment. A comparison might be made with the process of trying to go to sleep, for which one needs a firm intention, without subsequent efforts.

Many of the conditions described above are also required for fruitful research in the natural sciences. Thus, if any of those who participate in a physical experiment are tense or hostile, and do not really want the experiment to work, the chances of success are greatly diminished. Likewise, the aesthetic appeal of the experimental setup often helps to maintain interest and enthusiasm, but an attitude that consistently tends to damp these is evidently detrimental to the whole enterprise. In the study of psychokinetic phenomena, such conditions are much more important than in the natural sciences, because the person who produces these phenomena is not an instrument or a machine. Any attempt to treat him as such will almost certainly lead to failure. Rather, he must be considered to be one of the group, actively cooperating in the experiment, and not a "subject" whose behavior is to be observed "from the outside" in as cold and impersonal manner as possible.

The following analogy may help to give a more orderly overall description of the phenomena in the field. Consider a person whose hand has been paralyzed as a result of destruction of nervous tissue. If this person is to regain the use of his hand, he must somehow activate new nervous pathways. As to how he is to do this, he does not know. All he can do is, with all his energy, to feel out the possibilities of movement and to observe with great attention and alertness what movements actually take place. He cannot describe, or even think about, just what it is that he does in getting his hand to move. Moreover, he cannot at first produce controlled movements, which bring about consciously intended results. Rather, it is clear that the contact between brain and hand is brought about almost entirely by unconscious functions of the mind, which tend to be erratic and fortuitous. Of course, if he works with sustained interest and energy, he will generally find that his movements do begin to come closer to what he intended them to be. But it is also clear that if he is surrounded by people who do not believe that he can move his hand, or who, through hostility, bring about a state of psychological tension, then he will be less likely to be able to sustain the interest and energy needed for learning how to move his hand.

Those who work with such a person (e.g., the physiotherapist) must evidently share in the confidence that the ability to move the hand will eventually come about. The thoughts in the paralyzed person's mind, and those in the minds of his colleagues, are both important factors in bringing about success. The necessary confidence about the ultimate result must be maintained in the minds of all concerned, while at the same time there is a healthful capacity to be tentative and open-minded in statements about what particular results may have been achieved at a certain stage. And so reliable inferences can be made in physiotherapy, though by methods that are rather different from those used traditionally in the natural sciences.

The analogy between this field and that of psychokinetic research is fairly clear. The main difference is this: We can account for, and to some extent explain, the connection between the brain and the hand in the case of the paralyzed person (through the nerves that link them), but we have no way either to account for, or to explain, the connection between the brain and the object that is moved, bent, etc., in terms of what is now known to science. However, if we suppose that there is some *at present unknown* force, energy, or mode of connection, then we may also suppose that psychokinetic power may function in a way that is essentially similar to the power to move the hand. Thus, one might suggest that perhaps there is an unconscious "feeling out" of the connection. In many cases there is a visible "feedback" that enables a person to recognize that he has done something, and that permits him to try to go further along the same (indescribable and undefinable) lines. But there may be other forms of feedback. Thus, if the metal can respond to the brain in an unknown way, the brain may similarly respond to the metal. By being sensitively aware of this response, the person concerned might be able to tell when something had actually happened, even though the object in question was not sensually perceptible to him.

It is important, at this point, not to insist on having a potential theoretical explanation before one will seriously consider observing the phenomena themselves. Thus, when magnetic and electrostatic effects were first observed, it was impossible to account for them in terms of the then known forces, which were considered to arise only when bodies are in mechanical contact. Evidently, this did not prevent their being observed. The main aim of such observation is to give rise to an orderly account of the phenomena, which is first qualitative and then quantitative, e.g., first the qualitative observation that like charges repel, unlike charges attract, and then the quantitative observation that the force is inversely proportional to the square of the distance. On the basis of such an account, current field-theoretical explanations of electromagnetic phenomena were later developed. We propose a similar approach to psychokinetic phenomena, and in ways described earlier in this article, we have begun to carry it out.

In such research an attitude of mutual trust and confidence is needed; we should not treat the person with psychokinetic powers as an "object" to be observed with suspicion. Instead, as indicated earlier, we have to look on him as one who is working with us. Consider how difficult it would be to do a physical experiment if each person were constantly watching his colleagues to be sure that they did not trick him. How, then, are we to avoid the possibility of being tricked? It should be possible to design experimental arrangements that are beyond any reasonable possibility of trickery, and that magicians will generally acknowledge to be so. In the first stages of our work we did, in fact, present Mr. Geller with several such arrangements, but these proved to be aesthetically unappealing to him. From our early failures, we learned that Mr. Geller worked best when presented with many possible objects, all together on a metal surface; at least one of these objects might appeal to him sufficiently to stimulate his energies. In our fourth session, we had such a setup, which included, as described earlier, two small plastic capsules, each containing a thin disc of vanadium carbide single crystal. A clearly observable change in the disc within one of the capsules was brought about when Mr. Geller held his hands near them.

In discussions with magicians we have learned that the best conditions for a conjuring trick arise when the happening significantly precedes the observation. In the above instance we believe that the conditions were such that the failure to observe and record the precise moment of change is of no importance, because there is no known way of producing this effect within the closed capsule and no possibility of substitution. For this reason we conclude that this was something that no magician could have done.

Nevertheless, we realize that conditions such as we have described in this paper are just those in which a conjuring trick may easily be carried out. We understand also that we are not conjuring experts, so if there should be an intention to deceive, we may be as readily fooled as any person. Moreover, there has been a great deal of public criticism, in which the possibility of such tricks has been strongly suggested. For this reason it has often been proposed that a skilled magician should be present, to help to see to it that there will be no possibility of deception.

It is in the nature of the case, however, that no such assurance can actually be given. For a skilled magician is able to exploit each new situation as it arises in a different and generally unpredictable way. The corpus of tricks is not fixed, but rather continually changes and evolves. A particular magician could therefore say at most that he knew of no tricks that could have brought about a given set of observed phenomena. Of course, if several magicians of recognized proficiency were to conclude that what was done on a certain occasion did not involve any tricks, this could help create a presumption in favor of the notion that the phenomena are genuine. In principle, we would welcome help of this kind in decreasing the possibility of deception. It has been our observation, however, that magicians are often hostile to the whole purpose of this sort of investigation, so they tend to bring about an atmosphere of tension in which little or nothing can be done. Indeed, even if some magicians were found who were not disposed in this way, it does not follow that their testimony will convince those who are hostile, since the latter can always suppose that new tricks were involved, beyond the capacity of those particular magicians to see through them. Because of all of this, it seems unlikely that significant progress toward clearing up this particular question could be made by actually having magicians present at the sessions, though we have found it useful to have their help in a consultative capacity. We have learned in such consultations not to stop watching the identified specimen from the first moment when it reaches the hand of the subject until the bend occurs. We are familiar with the use of the human hair in producing small movements, with the use of mercuric salts in alcohol to corrode metals, and with the weakening in metals produced by continued bending to and fro. We recognize that there is a genuine difficulty in obtaining an adequate answer to criticisms concerning the possibility of tricks, and that a certain healthy skepticism or doubt on the part of the reader may be appropriate at this point. Indeed, it would be inappropriate if the scientific community did not at first react in such a way. However, we believe that our approach can adequately meet this situation.

It is essential that in at least some experiments conditions must be controlled in such a way that the possibility of deception is insignificant. Metal-bending and cleavage experiments are particularly suitable for this approach. Encapsulated specimens can play an important part, although up to the present we have been able to achieve success with only one such specimen.

We feel that if similar sessions continue to be held, instances of this kind might accumulate, and there will be no room for reasonable doubt that some new process is involved here, which cannot be accounted for, or explained, in terms of the laws of physics at present known. Indeed, we already feel that we have very nearly reached this point. We expect, however, to carry out more tests along these general lines and to report on them when results are available.

MY GELLER NOTEBOOKS

by John B. Hasted, Ph.D., Department of Physics, Birkbeck College, University of London.

What follow are two excerpts from an unpublished manuscript: "My Geller Notebooks," by John B. Hasted, Birkbeck College, University of London. They recount in considerably more detail the events that took place during two of Uri Geller's visits to Birkbeck College. The excerpts are important addenda to the previous paper because in them Dr. Hasted discusses not only more of the technical details of the experiments that he conducted, but also candidly evaluates the "controlled conditions" under which the work was performed, and some shortcomings in the experimental procedures.

The following two excerpts are published for the first time, with the permission of Dr. John B. Hasted.

Excerpt One

We had originally planned that only myself, Bohm, O'Regan, Bastin, Nicola, and Birkinshaw be present, but three other people were added to this number: Arthur Koestler, physicist Jack Sarfatti, and composer Mr. K. A. Appiah, who was writing music for Geller's gramophone record. Thus, the fifteen-square-foot room was a little crowded, although with discipline we managed to avoid too many difficulties. I had been fending off the press all day; not that they would have behaved irresponsibly, but because we needed all the peace and quiet we could get. The short periods during which Geller would be available to us must not be wasted.

When Geller arrived we showed him the equipment we had set

up, and he asked to make a start with the radiation monitor.* This was a commercial instrument, made by Mini-Instruments, consisting of a Geiger counter enclosed in a stainless steel sheath, and connected by cable to a control panel that registered the nuclear radiation pulses both on a ratemeter and as audible clicks on a loudspeaker. The counter is sensitive to γ-rays through the metal sheath, but for use with β radiation a part of the sheath could be slid open to allow the less penetrating radiation through.

β- and γ-rays are emitted by radioactive sources when the nuclei of the atoms decay spontaneously. Although the average number of decays in a given time is well known for each radioactive source, the precise moment at which each β- or γ-ray is emitted cannot be predicted from physical theory. It is a truly random event. Thus, if these moments could be changed by mental concentration, and an unusual number of β- or γ-rays counted, then we might have a clue to the understanding of this apparent randomness. Of course, there are ways in which a Geiger counter might be activated normally — for example, by a radioactive source concealed about one's person. I used the Geiger counter itself to search Geller for such a source, and found none.

When there is no radioactive source near the Geiger counter, only a few counts are registered each second; under our laboratory conditions, about one every two seconds. This radiation reaches the earth from extraterrestrial sources and is known as cosmic radiation. Thus, the instrument would record the time variation of the background count rate of cosmic radiation.

The pulse counts from the control panel of the Geiger counter were taken to a Harwell 2000 series ratemeter whose output was chart-recorded. (See Plate 54.) When the time constant is set at one second, pulse counts appear as small individual "noise" peaks on the chart (see Plate 54), provided that their rate is sufficiently slow. But when the count rate reaches, say, ten or a hundred per second, and remains there for several seconds, then much larger peaks appear on the chart, as is also shown in Plate 54.

* This session marks Geller's first visit to Birkbeck College: June 21, 1974.

The correct operation of this system was checked by exposing the counter close to a radioactive source; readings of the order of twenty-five counts per second were recorded (see Plate 54: test pulse). Care was taken to check that in the absence of the source the background radiation was not excessive, and that false pulses could not be produced by rough handling of the Geiger counter or its cable. Twenty minutes of constant background radiation were followed by a test pulse from the radioactive source, then by a further ten minutes of constant background radiation.

Then I handed the counter to Geller, who held it in both hands and tried to concentrate. We drew on the blackboard a picture of a mushroom cloud to help him to think of nuclear radiation. All the outward signs indicated that Geller was concentrating as hard as he could.

Within two minutes, two count-rate pulses, one of about twenty-five counts per second, were recorded (see Plate 54: a, b). Geller said that he felt some sort of shock, which I thought might have been electrical. But Geller did not see the chart record at this stage; we made no attempt to use "biofeedback," that is, to allow him to learn by watching the chart recorder. I was attempting to watch both Geller and the chart recorder. After sixteen minutes there was another pulse, c, and after a further five minutes a large pulse, d, during which Geller reported feeling a prickly sensation. We then allowed the apparatus to run for a further ten minutes without Geller's holding the counter. There was only background radiation recorded, and the apparatus was switched off.

During the experiment the gaussmeter and its chart recorder had been kept running, with the probe fixed to a table about two feet away from Geller. Nicola had been supervising the chart record, but I did not watch it myself. There had been small movements in the gaussmeter chart record, as there often are when people do not keep quite still. But there were two noticeable pulses, which Nicola told me had corresponded exactly in time with the count-rate pulses c and d.

I was already beginning to suspect that the origin of the Geiger counter pulses could be electrical rather than nuclear; we conducted further experiments on the following day. During a twenty-five minute session, four count-rate pulses, e, f, g, and h, were recorded, reaching maximum rates of about ten per second. A second Geiger counter was also exposed, but it was not touched by Geller, and it did not register either audibly or visibly during these pulses. Only the counter Geller actually held in his hands registered. A tape record of the loudspeaker clicks from this counter was also made, and although there were clicks corresponding to the first two chart record pulses, there were very few corresponding to the last two. The effects on the Geiger counter were not quite those that nuclear radiation would have produced.

After twenty-five minutes, all the witnesses except Arthur Koestler and me left the room, and Geller decided to make an extraordinary effort to produce a large pulse. Within three minutes he produced a count-rate pulse, k, which was well off the scale of the chart, and may have been as high as 200 counts per second (see Plate 54: k). What is interesting about this pulse was that it arrived *before* Geller intended it to. The transcription of the audio tape reads as follows:

Geller: "I'm gonna shout! . . . All right . . . *(knocking)* . . . *(deep breath out)* . . . I'm gonna count to ten and on ten it's gonna go one, two, three, four, five, six, seven, eight, nine"

Hasted (simultaneously): "It's going already."

Geller (shouting): "ten!"

Koestler (shouting simultaneously): "Um-ho . . . did you see that?"

Hasted: "I saw nothing, but it was ten times harder than anything we've had yet."

The peak on the chart recorder started when I said, "It's going already." No clicks were audible. The pen stayed off-scale until "did you see that?" at which point it returned to zero, and some clicks were audible. Geller felt some sort of shock, and Koestler also experienced a shock. They both were temporarily exhausted.

I verified that the Geiger counter was still operational, and was still proof against mechanical effects, such as a pulling of the cable or a knocking of the counter. Everyone came back into the room and Geller relaxed. My conviction was growing that the pulses were electrical in origin, but I did not see how electrical pulses could have entered into the circuit. Next day I realized that the stainless steel screening case constituted a return path for the circuit; I tried the effect of short-circuiting a 90-volt battery along the screening case. Even though the window was closed so that the screening case completely surrounded the counter, a count-rate pulse was produced every time I passed current through the case.

A Geiger counter is essentially a metal cylinder with a fine wire mounted axially (see Plate 54). It contains gas at a pressure of about 5 torr ($\sim$ 1% of atmospheric pressure), and a steady voltage is maintained between wire and cylinder, just insufficient to cause spontaneous electrical breakdown. The entry of nuclear radiation is sufficient to trigger such breakdown by collisional ionization. The electrical energy of the breakdown is rapidly dissipated, but the counter produces an electrical pulse, which is registered at a suitable amplifier. The counter quickly returns to prebreakdown conditions and awaits the next pulse.

But when a 90-volt battery is momentarily connected in the circuit, albeit across a piece of stainless steel, spontaneous breakdown occurs, and an electrical pulse will be registered irrespective of whether nuclear radiation enters. It may be that the dissipation of this energy produces secondary electrical effects, causing subsidiary breakdowns and further loudspeaker clicks, such as were heard after the largest chart record pulse. The ratemeter is simply an integrating circuit that would respond to a continuous breakdown much as it would to a series of pulses.

The most likely hypothesis to explain these experiments is that

Geller's hands produced transient voltages of the order of 50–100 volts.

These transients are about a million times stronger than normal; typical potential differences that develop, for example, between one human wrist and the other, are several hundred microvolts, but they vary in time with both heartbeat and breath, according to experiments that Dr. Birkinshaw conducted at the time. Presumably they are short-circuited when the body is immersed in a bath containing bath salts. Other areas of skin do not show these time-varying potentials; there is probably the equivalent of a high impedance separating these areas from the source of the time-varying potentials. But it follows that such a high impedance would protect the source, that is, the interior of the body, against shocks from surface effects. It seems likely that the source of Geller's potentials lies close to the surface of the body.

Let us consider the possibility that the effects are due simply to static electricity at the skin surface. Friction on very good electrical insulators produces a static charge, which can sometimes be discharged with the production of a spark. It would have to be an extremely powerful static charge to produce a voltage along the stainless steel case sufficient for the Geiger counter to break down. Frictional production of static charge acts by removing surface electrons from the insulator or adding them to it. Nevertheless, Geller had no cloth to produce the friction, and he was squeezing rather than rubbing the Geiger counter case; he held it quite still in his hands. His feet were not moving on the carpet. Those of us who have tried to produce static on metal surfaces without friction have had no success. There must be some mechanism by which the charge was produced, and since normal subjects cannot produce it one can legitimately call it paranormal. There have been reports from the USSR of subjects who have been able to produce static charge without friction and use it to apply forces to objects without touching them. Geller's Geiger counter pulses seem to have been phenomena of the same sort. But the hypothesis I wish to put forward to explain the source will have to await the description of even more surprising phenomena that occurred later in the year.

At the first Birkbeck session, the Geiger counter experiment was followed by an attempt to record any changes of magnetic field that Geller might be able to produce. We used a Hall-effect gaussmeter with the output signal chart recorded; the full scale of the chart corresponded to a 10-milligauss field.

Time variations of magnetic field are constantly occurring normally. The earth's magnetic field is more than 100 milligauss, and the Post Office Underground trains, which use an earth return, produce field variations of more than 1 milligauss when they pass underneath our laboratory. When metal objects are moved around, the balance of local electromagnetic fields can be disturbed sufficiently to register a change of magnetic field, which may also be about 1 milligauss. On one occasion H. M. the Queen Mother visited our laboratory, and I demonstrated how the departure of an underground train affected one of our electron spectrometers, which was sensitive to fields rather smaller than 1 milligauss. Suddenly there was an unexplained effect. When she had gone we found a hairpin on the floor.

Small changes in magnetic field are so easily produced by normal means that they are not very good phenomena for psychic research. Nevertheless, something might be learned from the chart record, provided that all present kept fairly still, and provided that Geller himself had no metal on his person. These conditions we secured, except for a small brass buckle on Geller's belt. We fixed the magnetometer probe to a table top, and asked Geller to concentrate on it and attempt to produce a variation of magnetic field. The probe was set at a forty-five-degree angle so that horizontal and vertical components of a field would contribute equally to the signal. For eight minutes the chart recorder trace was reasonably steady, although its response was more sluggish than that of the Geiger counter chart recorder. Then it became apparent to us that Geller had very little idea of what a magnetic field actually was, so we gave him a compass needle and asked him to concentrate on deflecting it toward him. There followed six more minutes of calm, although people were getting restive and producing a few small pulses, which were obviously due to the movements of metal.

Geller held the compass flat on the table, between his finger and thumb, and he moved very little in his wooden chair. Suddenly there was a jerk at the compass needle and a 2-milligauss deflection on the chart, which did not seem to arise from human movements. After seven more minutes, there was another apparently genuine pulse of about 2 milligauss, and the compass spindle jerked out of its bearings. These pulses are shown in Figure 1.

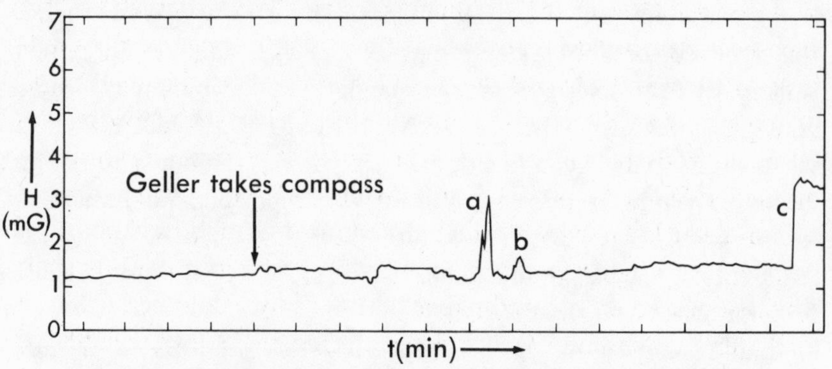

Fig. 1. Part of the chart record of time-variation of magnetic field measured by gaussmeter in vicinity of Geller's hands.

The compass we used was of unusual design; it consisted of a circular metal band with both top and bottom covered with a glass disc. The compass needle was carried on a spindle mounted in holes drilled in the center of the two discs. Thus it had no metal base.

If Geller's finger and thumb were to produce a voltage transient, then a current would flow through the metal band, and magnetic flux would be produced, essentially perpendicular to the compass needle. The latter might not be deflected strongly, but the vertical couple could well upset the spindle from its bearings. A magnetic field would be produced at the gaussmeter probe, which was about one foot away from Geller's hands. This corresponds to what was observed.

Although I cannot be certain that this is the correct interpretation of the experiment, it does confirm the hypothesis that Geller can produce voltage transients at his fingers when he concentrates sufficiently.

Encouraged by these early successes, we conducted an experiment to determine whether Geller could remotely exert a mechanical force on a delicate membrane. We used a capacitance manometer, the membrane of which responds to minute differences of pressure between the gas in two tubes. When both tubes are exposed to the atmosphere, as was the case here, the membrane is so sensitive that a wave of the hand several feet from one tube will be registered on the chart recorder. Both Geller and the witnesses refrained from moving, but several minutes of mental concentration by Geller failed to produce any result. We now switched on a helium-neon laser, which directed a spot of orange radiation in a parallel beam right across the room. The position of the tiny spot, which appeared on squared paper four m away, could be measured to better than 1 mm. Geller concentrated for a few minutes on bending the beam of light, but without success. I did not want Geller to get discouraged by too much failure, so did not continue any further.

Unexpectedly, Geller was not discouraged; in fact, he seemed to be growing in confidence. We talked about metal bending and I gave him latch keys, which encouraged him still further. When he reached what is sometimes called a "contact high," he wanted to attempt to make a bend without touching the specimen. Geller likes to have such specimens on a metal plate, so a sheet of steel was laid on the table, and the following selection of metal objects placed together on it:

1. Two key rings with keys attached to them.
2. Four loose latchkeys.

3. A thin steel tube containing a thermocouple.
4. A stainless steel paper knife.
5. A single crystal ingot of vanadium carbide.
6. A single crystal disc of molybdenum, 0.22 mm thick and 1 cm in diameter.
7. A single crystal bar of silicon.
8. A length of steel rod, one inch in diameter.
9. An annealed copper disc with a hole in the middle.

None of these objects had been in Geller's hands, and he did not touch them while they were laid out. Jack Sarfatti stretched his hand out above the objects, and Geller then put his hand on top of Sarfatti's. After a few seconds, Jack reported feeling a sharp tingle in his hand, and when both hands were withdrawn we examined the objects. The only one showing an obvious change was the molybdenum single crystal disc, which had been perfectly flat beforehand, but was now bent slightly. (See Plate 53.)

This single crystal, and some others we have used, had been given to us by Dr. Tony Lee, of the Cavendish Laboratory, Cambridge. It was of high purity, better than 0.99999. Some weeks later, when I showed the crystal to David Rooks, who was going to photograph it, we noticed that it was very slightly attracted to the tweezers he was using. Of course molybdenum should not be ferromagnetic, so I suspended the crystal between the poles of an electromagnet and found it to be quite as ferromagnetic as commercial molybdenum, which contains eighty parts per million of iron. I therefore sent the single crystal for neutron activation analysis to the Scottish Universities Reactor Centre. How this impurity got into pure crystal is still a puzzle.

The bending of the molybdenum crystal was impressive, and the witnesses became excited. It was difficult for me to maintain "controlled conditions," since Geller had worked very hard and now started to enjoy himself. He bent two latchkeys and my stainless steel paper knife, but not while sitting at the table; he walked into David Bohm's office, and later held the latchkeys under a tap; so I did not see the bendings sufficiently clearly. I weighed the keys, and in my excitement I made a mistake and concluded that one of the keys had lost weight. It was not until the next day that I discovered what I had done wrong with the balance. When I checked, I found that the key was actually unchanged in weight within 0.2 mg. Geller works well when he is excited, but unfortunately scientists do not. The afternoon's session concluded soon afterward; we had made several observations, the validity of which we were reasonably confident of, and everyone regarded the session as a success.

Excerpt Two

On September 9, Brendan O'Regan telephoned from the U.S. to say that Uri Geller was coming to London to work with a film company. We quickly made contact, and at 4:45 P.M. on the next day Geller arrived on his own at Birkbeck.* David Bohm and Nicola were with me, and Ted Bastin arrived soon afterward. We were by now sensitive to the disadvantages of crowded laboratories. Although the Geiger counter equipment had been made ready, we decided to concentrate on metal specimens.

Before he had been in my office for two minutes, I spoke of my experiences with the children** and handed him one of the stainless steel spoons that had been bent by the girl (under "controlled conditions"). Geller held the handle and did not touch the bend. Within a few seconds, and under our close scrutiny, the bend in the spoon became plastic. It quickly softened so much that the spoon could be held with one end in either hand and gently moved to and fro. I had never seen Geller produce a really plastic bend before,

* This visit marked Geller's last session at Birkbeck College: Sept. 10, 1974.

** Elsewhere in Hasted's "My Geller Notebooks" he presents evidence of psychokinetic abilities found in children who had either seen or heard of Uri Geller's metal-bending feats. Similar evidence is reported by Dr. John Taylor, Dr. Thelma Moss, and Dr. E. Alan Price in *The Geller Papers.*

and I asked him to hand the spoon to me in one piece. I took one end from his left hand into my right and one end from his right hand into my left. The acute angle, about sixty degrees, was essentially unchanged in the handing over. I could sense the plasticity myself, by gently moving my hands. It was as though the bent part of the spoon was as soft as chewing gum, and yet its appearance was normal. I continued a gentle bending movement for about ten seconds, and then decided that it might be more interesting to try to preserve the spoon in one piece than to pull it apart. As carefully as I could, I laid it on the desk. It was not appreciably warm. I did not dare to touch the bent part for fear of breaking it, and it lay on the desk apparently in one piece for a few minutes; but on attempting to move it I was unable to prevent it from falling apart, a "neck" having developed.

This was the first time that I had clearly seen a really "plastic bend," since these are much rarer than the slow bends I had observed previously. I do not think there can be any question of fraud when a really plastic bend is produced under close scrutiny, unless there is serious chemical corrosion, such as that produced by mercuric salts. Even then, the metal would behave quite differently, becoming wet, discolored, and brittle, but hardly plastic.

Chemical corrosion is accompanied by a change in weight; therefore I was pleased that I had recorded the weight of this spoon, as follows:

Original weight	24·3526 g
Weight after bend by child	24·3533 g
Combined weight of pieces after fracture	24·3529 g

These variations are within the limits of weight changes, both up and down, that have been observed in other bent specimens. The errors are due to dirt and to moisture condensation and evaporation.

We have not yet learned very much from the appearance of the fracture of this and other plastic bends. A stainless steel spoon, or a brass key, when broken by physical force, will display a brittle fracture in which the metal surface is formed into tiny cup- and cone-shaped patches. But the plastic bend fracture looks rather different from this, especially when viewed in the high magnification of the electron microscope. Paul Barnes arranged for his postgraduate students to take electron micrographs of a fractured spoon, and when these were examined various anomalies were found but no very definite new knowledge was gained.

Geller was interested to learn that the fractured spoon had not lost weight, and he concentrated on causing a loss of weight in a piece of zinc crystal, but with no success. However, the bent copper crystal, which was lying untouched nearby, appeared twisted as well as bent when I examined it. The twist was through an angle of ten degrees. Since the bent crystal was lying flat before it twisted, the producing of this twist without any touching of the crystal is difficult to understand, even assuming softening. But the mechanical properties of a copper single crystal are anisotropic, that is, they are different in three perpendicular directions. The x-ray analysis of the crystal may throw some light on the event, but has not yet been completed. (Ed.'s note: At the time this book went to press the analysis was still incomplete.)

The copper crystal had been resting on a machinist's metal surface plate, a hard steel block, fifteen inches by ten inches and about one-inch thick. Geller finds that his powers are improved by working on a large block of metal, and he soon felt sufficiently activated to attempt a bending without touching, in the same way as he had bent the molybdenum crystal. We laid out a collection of metal objects on the metal surface plate, and this time there was only one key; all the other objects were single crystals. These were of copper, zinc, silicon, germanium, chromium, nickel, and vanadium carbide.

In addition I laid out three encapsulated electron microscope foils, which Tony Lee had provided. When a specimen is viewed under an electron microscope, it must be thinned down to an extent that allows the beam of electrons to pass right through it. The specimen is formed into a disc of about 2.0 mm diameter, and 0.2 mm thickness; it is thinned down by special techniques until it is only ten or twenty atoms thick in the center, although its thickness at the edge is unchanged. I had been given three nickel crystal foils, and two of crystals of vanadium carbide V_6C_5. This material has the appearance of a metal, but it is harder than glass and rather brittle. The foils had been examined in the electron microscope, and so could be easily identified in a similar instrument. As is customary, each foil was encapsulated in a cellulose pill case, the sort that dissolves in the stomach and releases the powdered drug inside. These pill cases are made in two halves, one of which slides into the other. I had looked at the capsules when Geller had telephoned and had found the foils in good order, but I did not actually examine them closely when putting them out on the surface plate. The capsules had remained in their plastic box in a closed drawer of my desk in the meantime, and I had been in the room all the time. There was a strong presumption that they were unchanged, but in view of what was to happen I now regret this oversight; it detracts from an otherwise perfect session.

When all the specimens were laid out on the surface plate, I held my right hand, palm downward with outstretched fingers, a few inches above them, and Geller passed his right hand slowly above it. He said that the "power" could well be strongest in one particular place, and I might be able to sense where this was by feeling in my hand. Jack Sarfatti had experienced a sensation in his hand during the bending of the molybdenum, and Geller himself claims to have experienced sensations in his hands.

When Geller's hand was directly above my knuckles, I swear I felt in them a warm sensation, as though I were experiencing strong diathermic heating. I wondered if this might be radiant heat from Geller's hand being unusually hot, but a quick touch with my other hand told me that it was as cool as my own. So I said to Geller, "This is the exact place. Try to increase the 'power' here." He concentrated, with his hand still above my knuckles, and the capsule that was directly below them gave a little jump, like a jumping bean. I did not see this, since I could not see through my own hand; Ted Bastin reported it. Then I removed my hand, and I myself saw, below where my knuckles had been, the capsule give a little jump. Geller removed his hand, which had been about eight inches above the surface plate. Bastin and I examined the capsule without opening it, and found that although the capsule was undamaged only half the foil was there. A photograph of the fractured foil appears in Plate 52. Bastin took the capsule containing the fractured foil at once, and Geller never touched it. Bastin did not open it; he was going to Cambridge, and could ask Tony Lee to view it in the electron microscope.

I did not know quite how seriously to take my warmed knuckles, or how to answer the question of whether the effect was of physical origin or was purely psychological. I did experience slight discomfort in the knuckles for about two hours.

We searched the desk, which had been cleared for the session, and as much of the office as we could, but we could not find the other half of the foil. We decided to leave the office immediately, and arrange for a thorough vacuum cleaning of the desk and carpet. Fortunately, vanadium is fairly rare and small quantities of it can be detected by neutron activation analysis.

It is true that we never saw the half-foil reappear, but it did disappear under circumstances that led us to think conjuring was out of the question.

Next day Ted Bastin telephoned me from Cambridge; he said that Tony Lee and he had opened the capsule and examined the half-foil under the electron microscope. No substitution had taken place. The foil displayed a brittle fracture in the 100 plane, with a small proportion of conchoidal fracture. This would be typical of the mechanical failure of a brittle crystal such as vanadium carbide. The crystal is face-centered-cubic (as is common salt), with a superlattice of vacancies sufficient to make up the stoichiometric formula V_6C_5. Some small facets or ridges about 200 Å across were recognized running along the crystal; these might have arisen from a previous heat treatment, or as remnants of a cleavage in the 100 plane, or from polish damage, or they may have been oxide.

Lee and Bastin also examined the other encapsulated vanadium carbide foil, and tried to fracture it with pliers, holding it in tissue paper in a vise. It was a slow and delicate operation, and despite great care the broken half of the foil flew in the air and could not be found. The crystals are extremely springy, being under internal stress, so that they will fly apart rather than fall apart.

I supervised the vacuum cleaning of the office floor; the sweepings were sent off to Professor Henry Wilson at the Scottish Universities Reactor Centre for vanadium analysis by neutron activation. His colleague Dr. Whitley reported a high level (29 ± 6 μg vanadium in a 5 g sample), which at first surprised me. However, my shoes might have deposited this amount after my visits to the college workshops. Vanadium is present in small quantities in many types of steel, and therefore in the turnings and filings on a workshop floor. I am still sampling my floor sweepings to see what the typical vanadium level is.

David Bohm pointed out that the vanadium might actually have passed into the steel of the surface plate; I therefore arranged for drillings both from the center and from the edge of the underside of the surface plate to be analyzed. The levels were both 0.270 ± 0.016% of vanadium; this figure is below the maximum of 0.4% found in some types of steel. I concluded that there was no evidence that the vanadium had passed into the surface plate.

But from the session I had learned that genuinely rare elements and tracer elements may be useful in the study of metal-bending and disappearance phenomena.

A BRIEF REPORT ON A VISIT BY URI GELLER TO KING'S COLLEGE, LONDON, JUNE 20, 1974

by John G. Taylor, Ph.D., Department of Mathematics, King's College, University of London.

John G. Taylor is Professor of Mathematics at King's College. He has held Chairs of Physics at the University of Southampton and at Rutgers University, New Jersey. His present research interests include the problem of matter in extreme states, such as in black holes, and the development of a suitable theoretical framework for paranormal phenomena. He is the author of three books on popular science, a physics textbook, several science fiction plays, the book Black Holes, *and his most recent book on paranormal phenomena,* Superminds, *in which he presents his research with Uri Geller and expounds on the Geller Effect.*

In his first paper, "A brief report," Dr. Taylor recounts the sequence of events that took place the first time Uri Geller visited King's College. Taylor's second paper, "Analyzing the Geller Effect," is based on more work with Geller and on observations and reports of individuals who appear to be able to duplicate many of Geller's psychokinetic feats. (A more detailed presentation of Taylor's psychical investigations can be found in Superminds: A Scientist Looks at the Paranormal *[New York: Viking Press, 1975].)*

Both papers by Dr. Taylor are published here for the first time.

IN AN OFFICE at King's College I had set up several experiments designed to measure the pressure applied by Geller during metal bending. The two main ones were very simple. The essential apparatus for one of them was a balance of the type used to weigh letters and parcels; it was sensitive enough to measure weights to a quarter of an ounce. A brass strip about 20 cm long was taped horizontally to the platform of the balance. The major portion of the strip extended out from the platform, and Geller stroked the top surface of it while I measured, directly, by reading the scale, and by using an automatic recording device, the pressure he was applying. At the end of the test the strip had acquired a bend of ten degrees although Geller had at no time applied more than half an ounce (20 gm) of pressure. It was out of the question that such a small pressure could have produced that deflection. What is more, the actual bending occurred *upward* — *against* the pressure of the finger. Earlier, another subject gave a similar result, producing, with less than an ounce of downward pressure, a smaller upward deflection (two degrees) on a strip of copper.

While Geller was doing this experiment, we found it a little disconcerting, to say the least, to have the needle, which indicated the amount of pressure on the letter balance, also bending, as it moved, through seventy degrees.

The apparatus for the other test was a small cylinder imbedded in a strip of aluminum in such a way that one end of the cylinder, covered by a pressure-sensitive diaphragm, was flush with the surface of the strip. When pressure was applied to the diaphragm by a person's rubbing the strip gently with a finger, an electric current proportional to this pressure was generated by a device installed inside the cylinder. This pressure-measuring device had been used with various subjects, but no bending was achieved. In Geller's case the consequences were drastic. Holding the strip in one hand, he made it bend in the appropriate region so that the pressure could be measured. But as the bending occurred the mechanism in the cylinder suddenly stopped functioning. I took the apparatus from Geller and observed, to my horror, the pressure-sensitive diaphragm begin to crumble. A small hole appeared in its center and spread across its whole surface till the diaphragm had completely disintegrated, the entire process taking about ten seconds. After another three minutes the strip in which the cylinder was imbedded had bent a further thirty degrees.

Attempts to influence objects without contact yielded more information. Geller held his hands over a plastic container in which had been placed a small crystal of lithium fluoride; within ten seconds the crystal broke into a number of pieces. There was absolutely no chance of Geller's having touched the crystal. Throughout the experiment I could see a gap between his hands and the container holding the crystal. He also buckled a small disc of aluminum, which again was inside a plastic container. I held my hands between Geller's and the container in order to prevent any possibility of his directly manipulating the disc.

Geller was then led into another room to work with other pieces of apparatus. One of these was a standard strip of copper on which was glued a very thin wire. Distortion of the strip would cause a change in the electrical properties of the thin wire, which could be measured very accurately. Geller tried to bend the copper strip without direct contact, but had not done so after several minutes; there was no significant change in the properties of the thin wire. We broke off in order to start measuring his electrical output, but, turning around a few moments later, I saw that the strip had been bent and the thin wire was broken.

Almost simultaneously I noticed that a strip of brass on the other side of the laboratory had become bent. I had placed that strip there a few minutes before, making sure at that time that it was quite straight. I pointed out to Geller what had happened, only to hear a metallic crash from the far end of the laboratory, twenty feet away. There, on the floor by the far door, was the bent piece of brass. Again I turned back, whereupon there was another crash. A small piece of copper, which had earlier been lying near the bent brass strip on the table, had followed its companion to the far door. Before I knew what had happened I was struck on the back of the legs by a perspex tube in which had been sealed an iron rod. The tube had also been lying on the table. It was now lying at my feet, with the rod bent as much as the container would allow.

None of the flying objects could have actually been thrown by Geller as he was some distance away from them and would not have been able to get close to them without being spotted. I was not wholly surprised because an earlier occurrence in the corridor had led me to expect something of the sort might happen. I was walking along with Geller after the first batch of tests when a strip of metal, which had been left on the desk in my office, suddenly fell at my feet. We were at least seventy feet from the office when this occurred. I have to admit Geller could have brought the thing out of the room with him.

Later, I set a compass on a stable surface and asked Geller to try to cause the needle to rotate without touching it. This he did by passing his hands over it, achieving a rotation of up to forty degrees. Then I tried to do the same, keeping 10 cm away from the compass, as Geller had. It proved impossible. Even rocking or rotating the compass directly had little effect except when obvious violence was used. Nor could Geller have been using a magnet unless he could "palm" it with consummate skill at particular moments, for he appeared to be able to "switch" his magnetic effect on and off at will in spite of the fact that he might have been making similar hand movements. Nor could my two companion observers detect any such deceit.

The next step was to make further tests and especially to see if nonmagnetic material could be moved. But unfortunately Geller's timetable did not allow this. Right at the end of the session a comparatively loud click was heard at the far end of the laboratory. Looking toward its source, we discovered that the small piece of metal that had flown to the far end of the laboratory was no longer lying on the floor. We searched the laboratory, but it was nowhere in sight. Geller remarked that this was not the first time things around him had disappeared; the piece of metal had most likely vanished from the laboratory, he reckoned. After he left I made a more thorough search of the room, and finally found the piece of metal under a radiator at the end of the room opposite where it had been. How it had got there I do not know, but it clearly had not dematerialized, as Geller had suggested.

This left me in a state of even greater mystification than before. The bending of metal by known means had been shown to occur, as had the distortion of other materials. But objects had apparently been made to "fly" through the air, and a compass needle had been caused to rotate without the intervention of a visible mechanism. These events seemed impossible to comprehend; I should certainly have dismissed reports of them as nonsense if I myself had not seen them happen. I could always try taking the safe line that Geller *must* have been cheating, possibly by putting me in a trance. I had no video tape to support my own direct observations, though other people had seen the rotation of the compass needle. Yet I was sufficiently *compos mentis* at the time to monitor various pieces of scientific equipment while these objects were "in flight." I certainly did not feel as if I were in an altered state of consciousness.

ANALYZING THE GELLER EFFECT

by John G. Taylor, Ph.D., Department of Mathematics, King's College, University of London.

The Geller Effect involves the bending or breaking of objects, usually metal, by certain people in situations in which such results are scientifically impossible. The overt methods used are either a gentle stroking of the object or mental concentration on it without any direct contact with the specimen being distorted. At least fifty cases have been reported in this country, and similar numbers have been noted in other countries after visits by Uri Geller, the majority of the subjects being children. The effect itself is clearly a challenge to science, and requires a thorough investigation. This is especially attractive since the materials being distorted have structures that are reasonably well understood. What is more, the amounts of energy involved must be considerable because they cause metal objects to bend or break, so whatever mechanism is involved cannot be too elusive to be observed by reasonably sensitive apparatus. The prognosis for a complete analysis of the effect is therefore good.

The first question concerns the validity of the effect. Many instances of it have been reported under highly variable conditions.[1] The emergence of subjects with metal-bending powers has allowed more careful analysis with controlled surroundings. The repeatability of the effect due to the persisting powers of the subjects has permitted simple tests to be designed; they quite clearly validate the effect.[1,2] That does not mean that all cases of metal bending have to be accepted as belonging to the Geller Effect, but sufficient precaution can be taken to prevent fraud. The pressure being applied during stroking of a specimen can always be measured by the experimenter either holding one end of the object or attaching it to a suitable spring balance. Less certain, but still reasonable, is the very careful direct observation during the bending process itself. The majority of the results to be reported here involved the latter process, but only with subjects whose ability to bend material was already validated.

The next step in the scientific analysis of the Geller Effect is to determine the range of the phenomenon itself. This involves such things as the range of materials that can be affected, the variation of ease of bending according to the shape of the material, and the comparison of the powers possessed by different people. More technical questions, such as what associated phenomena — temperature change, current flow, etc. — occur in the metal or other material during distortion, also need to be answered, as do the possible forms of radiation that could be used to transmit energy to the specimen. There are also related disturbances that may be helpful to consider, and that are brought about specifically by the metal-bending subjects. In this paper we attempt to present preliminary data on these matters obtained from work with a number of young subjects (all under the age of sixteen) as well as with Uri Geller. (A microanalysis of the objects is underway.)

The final step is to determine the mechanisms involved in the Geller Effect. That is inextricably tied to the results of the experiments mentioned above, but it was felt appropriate to attempt as descriptive a discussion as possible before soaring to the rarefied atmosphere of theoretical analysis. Clearly the choice of experiments is partially guided by the mechanisms available. This must not prevent all possible mechanisms from being investigated without prejudice. The existence of the Geller Effect alone shows that the scientifically impossible can sometimes occur.

The range of materials that can be bent or broken is broad. The metals include copper, aluminum, brass, several forms of steel, tin, lead, zinc, and silver. The first four of these have been affected by subjects under conditions in which the pressure applied to the metals was measured or when there was no direct contact. The remainder have been distorted under less strict conditions but still when only gentle pressure appeared to be applied, and by children whose powers on the first four metals had been validated under strict conditions. Plastics have also been distorted by children. The plastics were tensile test specimens of polystyrene and polycarbonate. Ionic crystals have also been affected without direct contact.[2] Single crystals of both LiF and NaCl were fractured, the former with marked disintegration, and both fractures were made by Uri Geller. Silicon has been affected, as reported earlier.[2] Other materials have also been reported as being distorted; one was wood, though the experimenter has not observed this directly. It is clearly important to know the exact range of materials that are amenable, since important clues to the effect could result from such knowledge. In particular it is of value to learn if it is only materials with a certain degree of regularity in their structure that are at risk.

The next question is that of the effect of the shape of the specimen on ease of distortion. The results would indicate whether the Geller Effect involves the whole specimen being distorted or only a portion of it. To test this feature, standard specimens of different sizes were used with two subjects (A and B) whose bending powers had been validated on other specimens.[2] The first test involved five specimens of aluminum, each with a cross section of 0.6 x 0.2 cm. Every specimen was stroked gently by subject A for a period of seven minutes. The specimens were tested successively with a rest of two minutes in between each. The resulting degree of bending is given in Table 1. There is a clear relation of length of specimen to ease of bending, the best case being for that with a length of 19.4 cm. This result was supported by a similar test performed at an earlier time by the mother of subject A; the results are also given in Table 1. The times are not exactly comparable with those of the later test, but it was found that a strip about 20 cm long was bent most easily. Tests were also done under parental supervision with subject B. The results are shown in the table; the maximum length for the copper specimens used was 13.5 cm. Tests were also set up, again under parental supervision, with subject A using copper strips 2.6 cm wide. Here again the longest strip bent most rapidly. It is clear that the length of the specimen is of considerable importance in the bending process; the influence of cross section is not so apparent, and obviously more work needs to be done on this.

Table 1. Variations in the length of metal specimens and the ease of bending them

Subject	*Supervisor*	*Material and cross section*	*Details of bending*					
A	Experimenter	Aluminum 0.6 × 0.2 cm	*Length (cm)*	5.0	12.4	19.4	50.0	100.0
			Degree of bending	0	0	32	14	6
			Time (min)	7	7	7	7	7
A	Parent	ditto	*Length (cm)*	5.1	9.4	18.6		
			Degree of bending	0	125	178		
			Time (min)	8	4.75	2.75		
B	ditto	Copper 0.6 × 0.2 cm.	*Length (cm)*	5	10	13.5	15.5	
			Degree of bending	0	4	11	10	
			Time (min)	25	15	10	10	
A	ditto	Copper 2.6 × 0.15 cm.	*Length (cm)*	5.4	10.1	17.3	19.9	
			Degree of bending	0	0	4	15	
			Time (min)					

There are also data about the subjects with metal-bending powers. At least fifty such cases have been reported to the experimenter by reliable witnesses, though he has personally investigated only twenty-five of these cases, and of these only six were observed in action, making it possible to say they were genuine. There are only four adults among the fifty persons reported, all the others being under the age of sixteen; no adults are present at all among the six observed most closely by the experimenter. The youngest child observed is seven and a half (a four-and-a-half-year-old has been reported as having metal-bending ability, but the child's alleged talent was not directly studied by this experimenter). The average age of the children is about twelve, and they are roughly divided equally between boys and girls. The outstanding feature of these statistics is the complete exclusion of adults from the select group; its explanation might be found in physiological changes normally occurring at puberty.

It is also of value to investigate what is taking place in the specimen itself during bending. At the macroscopic level, measurements have been made of temperature changes by taping a 0.3-cm-long thermocouple to each specimen. No temperature changes of more than 2° C have been recorded during the bending process. This change is on the order of that expected when a specimen is touched by the hands. Microheating in the interior of a specimen could have escaped notice by such a measurement, but microanalysis to date indicates the absence of any such effects.

In a similar fashion any possible current flow occurring during bending was measured by means of wires soldered to metal specimens. Specimens of various shapes were used, the main ones being copper strips, each with a cross section of 0.6 x 0.2 cm and a length of 10 to 15 cm. The wires were attached at the mid point and near one end of each specimen. Changes of potential were measured on either D.C. or A.C. millivoltmeters. The sensitivity of the measurements was increased by a factor of 1000 by a suitable voltage amplifier. In three cases of bending of the Cu strips, one case involving a bend of over one hundred and eighty degrees, no deflections of the apparatus were recorded on the most sensitive scales. The corresponding potential differences were below 25 μV at D.C. and 0.1 μV over the frequency range of 1 Hz to 3 MHz.

Any radiant energy transferred to the specimen during bending was also accessible to measurement. The first type of radiation investigated was of the ionizing variety. A portable radiation monitor Type 5-40 with an x-ray scintillation probe Type 5-42, made by Mini Instruments, sensitive to 3–100 keV photons, or a larger Airmac radiation monitor 1021B was used in various tests with known subjects, the radiation probes being placed as close as possible to the specimen being affected. No readings above background radiation were observed, to within the accuracy of the equipment, in three separate sessions when bending occurred with five subjects. Nor were there any effects, during these tests, on the discharge rate of a gold-leaf electroscope. For example, in one test the electroscope deflection decreased twenty degrees in twenty minutes while bending occurred; a similar reduction, to within 5%, occurred due to normal charge leakage. The only way in which ionizing radiation could have been involved was if it were so highly focused as to have evaded the radiation probes.

Ultraviolet radiation was tested for by the use of metal strips coated with sodium salicylate and enclosed in quartz tubes. The strips were treated as specimens to be distorted, the attempts being made by subjects in reduced illumination so as to observe any fluorescence, appearing as a violet glow, produced by ultraviolet radiation. The strips were also placed nearby when standard specimens were bent. There were some violet flashes seen while the tubes were rubbed (though no bending of the treated strips occurred), but roughly the same number of flashes, and with the same level of illumination, were obtained by purely frictional effects at a different time. Otherwise no fluorescence occurred. The total fluorescence in all cases was less than that produced by illuminating the tube with a helium vapor lamp (Hg vapor calibration lamp A26-4812 at 5 W, UV Products, U.S.A.) at a distance of 20 cm; the amount of ultraviolet radiation that may have been involved during the bending sessions was clearly far too low to be significant.

A similar complete lack of success was encountered when we tried to detect infrared radiation from 2μ to 1 mm wave length by means of a germanium crystal detector connected to an oscilloscope. In two separate tests the detector was positioned next to the specimens being bent. In all cases there was at most a half-division change of the oscilloscope beam during bending; this is in contrast to the two-division deflection caused when hands were passed in front of the detector at about the same distance, 10 cm, as the specimens that were being bent. The possibility of static magnetic field effects during bending was also ruled out for numbers of subjects by using a milligaussmeter (Type M Magnetometer, Newport Instruments) in two sessions; no deflections were observed, while bending occurred, to within the noise level of the instruments on the most sensitive scale.

It is possible that one or another of the above forms of radiation could still be involved with the Geller Effect, but in too narrow a beam. To test this hypothesis, direct attempts were made by subjects to affect the various measuring instruments. No modifications above those ascribable to experimental error were obtained with the infrared or ultraviolet detectors (except for breakage of an axle on the chopper blade in front of the germanium crystal) nor with the milligaussmeter. This was not the case with the Geiger counter.

The first clear evidence that a Geiger counter could be affected occurred when the portable radiation monitor was tested with Uri Geller. In the presence of two independent observers, Geller caused the counting rate to be increased by a factor of twenty-five above the background radiation on three separate occasions, and by a factor of 50, 100, and 500 times above it on one time for each. The duration of each of these high count rates was about three seconds, except for the highest rate, which lasted five seconds. In each case Geller held the probe in his hands and appeared to exert some physical force, though a test afterward showed that distortion of the probe was very difficult to achieve. Since this result was so unexpected, the effect on the Geiger counter was tested by the more satisfactory method in which the subject was not allowed to touch the radiation monitor at all; the output was also recorded automatically by allowing each output pulse to charge up a condenser whose slower discharge across a resistance was recorded on a Servoscribe millivoltmeter. The results obtained supported those found with Geller. The case of a sixteen-year-old girl, whose metal-bending powers were suspected but had not been validated, was outstanding. She obtained deflections up to twenty times greater than the background radiation. A group of seven subjects who were not metal benders produced deflections about forty times greater than background radiation. The smoothness of the background readings over three hours of monitoring was an indication of the satisfactory functioning of the instrument, which had been thoroughly overhauled the preceding week.

None of the subjects was able to influence significantly the rate of discharge of an electroscope. There is clearly a paradox here, since the latter result indicates that it is most unlikely that ionizing radiation which is the cause of the modification of the Geiger counters. The problem, then, is to discover what the cause actually is, for it may well be closely linked to the mechanism producing the Geller Effect itself.

A final phenomenon, which is clearly relevant, is the subject's power to move objects. This was observed with Geller, who caused a compass needle to rotate smoothly from its equilibrium position through forty degrees and remain deflected for a period of four seconds. This occurred three times, the third time in the presence of three other witnesses. It was not possible to duplicate this phenomenon by moving the body in such a way as to cause the compass needle suspension to vibrate, since any such motion added a vertical oscillatory component to the rotation of the needle; none was observed with Geller. Again, the cause of this may be relevant to the Geller Effect.

In conclusion, we can say that the Geller Effect depends on the gross shape of specimens, especially their length; in involves very little change of temperature or flow of current in the specimen, and is very unlikely to be caused by ionizing, ultraviolet or infrared radiation. Nor are static magnetic fields involved. Further investigations of these questions are now underway. Other phenomena affecting Geiger counters and rotating magnets also need further investigation to determine their mechanisms and the light they may throw on the Geller Effect and on the extrasensory powers of human beings in general.

REFERENCES

1. J. G. Taylor, *Superminds: A Scientist Looks at the Paranormal* (New York: Viking Press, 1975).
2. J. G. Taylor, "On the Geller Effect," *Psychoenergetic Systems*, No. 5 (yet to be published).

REPORT ON A MEETING WITH URI GELLER AT THE ROYAL GARDEN HOTEL, LONDON, OCTOBER 30, 1972.

by Edward W. Bastin, Ph.D., Language Research Unit, Cambridge.
Tim Eiloart, correspondent for *The New Scientist*.

Edward W. Bastin holds doctorate degrees in both physics and mathematics. He won an Isaac Newton studentship to Cambridge University, and for a time was Visiting Fellow at Stanford University, California. Dr. Bastin's current interests are in physics, mathematics, and parapsychology.

Tim Eiloart studied chemical engineering at Trinity College, Cambridge. He spent twelve years setting up and running a number of companies, including Cambridge Consultants. Since 1970 he has been a free-lance journalist and business correspondent for The New Scientist.

On his way to the U.S. in late 1972, Uri Geller stopped off in England, where he met Dr. Edward "Ted" Bastin of the Language Research Unit at Cambridge. The following report tells of that meeting and of the events that Bastin and others witnessed at the Royal Garden Hotel in London. This is a conversational paper; it is printed here because it presents an early picture of Geller and the feats he performed before any scientific testing of him was undertaken. About a year and a half elapsed between this first informal meeting between Geller and Bastin, and the subsequent testing that Dr. Bastin and his colleagues undertook at Birkbeck College.

Published in Theoria to Theory, *Macmillan Journals Ltd., Vol. 7, Jan. 1973.*

Ted Bastin

The meeting began with Geller attempting some quite ordinary "thought transference" tasks, which were at first not very successful but became more successful later on. It seemed that Geller liked to "warm up" in this way — indeed, he himself said that this was so. He also said that if there were few people present then he needed to have a deep warm relationship with each. If there was a large audience this did not matter so much (Geller is used to giving music-hall demonstrations of his powers).

Geller then asked for some fairly small metal objects — preferably of a rather personal, familiar sort. He didn't like money. No one proffered a ring, and all we could find were spoons. One was a stainless steel spoon that Bastin found in Puharich's bathroom while looking for metal objects. It turned out to be a spoon Puharich used for taking medicine. The rest were teaspoons belonging to the hotel. These latter were silver-plated and quite robust (probably with a cupro nickel base — it was later confirmed that they were E.P.N.S. [electroplated nickel silver]). Geller asked Eiloart to hold these four spoons loosely in his hands, which were cupped, with the spoons vertical and hands and spoons resting on the table. Geller then put *his* clasped hands an inch or two above the spoons — not in contact — and appeared to concentrate his thoughts upon the spoons. He concluded this "concentration" with a tightening of the clasp, which usually made his fingers click. Geller then said he thought nothing had happened. Eiloart released the spoons onto the table.

A minute or so later Bastin asked if the others thought that the stainless steel spoon had flattened its handle. No one was sure. Bastin picked it up and immediately dropped it involuntarily because it felt somehow "alive." Then all saw that the bowl of the spoon was bent sideways, and some discussion took place as to whether the spoon could have been distorted as much as that before the experiment without this having been noticed. It was thought this was most unlikely since the spoons had been scrutinized when they were collected. This spoon continued to deform slightly in that the bowl took a sharper angle to the handle in the symmetry plane (the first movement had been at right angles to the symmetry plane).

In the next experiment Geller said he would try to move the hands of Bastin's wrist watch (which had a segmented stainless steel strap). He laid the watch on the table face up and made the same motions as were described for the spoons. Nothing happened. (During this attempt and the next ones, everyone watched to see if there was daylight between Geller's hands and the watch.) Geller then tried with the watch turned face down, and this time it was found that the hands had moved from a quarter to five (the correct time) to a quarter past three. The new position was a "possible" one in the sense that it could have been reached by turning the watch handle. The watch was still going, and Bastin returned the hands to the correct time after everyone had observed them.

Half a minute later Bastin thought he saw the back of the watch (then lying face downward) begin to go concave. In fact, this was an illusion and was probably caused by a deformation that had started in the metal strap at the end that was connected to the watch. Two links had been considerably twisted. Eiloart then examined the strap and made estimates of the angle through which it had twisted. It took about ten minutes to reach the state in which it finally settled, by which time the four end links had been twisted. The twist might have been produced by manually applied force, but it seems more likely that the strap would have broken.

The last phenomenon to be observed occurred when Geller made a movement to pick up one of the spoons (it is not certain whether this was one of the original set) that was lying in a saucer in order to stir his coffee or put in sugar. He lifted the spoon (as I saw out of the corner of my eye) by the end of the handle, and as he did so the bowl of the spoon fell off and clattered into the saucer. Everyone then looked, and Geller became excited, saying, "Look what has happened." Eiloart then took a rather similar spoon (no exact duplicate could be found) and bent it backward and forward as far as it would go, using all his strength. It took about twenty such flexures for the spoon to break, which it did, and in a place similar to the fracture of the first spoon.

The affected pieces of metal from the various experiments were placed in separate plastic bags together with brief notes to describe what had happened in each case.

The only general remark I am able to make about the fractures from a physical point of view is that the easiest way to imagine them would be to consider the metal becoming momentarily plastic at the relevant point, and then being subject to gravitational and inertial forces for a moment.

Tim Eiloart

My first impression of Uri was of an immensely enthusiastic person who really seemed pleased to encounter us. All smiles and friendliness.

He sat us down and warned us that he would not be able to do as well if he had not got a big audience or if we were skeptical. (This warning seemed to rule out any really skeptical investigation or thoroughly scientific procedures, so what follows is put forward as an honest description of Uri's way of working, not as proof of his paranormal powers.) Then he said he was able to do two sorts of paranormal thing, one being telepathy and the other being action at a distance. I expressed surprise about the telepathy, which I had not previously heard of. He then said yes, and asked Ted to write two series of three numbers on a sheet of paper. Ted did so, putting the numbers in groups of three. Then Uri asked Ted whether he could remember the last of each series. Ted couldn't and I could so Uri asked me to transmit the numbers. He seemed quite sure he could get the first after a while but not the second (or maybe the other way about). He then got the one he thought he could get.

Next we tried my sending a picture. Uri was blindfolded when I drew it, and in most other cases was apparently looking away or was blindfolded. He was wishing to transmit this to Ted and we stood in various positions with Ted next to him and me on various sides of him. He admitted defeat after a while and Ted said, "Was it a castle?" As he said so, Uri said, "Was it a house with a big chimney?" Uri was right, though Ted was also pretty accurate. Ted also asked about squares, which were prominent in the windows.

Uri tried to guess a tree and got a circular thing with two lines, but they were horizontal, not vertical, beneath it. He tried to draw what I was holding, which was a comb, but "could have been a comb or pen." He drew a sort of cigarlike object, in fact, and was disappointed that it was about 5 mm too long. He had hoped to get the right length to within 1 mm or so.

He tried to soften some spoons and bend them. After he had done so, one was very bent, although it was just conceivable that we had missed noticing it was bent when looking at them before he tried. At the time, I held the spoons in my hand and he held his hand over mine as if warming them with body heat. He had previously failed to make any impression on an individual spoon as far as we could see, though the curvature of the handle might have changed a little. I doubt that.

At a very early stage Uri had tried to transmit colors to Ted, without any success, and had transmitted green to me (though I never felt any conviction and felt I was merely guessing).

He then tried to change the hands on Ted's watch, but without success.

Next he did some more guessing of pictures from Ted. He got one impression of "a box-shaped thing on circles with lines beneath which could have been a train." In fact, there was a box-shaped church on some lines of hills but no circles we could see. Later I held the piece of paper up to the light and the word *Green* appeared where Uri had written it, when transmitting it to me, in rounded script where the wheels would have been. (Uri never saw this interpretation of the circles.)

I went to the john and when I was coming out Uri was trying to alter the hands on Ted's watch again. It seemed to work. The hands went back an hour and a half. I had not seen them previously and could not say that the effect was real; I had only Ted's word for it. Then he tried to alter Ted's watch and produced a very pronounced twist in several of the links of the strap. This appeared to increase and spread from one link to another. Eventually the first link went through about one hundred and thirty-five degrees and other links through ninety-, sixty-, and forty-odd degrees. I saw a few days later that all the links were nearly back to normal and the effect could hardly be credited anymore. Ted was wearing the watch and the tension on the strap would tend to straighten the links.

The last effect was when Uri picked up a spoon to show us something about it and it snapped in two. In fact, although the spoon was a few feet from me, I was not looking at it directly. I could see it from the corner of my eye. I heard a bang as soon as he picked it up, and Uri leaped with delight because it had broken in two. He could just have palmed it without anyone seeing. It was broken as though it had bent double first, which is inexplicable, too, since it certainly did not seem to be bending double. Put this another way: if it had broken alone this might have been less odd than the fact that it bent double and then broke as he picked it up. As a piece of spoon to palm, it was an odd choice. On the other hand, bending with subsequent breaking is standard Geller practice. Uri also tried to guess numbers from Ted, which did not work too well. He guessed 10 for 5 but got one other number right; 4 I think. He failed to get a picture of a boat from me but got a picture of a face with hairs coming out of it from Ted. I was watching Ted draw this and felt that it was a face. In fact it was a cat's face with long whiskers.

In summary, the watch strap was the best piece of work apart from the spoon, which could have been a trick. The watch's changing its hands should have impressed Ted most, perhaps. I did get the feeling that the telepathy was real and either a correct image came to Uri or he refused to guess in most cases. Only the single wrong number with Ted was a positive failure.

If Uri and Puharich were working an elaborate double act, it would have been possible to do some of the guesses, though a radio transmitter would have been needed for the cases where Uri was blindfolded and Puharich would have been an accomplice.

If we were hypnotized it would have been possible for Uri to twist the links in the watch strap to their original final twistedness, using pliers without our noticing, and to change its hands. However, the twist, which is now visible, could be produced with a quick hand movement.

Insofar as Uri cannot operate well with skeptics, it would be very difficult to test his powers properly, since he could always employ quite sophisticated tricks up to the point that the crosschecks stopped him, then plead skepticism. I did try writing down the state of the watch strap at 5:10 or so, when it seemed to be twisting more every few minutes, and at that time had stopped changing, as far as I could see. He does seem very genuine and might well be self-deluded if he is hoaxing. But then it is impossible to say how anyone could not be aware of such a depth of trickery if that were the case. It would need to be some kind of walking trance state, I guess.

Coda *by Tony Bloomfield, journalist*

At 10:00 A.M. on the morning after what Bastin has described, a further meeting was held at 52 Berkeley Square. Those present, aside from myself, were Uri Geller and his young cousin, Andrija Puharich, and Ted Bastin.

Geller began with "thought transference" experiments, in which he tried to guess simple line drawings and digits that I had drawn on a piece of paper. He had varying degrees of success with this, but the last attempt was strikingly successful. I had drawn a circle with a vertical diametric line, and began to hold the figure in my mind. He then reproduced the figure on his paper with complete assurance and no delay, and we both held the figures up for the others to see. This experiment convinced me that Geller was succeeding genuinely, though, of course, the elaborate precautions customary in this kind of experiment were not taken.

We then turned to metal objects. Geller wanted objects with some personal "character," and I produced a very heavy object like a marlin spike. Geller said he thought that would be too strong for him to affect, and this turned out to be true. After that we were again reduced to the spoons, which had come in with the coffee I had ordered. They were again quite heavy silver-plated spoons. Geller asked Bastin to put his hands over one spoon, which he did in such a way that we could see the spoon and could see daylight between the spoon and his hands. Geller then put his own hands above Bastin's and concentrated on the spoon. It was just as he stopped that we saw the handle of the spoon begin to distort slightly and I immediately said, "That's it; it's going." Then I drew the meeting to a close as I had a further engagement.

I put the spoon in a drawer in my desk although Geller had wanted Bastin to take it away for some reason we did not fathom. Later it was put on a filing cabinet in my secretary's office, where she commented on how badly it was bent. I told her the spoon was to be left on the cabinet and not to be touched by anybody. After about an hour the spoon handle was seen to have become much more bent. The spoon stayed there for some time; it was then seen again in the afternoon and then placed under lock and key for the evening.

At the same time a second spoon had been brought up from the kitchen. This spoon was in a sugar bowl and no attention was paid to it by any of us. However, when we came to send the sugar bowl out of the office, we noticed a "mangled" spoon in it. I asked my secretary, who said it had been slightly bent but not as badly as the condition in which it was being returned. However, as nobody was paying any attention to this spoon, no comment can be made on exactly when it became so much more bent.

Both incidents are significant because my secretary was quite a new person on the scene. She had not been subject to any possible collective hallucination or hypnotism on the part of Geller. In fact, she had neither met nor known any of the people present in my office that morning.

Later the same day I met Geller and Puharich in the same room, and again a spoon was bent in much the same way. One other incident took place while Geller was there that reminded me of the phenomena of poltergeist infestations. A heavy metal knob, which was one of a pair screwed onto the tops of the corners of my electric imitation coal fireplace, suddenly clattered to the grate. There was no reason to think that anyone had unscrewed it and left it in an unstable position.

THE URI GELLER REPORT

by Albert Ducrocq, Ph.D., INSERM Telemetry Laboratories, Foch Hospital, Suresnes.

Albert Ducrocq has research interests in astronautical engineering and cybernetics, and is Director of the French Society of Electronics and Cybernetics. He is the author of numerous scientific papers and has presented a portion of his work before the Scientific Academy of Paris.

Seven experiments were conducted with Uri Geller at INSERM (the National Institute for Higher Studies and Medical Research), Telemetry Laboratories in April 1975. The work was under the direction of Dr. Albert Ducrocq; others present were Dr. Hermann (an internist), Dr. Cherrier (a cardiologist), Dr. Warusfel (a mathematician and a professor at Louis le Grand), Dr. Aimedieu (general practitioner at the Center d'Aeronomie de Paris), Dr. Arfell (Director of the INSERM Telemetry Laboratories) and his assistant, Mrs. Laurette. Attempts were made to monitor Geller's brain waves during certain telepathy and PK experiments. But Geller found the electrodes pasted to his head "distracting," and felt that he could not perform at his best while they were attached to him. And indeed he did not, as Ducrocq reports. Before the experiments the French scientists searched Geller thoroughly for any hidden metallic or magnetic devices, and found nothing. Ducrocq's report is brief, with only a few comments made on each of the seven tests that were performed. This is unfortunate, for it is hard to get an overall picture of the events that took place.

Published for the first time, with the permission of the author.

During our seven experiments with Uri Geller, only laboratory personnel were present: it had been one of the conditions we set down, and furthermore, Uri Geller himself asked his two companions to stay outside the laboratory.

Mr. Geller wore complete telemetering apparatus, which monitored his brain waves, during all of the experiments. (See Plate 55.) He was able to move about the room very little, and never for a moment was he out of our sight. The testing ran two hours and forty-five minutes.

One observer was chosen, by Mr. Geller, to wear telemetering apparatus similar to that which he wore. The purpose of this was to compare the electroencephalograms of Geller and the person he would be trying to communicate with telepathically. Both sets of data were recorded simultaneously on the same roll of paper; the twenty recording tracks were divided into two sets of ten, one for each person. Before the experiments began we searched Mr. Geller for any apparatus he might have that could influence our tests, but found none. He was wearing blue jeans and a short-sleeved shirt.

1) The Compass Experiment

Uri Geller had to cause deviation of the magnetized needle of a compass brought to the laboratory by Dr. Albert Ducrocq. The compass was set on a sturdy table and Geller concentrated on it. He never touched the table or the compass; in fact, both his hands were held by two of the scientists present. After several unsuccessful trials, Geller was able to move the needle a few degrees both clockwise and counterclockwise. The needle moved three times, slowly and with difficulty, as if it were activated by a force just barely capable of moving it. Another attempt to influence the compass was made at Geller's suggestion. He asked that all of the persons present form a circle around him and the table. This time when he concentrated on the compass the deviation of the needle increased perceptibly. (See Plate 56.)

2) The Watch Experiment

A watch had been brought to the laboratory by Dr. André Warusfel. According to a clockmaker, the watch did not work because it had a bent axis. Mr. Geller placed the watch in one observer's open hand. He stroked it slightly several times with his fist and then kept his hand on it, with his fingers spread out. After about two minutes, I thought I heard the watch ticking. When I checked, I found that it indeed had begun to run, and it was still running at the end of the day. Since then, any agitation will get it started, but it will run at a very slow speed.

3) The Galvanometer Experiment

Dr. Cherrier had brought a galvanometer with him to the laboratory in the hope that Geller could influence the device. However, despite Geller's many attempts, he was not able to effect deviation of the instrument's needle.

4) The Key Experiment

A key belonging to one of the observers was used for this test. Geller asked the owner of the key to hold it loosely by its top between his thumb and index finger. Geller began to stroke the tip of the key. After two minutes, the key bent.

The key was photographed and covered with a glass dome. Geller then tried to increase the key's curvature. However, nobody was able to tell if the attempt was successful.

Later, however, Geller took the key and placed it on the metal platter of a record player. He concentrated on it, and the curvature of the key perceptibly increased. (The key bent upward, the "force" being opposed to gravity.)

It must also be said that later, in another room, during a meeting at which the results of the tests were to be announced, Geller bent the key belonging to a highly skeptical journalist, Michel Polacco, in front of several observers.

5) The HP 65 Calculator Experiment

A calculator had been brought to the laboratory by Dr. André Warusfel. A magnetic program, which gives the machine the ability to handle vectorial multiplication, was tested in the calculator. But after Uri Geller had stroked the magnetic program element several times with his finger, it was repeatedly refused by the calculator, as if its program had been totally upset.

6) The Dice Experiment

I had brought to the laboratory an ordinary die. Geller took it in his hand, kept it there for a while, then wrote on a piece of paper the figure 2 (and the word *two*), and gave the paper to André Warusfel. He asked Warusfel to put the die (which I checked to make certain it was the same die I had given Geller) in a metal box (an empty film container) and close the top. While Dr. Warusfel shook the box, Geller concentrated on it. At one point Geller told Warusfel to stop shaking and open the box and throw out the die. It rolled onto the floor and went several yards. It stopped upright on the number 2.

7) The Telepathy Experiment

Several telepathy tests were conducted between Uri Geller and one researcher, with both subjects wearing similar electroencephalographic gear. No telepathy was possible. Geller felt that the recording instruments were bothering him, so the devices were removed and another set of tests begun. Geller had immediate success. Dr. Tovar, who had unexpectedly walked into the room, was asked to make two drawings. Geller recreated both pictures. Even the proportions were the same, the only difference being that the drawings were reproduced upside down.

A MAGICIAN LOOKS AT URI GELLER

An Excerpt, Translated from the Danish, from *Uri Geller*, by Leo Leslie.

Leo Leslie is a professional magician living in Copenhagen, Denmark, and an administrative employee of the local government. He is acknowledged as one of Scandinavia's leading experts on the history of magic. Mr. Leslie is cofounder of the Magic Ring — a society of magicians — and former editor of Cyprianus, *a Danish journal for professional magicians. He currently holds the honorary title of consultant-adviser in all matters concerning magic for the National Museum of Denmark. For years, Mr. Leslie has specialized in exposing fraudulent mediums.*

In January of 1974 Uri Geller visited Copenhagen and appeared on a local television show. Because Leo Leslie was a magician, he was called in by the studio before Geller's arrival to instruct the members of the show in the magic tricks he thought Geller would attempt to use; Leslie felt certain, for example, that Geller used a chemical to soften metal objects before he attempted to bend them. For the taping of the show, certain precautions were taken: members of Geller's personal staff were barred from the studio, and throughout the performance one camera always remained focused on Geller's hands. Although Geller apparently displayed telepathy and psychokinesis during the taping, Leslie, a skeptic, still was not convinced that what he had seen was genuine. After the show he and Geller got together in one of the backstage dressing rooms, along with a local journalist, a photographer, a psychologist, and one woman from the television studio. The excerpt from Leslie's book dealing with what occurred in the dressing room is presented here.

Because of the geographical arrangement of the papers in this book, Leslie's account of his experiences with Geller appears separately from the papers by magicians Artur Zorka and William Cox.

The material that follows has been excerpted and translated from the book Uri Geller, *by Leo Leslie, Samleres Forlag, 1974.*

I TOLD GELLER I was still skeptical despite what I had seen him do on the television show. He asked what he could do to convince me of the genuineness of his paranormal powers. "Well," I said, "you could either bend one of my keys or attempt, if you can, to read my thoughts." Geller responded enthusiastically. "OK," he said. "Make a drawing." He asked me to sit at one end of the sofa with my back to him while he sat at the opposite end with his back to me. I decided to draw a flower. (From the psychologist who stood near Geller and observed his every move, I later learned that Geller started to draw a flower immediately, even before I set my pencil to the paper. He had finished his drawing before I had even begun mine.) "Are you finished?" Geller asked me. I told him that I was not, and that I was still concentrating on the object I had decided to draw.

"Then we must start over again," said Uri, "because I have already received an image and finished my drawing." He thought this attempt had failed.

Now I drew a flower and took some time putting finishing touches on it. But apparently Geller was receiving nothing. "I don't think I can do it," he said. "Are you having difficulty concentrating on the object?" he asked. I told him that I was, but still I asked to see whatever sketches he might have made. He turned around and said, "I can only get the image of flowers." He had drawn a crude sketch of another flower.

My suspicions of him had begun to fade. There was no chance that he could have cheated. None of his own people was present in the room. The girl from the studio sat at Geller's end of the room and she could not possibly see my drawing. A photographer roamed about the room, but he said nothing and did nothing but take photographs. Geller could not have used accomplices or relied on secret signs to receive the drawings.

What about the possibility that Geller relied on "sound readings," that is, the reproduction of lines from the sound impressions a pencil makes on paper. Because I am an experienced mentalist, I intentionally had distorted the sounds my pencil made while I drew the flower. In addition, I spoke constantly during the time I was drawing — partly to drown out sound from my pencil and in part actually to confuse Geller. I believe that sound-reading must be ruled out as a possible method by which Geller could have received the drawings.

Could Geller have used a "thumb-writer"? This clever little magician's aid is a tiny metal clip, filled with lead, which is held tightly underneath the thumbnail so that the lead point sticks out slightly. With such a device, an accomplished mentalist can, in a moment, reproduce a simple drawing or a small series of numbers on a card behind his back. When the mentalist pulls the card from behind his back, it looks as if the drawing had been there all along. Being a practicing mentalist, I will not go into complete detail here on exactly what else a person experienced with a thumb-writer can achieve. The only thing that must be stated is that the psycholgist at Geller's end of the sofa saw Geller draw both flowers *before* he said he "gave up." I have to admit that I believe Geller actually read my thoughts.

After his demonstration of telepathy Geller tried psychokinesis. A nickel-plated, enameled key was given to Geller. He asked the journalist who was present to hold the key between two fingers. Geller then rubbed it a couple of times, very lightly, with his forefinger. "I can't do it," he suddenly said. "You have done something to this key. I cannot get in contact with the metal." I immediately suspected that Geller probably uses a chemical to soften metal, and that with the coating on the key he felt defeated. I took the key from the journalist and studied it closely. But while I sat looking at the key the enamal suddenly started to crack, and a second later strips of the nickel plating curled up like small banana peels, while the key actually started to bend in my hand. I don't know who was more excited, Geller or the rest of us in the room. I only know that we were all thrilled.

The judgment of all of us who were present for what occurred was one of total endorsement of Geller's paranormal claims: both his ability to bend metal and his talent for receiving telepathic signals. When I am asked about the strength of my own conclusions as to what I witnessed, I can answer only that while Geller was in Copenhagen I did not catch him in any deceptions. Therefore I have to continue to rely on my own judgment and experience as a mentalist; they tell me that Uri Geller is genuine.

THE URI GELLER EFFECT

by E. Alan Price, M.D., The South African Institute for Parapsychology, Johannesburg.

E. Alan Price is a practicing diagnostic roentgenologist in South Africa, and a former senior radiologist at the Johannesburg General Hospital. He is also Research Project Director for the South African Institute for Parapsychology, and the author of numerous papers on medical, radiological, and parapsychological subjects.

Uri Geller visited South Africa during the summer of 1974, giving lectures in Johannesburg, Pretoria, Durban, Cape Town, and Port Elizabeth. During his visit and shortly afterward, many individuals reported that they had spontaneously developed Geller-like talents. Dr. Price appealed to the public through the press and radio to send in accounts of the experiences they thought were related to Geller's visit. Thus, his investigation is a "field study." His task was laborious and lengthy, for it was essential to establish a certain degree of reliability in the many reports he received. Dr. Price's paper presents the investigative methods he used in weeding out the "good" from the "bad" anecdotes, descriptions of a number of the actual incidents that were reported, and his careful analyses of their substance and significance. Although Price's study cannot offer proof of paranormal happenings among the general populace, taken with the laboratory observations of Drs. Thelma Moss, John Hasted, and John Taylor, it presents a strong case for the existence of psychical talents in average, normal individuals.

Published for the first time, with the permission of the author.

OVER THE PAST FEW YEARS a young Israeli psychic demonstrated in various capitals of the world, on radio and television, certain telepathic abilities as well as remarkable psychokinetic powers to bend metal and to start watches and clocks that have been out of order for varying lengths of time. He was investigated at the Stanford Research Institute by Russell Targ and Dr. Harold E. Puthoff,[14] who have confirmed his extraordinary extrasensory perception under conditions of sensory shielding.

From the very beginning of Mr. Uri Geller's appearance in Europe and the United States, strange phenomena have been reported by various individuals who witnessed Mr. Geller's live demonstrations, or saw him on television, or listened to him on the radio. These reports stated that, on following Uri Geller's instructions, they too were able to bend metal objects simply by stroking them and willing them to bend, without applying any physical force whatsoever. Other reports referred to clocks and watches, which have not been going for many years, starting to "tick" once again without the direct physical intervention of Uri Geller. The reports also stated that in many instances the metal objects or watches reacted without being touched or stroked, and at a time subsequent to the broadcast or demonstration. It would appear that Uri Geller triggered off an inherent latent psychokinetic ability, on a hitherto unprecedented scale, in the population group that either saw him or listened to him. It is to this phenomenon that one refers as "The Uri Geller Effect." At the moment it is not possible to be certain whether the Uri Geller Effect is due to the psychic ability of Mr. Uri Geller alone or to the arousal of latent psychic powers within the individual who experiences the Uri Geller Effect.

By definition, therefore, the Uri Geller Effect occurs at a variable distance from the physical presence of Mr. Geller. This distance may vary from a few meters to hundreds or thousands of kilometers. Under these circumstances a possibility of trickery or sleight of hand, misdirection, or any other method of cheating is not conceivable. The only alternative explanation to that of a paranormal phenomenon is the possibility of conscious or unconscious fraud on the part of the person reporting the experience. At a later stage I shall deal with the evaluation of the evidence of the present series of cases.

The Source of the Material and the Method of Its Collection

Mr. Uri Geller visited South Africa from mid-July to mid-August 1974. He gave lecture-demonstrations in Johannesburg, Pretoria, Durban, Cape Town, and Port Elizabeth. He appeared four times on the radio but on only one occasion did he appeal to listeners to attempt to produce the same phenomena he was producing in the studio, and to telephone the results to the studio. He met people at various private functions and appeared at a charity evening in Johannesburg. From the beginning of his visit it became apparent that numerous phenomena occur outside the direct physical presence of, or contact with, Mr. Uri Geller. I then decided to launch a project that would attempt to collect, record, and analyze the various experiences that were reported to be taking place throughout the country. The method adopted was to insert in the programs a circular appealing for reports on any experiences a person might have had or witnessed during or after the lecture-demonstration. We also appealed to the public through the press and the radio to report to our institute any phenomenon that may have occurred and seemed to be associated with Mr. Uri Geller. We have also obtained a tape recording of the telephonic reports by various people who phoned the offices of the South African Broadcasting Corporation following Mr. Uri Geller's broadcast and the appeal to the listeners to report immediately any phenomena that may have occurred in their homes or to them personally. Many of these people who telephoned gave their names and addresses and we subsequently wrote to them. It has to be stressed, however, that the response of the public to isolated single appeals through the press or radio produces a poor response. The general public is most apathetic and very lazy in coming forward to any such appeal no matter what the scientific project may be. In the case of parapsychology, the subject is further bedeviled by a reluctance of people to be associated with the investigator of paranormal phenomena. It was, therefore, very hard work, and a great amount of perseverance was required to accumulate the 137 reliable case reports. This is probably not more than 10 percent of the total number of phenomena that have occurred throughout the country.

A questionnaire was subsequently sent to all the people who reported such phenomena. About 85 percent completed the questionnaire.

The reports can be divided into two groups. The first group deals with Uri Geller and his personal demonstrations and appearance. The second group, and this is the group we shall be dealing with in this paper, deals mainly with the Uri Geller Effect on members of the population or audience who had no direct physical contact with, and were not subject to the intervention of, Uri Geller.

Order of Presentation of the Cases

There are obviously many ways in which the reported experiences may be grouped. My order of presentation is of course arbitrary. I have endeavored to group the cases in such a manner that each group will demonstrate a certain aspect of the conditions under which the effect manifested itself. I propose to relate to this paper only some of the experiences reported to us. No change was made in the language or substance of the reports. In certain cases, however, irrelevant material was excluded. Space does not permit the publishing of all the cases in detail. Only the initials of writers and percipients or experients are published, as anonymity was promised to all participants of this research project.

The Uri Geller Effect Produced Among Members of the Audience During a Stage Demonstration

Case No. 30

This report was sent to us by Dr. T.E. of Johannesburg on December 24, 1974.

The event took place on the 17th July at approximately 10:00 P.M. during a demonstration by Uri Geller at a charity premiere at the Carlton Hotel Ballroom. I was holding a teaspoon in my right hand, between thumb and middle finger, concentrating on bending the spoon through the medium of Uri Geller's efforts, when I experienced a warm, tingling sensation in the thumb and finger, and the spoon began to bend. As I was skeptical about the "powers" of Geller, I would not believe my eyes and started to shout, "The spoon is bending!" and displayed it to people around me, including my wife and professional colleagues.

The spoon kept on bending, and the more it bent, the more jubilant and excited I became until I reached a stage of almost "hysteria." I kept on shouting, "Look, the spoon is bending more and more!" The "spoon bending" was continuous and lasted about four minutes and at the end the teaspoon was bent into a *U* shape. (Here Dr. T.E. drew the shape of the spoon before and after it bent.)

The following information was obtained from his completed questionnaire. Dr. T.E. is a forty-four-year-old male specialist gynecologist and obstetrician in private practice. He is married. He was a complete skeptic about the possibility of such an experience before it happened. He is a confirmed believer now. He stated that he did have a previous psychic experience. He believes, however, that his present experience was induced by Uri Geller, and does not think that he could repeat it on his own. There were nearly one thousand people in the audience and he was surrounded by his family and friends during Uri Geller's performance. The delay in remitting this report to us appears to be due to the fact that Dr. T.E. emigrated to Israel in the interim.

The Uri Geller Effect Produced a Day Before and Repeated the Day After a Stage Demonstration

Case No. 43

The following letter, dated August 16, 1974, was received from Mr. P.J.M. H.-J., a sixty-three-year-old director of a large electrical company.

In reply to your circular inquiry following the visit of Mr. Uri Geller, I would advise you as follows:

1. On the day before I saw his performance at the Colosseum, I bent a key. It took me the best part of thirty minutes, and there were no witnesses. I told my wife and showed her the key and she promptly told me that she did not believe me.

2. The following day my wife and I saw the performance at the Colosseum.

3. On the day following the visit to the Colosseum I was telling three of my colleagues at lunch of the events outlined in 1. above. They promptly agreed with my wife, but suggested that I show them how I did it. This I did, and rather to my surprise, the second key bent. This occurrence being observed by two of my codirectors and my administrative manager — the latter stated that he felt something as the key bent.

This incident is, therefore, well corroborated.

On the second occasion, the key bent in a couple of minutes, and after bending I had a marked tingling sensation on the ends of all my fingers, which lasted for perhaps five minutes.

Both keys are available for inspection at any time.

Yours sincerely,
(signed) P.J.M. H.-J.

In reply to an inquiry from us with regard to this sensation, which he had experienced while he was bending the abovementioned keys, we received the following reply on September 24, 1974.

In accordance with your request to me, I wish to confirm that, as I am stroking a key with the intention of bending it, there comes a time when the smoothness of the key gives way to a feeling as though the key was crystallized, and it is at this point, in my opinion, that if you are experienced, you can keep the object in this condition, and it will bend. This has been my experience with two keys and a spoon, but I think it is only fair to say that I do not have great difficulty, even now that Uri Geller has left the country, in bending an object to this crystallized condition, but I am unable to hold it there, and after a moment or two it goes back to its former smooth surface, and I have, therefore, failed to bend the object.

We then requested corroborative signed statements from the three colleagues who witnessed the bending of one of the keys. We subsequently received the following letter:

This is to advise that some months ago we were having lunch with Mr. P.J.M. H.-J. when a discussion arose regarding Mr. Uri Geller who was at that time in South Africa.

During the discussion, Mr. P.J.M. H.-J. demonstrated to us that he was able to bend a residential key by slowly stroking it. We all saw the key bend after a short interval of time.

(signed) Mr. G.C.G. — Financial Director.
Mr. E.B.B. — Director.
Mr. R.H. — Administrative Officer.

In reply to our request to have the keys examined, the following was received on November 8, 1974.

As requested in your circular letter of the 5th November, I am enclosing my two bent keys. I hope you are not going to keep them too long, as one of them is my garage key, the other is the key to an inner drawer in my safe, so it will be rather inconvenient to do without them, but I do have a duplicate to the safe key. I have tried to bend other keys after Geller's departure, but had no success.

The Uri Geller Effect Produced Among the Population During and Following Radio Broadcasts

Mr. Geller appeared on four radio programs. He twice appeared on the very popular program, "Deadline Thursday Night." The first one was in the Johannesburg studio on July 11, at 7:30 P.M. and the second one at a Cape Town studio three weeks later, on August 1. He also appeared on "The Voice of Science" program with Professor Arthur Bleksley, Dr. Gordon Nelson, and Mr. Robin Jackson of the South African Broadcasting Corporation. The following reports were sent to us by Mr. Timothy Bungey, who was the producer of the radio program "Deadline Thursday Night," and Mr. Adrian Steed who was the announcer during the program and partook in key-bending and telepathic tests.

Case No. 19

This report was sent to us by Mr. Timothy Bungey, who is a broadcaster and radio producer, and was responsible for the radio program "Deadline Thursday Night."

I did not attend any of Uri Geller's theater shows, but as the producer of "Deadline Thursday Night" I was present on both occasions when he took part in a broadcast on Springbok Radio.

The first occasion was July 11th, 1974. We prerecorded the last two thirds of the program and arranged with Mr. Geller that he would take up the first ten minutes "live" in the studio. We also arranged to record listeners' reactions over the telephone in a separate studio, and although Mr. Geller warned us that there was often some delay before people managed to bend knives and forks, the calls in fact started to come through before he left the main studio. As you already have dubbings of these calls, we do not need to elaborate on this aspect.

At Mr. Geller's request, so that he did not feel hemmed in, I did not allow anyone else in the studio other than the presenter of "Deadline," Adrian Steed; the Continuity Announcer on duty that evening, Paul Beresford; and the inevitable disc jockeys. There were a large number of onlookers, including Mr. Geller's own entourage, and the other members of the "Deadline" team, and, since the word had got round the building swiftly, there were a dozen or so members of the S.A.B.C. staff watching as well. Some were in the passage, looking through the windows, others in the control room that overlooks the main studio, and still more were in the adjoining continuity studio. All told, there must have been some thirty to forty people including myself.

Mr. Steed opened the program in the usual way and then introduced Mr. Geller. He explained what he was going to try and do — bend metal objects in the studio, mend broken watches (we had supplied various items beforehand), and tell the listeners how they could do the same. He asked for Adrian's key ring, selected the car key, and started stroking it gently. Within a matter of seconds (not more than thirty seconds) the key began to bend. One may put it down to mass hypnosis, but there was no doubt in the minds of everyone present that the key actually bent to an angle of roughly forty degrees. After this, he took a couple of broken watches, placed his hands over them, concentrated, and — presto! they began to tick again. Then he explained to the listeners how they could do the same. "You must *want* it to happen," he said. "Just take the knife or the fork, stroke it gently, and *will* it to bend." You can learn the results from the dubbings we sent you. (The dubbings of almost all the telephone calls are in our possession. E.A.P.)

After a brief chat with Adrian Steed, Mr. Geller left the studio and the program continued. As I said earlier, the calls had already begun to come through and they had been answered by "Deadline"'s assistant editor. Then Mr. Geller took over for a while, asking each listener who phoned what had happened; and when he had to leave, the editor, Bryan Chilvers, continued taking the calls.

We later learned, although this I did not see in person, that the continuity studio suffered strange happenings after Uri Geller left.

The turntable on which he had been demonstrating his powers to the technicians before we went on the air with "Deadline Thursday Night" suddenly refused to function anymore. (He had taken a metal object and rubbed it on the surface.) A switch that no one in his right mind would touch while we were on the air somehow managed to switch itself off. And then one of the monitors gave up the ghost and so a bewildered Paul Beresford and crew were forced to move to an adjoining studio.

That was the first occasion. Three weeks later, when Mr. Geller was in Cape Town, and as we had had such a fantastic response to the first broadcast, we decided to ask him to try some thought transmission with Adrian Steed of our Johannesburg studio. This time, as we had no idea how long it would take, we played safe and prerecorded the session. It was later edited and played into "Deadline Thursday Night."

There was a slight misunderstanding at the outset. Mr. Geller had been under the impression that he was simply going to thank South Africa for the wonderful reception (his agent had passed on our request incorrectly) and at first he was somewhat reluctant to try a thought transmission so soon before appearing on the stage. But at length he agreed to try, and over the line from Cape Town he tried to transmit an image into Adrian Steed's mind (he was in Johannesburg, 900 miles away). Adrian sat in the studio with a piece of paper and a pencil, and he was told to draw what came into his mind. After a couple of unsuccessful attempts, he tried another picture and this time Adrian drew first of all a circle, then a *V* lying sidewise. These were separate items. Then he said to Uri Geller that he felt they should come together and at length he attached the sideways *V* to the circle. After that came an eye — and the result was a childlike drawing of a head.

Mr. Geller sent his original drawing to Mr. Steed later on and there was a distinct resemblance though it was by no means an exact copy.

Case No. 110

Mr. Adrian Steed was the presenter of the program "Deadline

Thursday Night" and he sent us the following letter dated October 4, 1974.

> During the now well-known broadcast by Uri Geller I had the experience of seeing one of my keys bent before my eyes by Uri's stroking it with his fingers. During the same evening I saw him stroke a spoon until it broke. Uri also moved the hands of my watch back an hour by rubbing the back of the watch.
>
> Only this last week I have noticed that two more of my keys are now bent. Whether this is because they were attached to the same ring that Uri handled or whether I managed to duplicate Uri's feat, I don't know because, I must admit, I tried the stroking myself — not in Uri's presence. I certainly wasn't aware of their bending when I did the stroking but they are available for examination.
>
> Uri also attempted either one or two weeks later to transmit a picture to me from Cape Town. I succeeded in receiving the image of a circle, a triangle, and a circle, all of which seemed to be a face with a nose and an eye. That in fact was what Uri had tried to "transmit": a face. He was very and genuinely excited because prior to the experiment he had expressed serious doubts about achieving anything. Unfortunately I did not keep the drawing, but Timothy Bungey (radio producer) can verify what I say.
>
> I feel obliged to tell you that in spite of my experiences I can't help feeling skeptical. I am not a nut or weirdy, but I cannot help — in spite of my skepticism — feeling that there are more things in heaven and earth undreamed of in our philosophy.

There appears to be a slight inconsistency in the date of the second transmission of the program "Deadline Thursday Night." According to Mr. Timothy Bungey, it was three weeks after the first program, which would make it August 1, whereas according to Mr. Adrian Steed it was one to two weeks later.

The response from the public to the request by Uri Geller to call the studio was, as Mr. Bungey states, fantastic. One has to listen to the tape recording of these telephone calls to appreciate the tremendous impact it has made on the various people who had experienced the Uri Geller Effect. These calls came from all over the country, and the telephone lines became jammed at the studio. Reports from other parts of the world, such as Germany, England, and France, tell a similar story.

Case No. 76

This report was received from Dr. Gordon Nelson on October 29, 1974. He was one of the participants in the radio program "The Voice of Science."

Recording Session, Voice of Science, S.A.B.C. — 8th August, 1974.

In the company of Dr. Arthur Bleksley, Mr. Robin Jackson of the S.A.B.C., Uri Geller bent a teaspoon belonging to Dr. Bleksley. He then took my watch, clenched his fist over it, and handed it back to me, one hour slow exactly.

During the recording Mr. Geller moved to a point about 2 meters from the table facing away from it. He asked Robin Jackson to make a drawing, came back and asked if it was finished, and produced a piece of paper with the identical drawing.

After the recording, at home, I was idly stroking a silver teaspoon during a conversation. After some minutes I lifted the teaspoon and noticed it was bent.

Shortly afterward, while having a drink at a neighbor's home, I was equally idly stroking a small alarm clock, which had not worked for some time. This suddenly began to go. I had the same experience one minute later with a second alarm clock, which had also not worked for some time.

I can offer no explanation of Uri Geller's spoon bending.

The episode involving my watch may have been a matter of rapid and dextrous manipulation. The "telepathy" involving the drawing could have been accompanied by very rapid sketching, in which Geller is a master. My subsequent experience with the spoon may have involved excessive "pressure" (my relatively strong hands on the silver spoon, which is fairly soft). The matter of the clocks may have been due to chance or temperature changes or both.

The above three reports (Case No. 19, Case No. 110, and Case No. 76) were sent to us by people who were directly associated with, or involved in, the three broadcasts in which Uri Geller participated. The following case reports are from people who were listening to these programs and had certain experiences that, according to our definition, are apparently the result of the Uri Geller Effect.

Case No. 22

This report was sent to us by Mrs. E.C. of Somerset West, Cape Province, on August 9, 1974. Somerset West is about 900 miles from Johannesburg.

My husband and I were concentrating on stroking two knives on the Thursday evening "Deadline Thursday Night" broadcast with Uri Geller (the Uri Geller experiment referred to). Timepieces in our house that were stopped permanently as far as we knew were two wrist watches and a brass carriage clock that was given to my husband's mother as a wedding present about 1890. This had not been going for some years and when it did go it gained about six minutes a day. We had taken it to several watchmakers who said that a part was worn and would have to be handmade and the whole clock taken down to fit it — such a big job it was hardly worth doing. One of the watches was probably in need of a clean but so impossible was it to start that I had been wearing a gold watch I usually keep for evenings as my everyday wrist watch for months. They either would go for a few seconds or stop. All three were ticking merrily after Uri's broadcast and they have been going ever since. My husband adjusted the clock and it now keeps perfect time.

Her husband, who is a retired farmer and ex-naval officer, corroborated the statement.

In a further letter, dated October 29, 1974, she states that the clock was useless as a timepiece and had been kept as an ornamental clock for sentimental reasons and two watchmakers had declared it irreparable. It has been going ever since that evening. She also stated that the knife she was stroking bent very slightly and she felt a tingling while stroking the knife.

Mrs. E.C. is fifty years old, her academic qualifications are matriculation, and she is a housewife. She has had previous psychic experiences.

Case No. 56

Mr. S.K. phoned the studio from Witbank, which is 100 miles from Johannesburg, from where the broadcast was made on July 11 at 7:30 P.M. We subsequently listened to the tape recording of his phone call. He was extremely excited and said that he had an old antique clock hanging on the wall. He was standing on a chair and stroking the clock. Suddenly the door was flung open and the pendulum thrown out. "We were all rather startled and amazed," he said. Mr. S.K. gave his name and address to the man in the studio. We subsequently wrote to him and sent him a questionnaire. We received the questionnaire on October 14, 1974. He confirmed in writing the above experience. Mr. S.K. is fifty-four years old, married, and is a director of companies. He has had previous psychic experiences and he is a spiritualist. He believes that his experience was induced by Uri Geller.

Case No. 100

The following letter, dated August 16, 1974, was received by us from Mr. W.L.S. of Port Elizabeth, Cape Province. Port Elizabeth is about 700 miles from Johannesburg, from where the broadcast was beamed. This program, "The Voice of Science," had been prerecorded.

My wife and I witnessed one of those amazing occurrences *after* the Science Hour broadcast a week ago today. We were listening casually, not realizing at first that Mr. Uri Geller was on the air together with you gentlemen. Had I known beforehand I would have recorded the broadcast for further experimentation.

My wife and I were sitting over a cup of afterdinner tea in our lounge when Mr. Geller suggested that the audience should try to "bend metal." I took the teaspoon from my saucer and laid it on the small lounge round table next to the cup, and asked my wife to concentrate on bending it. I gave it a try myself for about a minute or so, watching the spoon, then gave it up as a bad job, but listened intently and very interestedly indeed. My wife still had her eyes shut, maybe concentrating on that spoon. Then both of us forgot about the spoon and did not give it any further attention as nothing had happened and both of us had been skeptical that anything would happen. At the end of the broadcast I suggested to my wife that we should also try the other experiment with the copying of the drawing. My wife, however, picked up the empty cups and saucers and left the lounge for the kitchen for some fresh brew.

I had my mind on how to go about the paper-drawing experiment and the contents of the whole of the broadcast. Turning away from the hi-fi set I noticed out of the corner of my eye that the spoon I had taken out of the saucer and put on the table and that my wife had forgotten to take to the kitchen, *had bent through an angle of about forty degrees.* When I looked closely, I did not want to believe my eyes. The weirdness of it all caused in me what I would call a primitive fear reaction of the unknown; I had goose pimples all over me, and my hair started to rise. I shouted out to my wife in the kitchen and called her to come and see for herself.

My wife first thought that I was playing the fool with her and I was at first not sure that my wife had not played the fool with me. We had another spoon of identical make. I asked my wife to bend it with her hand. This was a great effort for her, and caused the metal to make deep red marks in her flesh. I then tried to bend another spoon myself, which I was easily able to do with my greater strength and by applying leverage. I waited a week to write to you about this. It would be quite out of character for my wife and myself to keep up a pretense so long. I am now positive *that this spoon bent without having been touched by either of us.* I am the

President of the Observatory Society and met Professor Bleksley many a year ago when I was the secretary and he delivered the lecture to us in the Port Elizabeth City Hall.

Mr. W.L.S. is sixty-four years old. He is a radio engineer and has his own business. He studied law at Berlin University. The experience occurred approximately a minute after the close of the broadcast. His wife, Mrs. V.K.M.S., is forty-four years old. Her academic qualifications are B.A. (Birmingham), Dr. of Theology *Honoris Causa.* She is well disposed to such psychic experiences. Her personal psychic experiences are of a religious and mystical nature.

The Uri Geller Effect and Distance

From a study of many of the cases reported to us, it would appear that distance did not seem to prevent its manifestation. The following is a case in point.

Case No. 56

This particular case was described earlier in this paper *(vide supra).* As stated earlier, the individual was in Witbank, which is 100 miles from where Uri Geller was at the moment of broadcast.

The following is another interesting case report. In addition to the fact that it demonstrates that distance does not prevent the manifestation of the Uri Geller Effect, it also shows that the manifestation may occur some time after the event was triggered off by Mr. Uri Geller and that it may take place without the immediate conscious effort of the experient.

Case No. 55

Mrs. B.K. of Durban wrote to us on July 26, 1974, as follows:

"Deadline Thursday Night," 11th July, 7:30 P.M. I have a machine key made of steel belonging to my mother. I got the same out and started stroking it as Uri Geller spoke. Nothing happened so I put the key down, switched off the radio, as "Deadline" 's singing irritates me. I went on reading until about 11:30 P.M. I turned to switch off my bedside light when to my utter shock the key had bent nearly double. When I showed it to a locksmith he said the breaking strain was about fifty pounds. To say I was astonished is to put it mildly. I took a long time to fall asleep.

Durban is 383 miles from Johannesburg's broadcasting studio, where Uri Geller made the broadcast "live." This broadcast was not prerecorded. Mrs. B.K. is fifty-seven years old and is widowed. She is a director of a company. She was previously doubtful but prepared to consider such possibilities. Now she has a confirmed belief in such experiences. She did have previous experiences of a psychic nature.

The Uri Geller Effect and Time

Many of the reports indicate that the effect manifested itself during Uri Geller's demonstrations or broadcasts. Some reports indicate, however, that the transference occurred before or after Uri Geller's direct attempt to produce the effect. The following is an example of a report that indicates that the effect became apparent before Uri Geller's attempt to produce it.

Case No. 25

Mrs. G.M.C. wrote on October 8, 1974, from Durban.

As requested, I am writing to tell you of my experience. I wrote to Dr. Arthur Bleksley at the S.A.B.C. some weeks ago. [This letter was not referred to us.] I don't know if the following will be of interest to you and I am afraid I cannot remember the date on which it happened. I didn't see Uri Geller on stage but I am sure I saw him in West Street (the main street in Durban), and he looked straight at me. It was on the day that he was to "open" at the Playhouse Theatre in Durban. At 6:50 P.M. I was sitting alone in my flat and thinking that a clock looked rather dusty. I picked it up and started to rub the glass over the dial. I must add that the clock is about 100 years old and had not worked for at least fifteen years. As I polished it I wished that I could see Uri and to my astonishment the clock started ticking and it is still working. At the time Uri was not speaking on the radio and had not appeared on stage. I was very surprised and couldn't understand it although I was thinking of Uri.

I would have written to you before but have been ill, as you can see from my bad writing. I hope that I have not wasted your time.

Mrs. G.M.C. is over sixty years old and widowed. She has had no psychic experience before.

The following is a report that would suggest that the Uri Geller Effect occurred after the appearance of Uri Geller at the Playhouse Theatre in Durban.

Case No. 45

Mr. A.N.H. wrote to us on August 17, 1974, from Hilton, Natal.

In response to your request on the wireless for incidents consequent on Uri Geller's meeting, I have the following to report. Some twelve to fifteen months ago the electric clock attached to my stove suddenly stopped. The first electrician called in to mend it and said it had been struck by lightning. I pointed out that the plate and oven worked! As the quote to mend it was rather high (R30.00) we decided to leave it. Toward the beginning of July this year, one of the plates went out of order so we called in the Maritzburg agent to mend it and have a look at the clock also. The plate was fixed but he reported that the clock was beyond repair and we would need a new unit, which would cost R45.00 plus labor and three months' delay. Again we decided to leave the clock. On Thursday morning, the 25th July, the morning after Uri Geller was purported to have said in a show somewhere in Natal that "all clocks that hadn't gone for some time will start," the clock was working and has kept perfect time ever since.

Mr. A.N.H. is a teacher in a well-known private school. His wife, Mrs. J.E.H., who is also a teacher, confirmed this report on October 13, 1974. Here is what she wrote:

My electric clock attached to my Frigidaire stove (new one) stopped. When an electrician was called in he said it had been blown out by lightning. Another man said it was finished and we would have to buy a new one. We left it for a while and just before my daughter's wedding I had a great longing to have my electric clock in the kitchen. So great was my longing that my husband decided to buy a new one for me. It was rather costly as it was a beautiful stove and we were debating this when I heard over the news that Uri Geller was going to set clocks going in Natal. I was very interested but in no way thought it would be mine, as the electricians were so adamant it was finished, or rather blown out by lightning. The next morning, when my husband made me my early morning cup of tea (6:00 A.M.), he dashed into my bedroom and told me to get up and come to the kitchen. I couldn't believe my eyes when I saw the clock was working. It was a miracle. When we told the electrician Uri had got my clock to go, he was amazed too.

Mrs. J.E.H. is fifty-eight years old and states that she is well disposed to the possibility of such an experience and is now a confirmed believer in such experiences. She believes that the experience was directly induced by Uri Geller.

Comment: As neither Mr. nor Mrs. H. looked at the clock the evening before, it is not possible to be certain when the clock started going again.

The Manifestation of the Uri Geller Effect when the Experient is Handling the Object

On studying the various reports, it became obvious that the Uri Geller Effect may manifest itself in some instances when the experient is handling the object and in others without any direct physical handling of the object.

Case No. 46

This report relates to an experience when the object was handled by the experient. Mrs. J.H. of Johannesburg, who has a Bachelor of Arts Honors degree in psychology, wrote to us at the end of August 1974 (her letter is undated).

My daughter, Debbie, volunteered to go onto the stage at a performance of Uri Geller. She was asked to write the name of a capital city and draw a simple picture. She chose Reykjavik as a capital that Uri had never heard of. He "received" all the letters from the audience in a slightly mixed order but then called on Debbie to transmit the name correctly. He asked the audience how many of them had heard of Reykjavik and by a show of hands almost 40 percent of the audience had not heard of it.

In the second half of the program Debbie, who was *not* on the stage, held a cake fork in her hand, which she stroked gently. The cake fork "melted" and is now bent into a complete *U* shape and will be submitted to you should you request it.

Since that evening, she is able to name the numbers of playing cards face down.

An interesting "aside" is that she had been seriously ill on the evening we had booked for her to attend the performance and was unable to see the show. She was almost unreasonably disappointed but I managed to book a seat for her two days later. She made a dramatic recovery, attended the show, and despite the fact that she is a very shy person, seemed almost magnetized on the stage, with dramatic result!

We wrote to Mrs. J.H. and asked for a report from her daughter and sent her a questionnaire to be completed. We received the following reply:

After some telepathic work with Uri Geller on the stage (transmitting a picture into his mind and giving him a capital city) I returned to my seat, certain that I would bend my own fork.

I did not try to force the fork to bend, but rather pictured it bending in my mind — I gave it a "loving" look. The fork continued to bend all the way home until it was in a full horseshoe shape. The metal did not get hot but became pliable, like putty. (The metal seemed too pliable to break completely.)

The following morning I guessed twenty-six cards correct out of thirty-four cards that I placed face downward. I guessed their suits and their numbers. I always felt quite sure of the cards that were correct, and guessed at the eight cards that were wrong.

That morning I also managed to bend a teaspoon slightly.

I have not been able to do anything in this field since then.

In answer to certain inquiries in our questionnaire, Miss D.H. states that her experience was accompanied by a sense of affection and a real belief that the metal will bend. She also had a feeling of warmth and tingling. She had previous psychic experiences, such as dreams about the future, and winning races, etc.

Case No. 51

This report describes the manifestation of the Uri Geller Effect without the experient's handling the object.

Mrs. R.J. of Port Elizabeth wrote to us on August 2, 1974.

Briefly: I attended the Uri Geller performance plus lecture on the 22nd July, 1974. Toward the end of his show, he mentioned that people might find that they had bent keys in their possession. When I took mine out of my bag, I found that my front-door key was bent. People around me were impressed. When I arrived home I found it was now twisted. The following day I found another key badly out of alignment and a few days later I noticed that the key to the cellar, which I don't use often, was slightly out of alignment.

Mrs. J.R. is sixty-seven years old and married. She has a B. Economics degree. She had no previous psychic experiences but is well disposed to the possibility of such experiences. She has stated that the keys are available for examination.

Cases Nos. 16, 7, and 8

These are reports from three people concerning the same experience, in which they were all involved. As in the previous case, the Uri Geller Effect manifested itself without the experient's handling the object.

Case No. 16

Dr. E.G.B. and Mrs. B. of Kempton Park, Transvaal, wrote to us on October 11, 1974. Dr. E.G.B. is thirty-three years old and is a general medical practitioner.

We went to the Uri Geller show purely for entertainment. We took no spoons, broken watches, etc. with us. However, my husband has a fairly large bundle of our keys and other keys, which he always carries with him and which he put in a friend's handbag, mainly because she had a large bag that evening. We all forgot about those keys during the evening, and certainly no one touched them.

After the show we had coffee at the restaurant directly opposite the theater where, for the first time, our friend handed back the keys before she and her husband drove home in their own car. As she took the keys out of her bag and handed them across the table to my husband, a piece of key fell onto the table. No one had given those particular keys another thought and naturally we were all very surprised. It was the key to the front door of the surgery and was broken off neatly from the round piece still hanging on the key ring. The key next to the broken key belonging to a wrought-iron door in our house is a Yale key and this was bent. Both those keys were in perfect condition before the show. Of this we are positive.

The next morning, however, we noticed that the Yale key had evidently bent considerably on its own during the night, as it was much more bent than it had been the previous night.

This letter was signed by Mrs. B., and Dr. E.G.B. confirmed it when he returned the completed questionnaire. Dr. E.G.B. states in his questionnaire that before this experience he was doubtful but prepared to consider the possibility. After this experience, however, he is a confirmed believer in such experiences. He had never had any psychic experiences personally and the keys are available for examination. This event occurred on the night of August 7, 1974, at an evening performance at the Colosseum Theatre.

Case No. 8

This report came from Mrs. M.A.A. of Kempton Park, who is thirty years old and in whose handbag the keys were placed during Uri Geller's demonstration on August 7. She wrote to us on September 27 about this episode, which also appeared in the newspaper. She confirmed the report in the newspaper and added the following remark: "The experience was accompanied by a feeling of amazement. However, my husband was absolutely in a state of shock."

Case No. 7

Mr. B.A. is the husband of Mrs. M.A.A. in whose handbag the keys were placed, as reported above. He is thirty-six years old and holds a B.Sc. degree in chemical engineering. He makes the following remarks:

Being an amateur magician, I was most skeptical about Geller. I was not at all impressed by his stage presentation, which I can perform by "standard conjuring methods." However, I have no explanation for what happened to the keys held by my wife after the show. I am not prepared to say that this was in fact caused by Geller, but can find no logical explanation.

Spontaneous Occurrence of the Uri Geller Effect (Unrelated to Geller's Public Performances, Radio Broadcasts, or Private Meetings)

Case No. 20

Mrs. L.C. of Rosebank, Johannesburg, wrote to us on August 25.

I would like to report an incident that occurred while Uri Geller was here although I never saw him or never even listened to him on the radio.

On Friday, July the 19th, at about 2:30 in the afternoon, I went to Sandton City to do some shopping. As far as I can remember, my route was as follows . . . from Rosebank to Goldfields Supermarket and a bookshop in Sandown, then to Sandton City. I noticed that the escalators were not all working at the time. Coming home at about 3:30 in the afternoon and taking out my front-door key to open the door, I found that it was bent so that I could not use it. The key is on my key ring with my car keys and while I did my shopping the ring was either in my hand or in my shopping bag. I cannot remember anything that would have caused any damage to the key. It had certainly worked very well when I came home from work at 1:15 that same afternoon. There seems to be no explanation for the bending that I can see. I would have noticed if the key had been caught anywhere during my shopping trip.

Mrs. L.C. is forty-one years old. She is married and her academic qualifications are "candidate of philosophy from the University of Helsinki." She is a part-time teacher and part-time bookkeeper. She states that she did have previous experiences of a psychic nature and she believes that this experience was induced directly by Uri Geller.

The Uri Geller Effect Following a Prerecorded Radio program

The manifestation of this type of effect following a prerecorded program would suggest that the response or association of the experient is related to the radio voice rather than to Uri Geller as a person. A number of such experiences were reported.

The radio program "The Voice of Science" was prerecorded on August 8, 1974, and broadcast the next day. Thus, all reported experiences relating to this program were triggered off by an electronically produced voice. Some of the previously described cases fall into this category. Here is an additional case.

Case No. 69

Mr. R.D.Mc. of Springfontein wrote to us on August 16, 1974.

My wife and I were touring the Eastern Transvaal and were in bed in our Combi at Loskop Dam.

We happened to be listening to the program on the air when you were interviewing Uri Geller. The program was "The Voice of Science," Friday the 9th August at 7:45 P.M. When Uri Geller invited listeners to take part in his metal-bending exercises, my wife, whose age is sixty-four years, took a heavy tablespoon and held it with both hands and after a minute or two the handle was bent at an angle, I should say of near forty-five degrees. I was dubious and straightaway tried to straighten it, but can assure you that she had not the power to bend it at will. She told me that while holding it she could feel it bending on its own. I might add that she is suffering from arthritis in her hands, which means that it is quite impossible for her to do the bending."

Mrs. Mc. was a nurse but presently is a housewife. She had previously had experiences of a psychic nature. She believes the experience was induced by Uri Geller and is now a confirmed believer in such experiences.

Spontaneous Disappearance of the Changes Produced by the Uri Geller Effect

A number of reports indicated that the metal objects have either partly straightened themselves or completely returned to normal after a lapse of time. The following is an interesting report of such an occurrence.

Case No. 105

This report was sent to us by Miss G.S., who was closely connected with the public relations aspect of Mr. Uri Geller's visit in South Africa.

Having been in close contact with Uri Geller during his visit to

South Africa, I naturally saw most of his performances. After the charity performance at the Carlton Hotel we all went to the home of Dr. E.A.P. for a party. During the party I asked Uri to bend a personal key of mine. We went into the kitchen, as this seemed to be the only room without people around. He was a little tired of bending keys and said he would do mine very quickly. The key that I gave him was the key to my mother's flat . . . a solid silver-colored slightly tarnished Yale key. In a matter of seconds the key he stroked very gently bent. In fact it bent so quickly that I asked him not to let it break. The key bent from the center at about a seventy-degree angle. This key has been with me personally ever since that evening (the 17th July, 1974).

On Sunday, November 3rd, that is, 3½ months after the key was bent, I was at my sister's home in Florida, and for some reason took my bunch of keys out, and the key that Uri had bent was dead straight. The last time I recall seeing the key bent was on Friday, November 1st.

I can give you the names of at least ten people who saw that particular key bent and who have also seen it since it straightened.

I will be delighted to give you this key should you require it for research purposes. I must point out that at all times I have been a positive believer of Uri's psychic powers, even before he actually arrived in South Africa.

Should you require any further information, please do not hesitate to contact me.

This letter reached me in the middle of November 1974.

The Uri Geller Effect and the Mini-Gellers

One of the most interesting manifestations of the Uri Geller Effect is described in the reports we received from adolescents, children and their parents. These reports claim that, as a result of seeing, listening, or reading about Uri Geller, the people reporting were, and in many cases still are, able to perform metal-bending and watch-"repair" feats similar to those of Uri Geller. A detailed laboratory study of these mini-Gellers is planned for the future if funds and time will become available. Up to the moment we had neither the time nor the facilities to undertake such a study. From a pilot laboratory experiment on one mini-Geller, undertaken at the end of 1974, it became apparent to us that very sophisticated and tightly controlled conditions would be required to assess these mini-Gellers.

In this paper I will deal with the reports that we had received from our mini-Gellers.

Case No. 87

This report was received from Dr. D.C.P., the father of Elizabeth-Ann, who is nine years old. Dr. D.C.P. has a Ph.D. degree and majored in industrial psychology. He is a management consultant and a registered industrial psychologist. He is a great personal friend of mine and I do not doubt his integrity or powers of observation.

Report on Elizabeth P.

Thursday evening, 11th July, 1974. The time was approximately 7:25 P.M. and the family was gathering in the study to listen to the program "Deadline Thursday Night" on Springbok Radio. Interest was stimulated by a radio announcement that Uri Geller would participate in this show. I received a long-distance call, which kept me occupied long enough to miss most of Uri Geller's demonstration. However, I came on the scene to hear the radio announcer expressing his amazement in no uncertain terms that Uri Geller had just bent his key. Uri Geller then invited the radio listeners to get hold of any object, such as a spoon, key, or an old watch, and try to do the same. The family, that is, my wife and two daughters, aged 9 and 6 respectively, promptly fetched spoons from the kitchen and started stroking them. I looked on with a cynical eye as I was under the impression that the program was canned. (I later discovered that Uri Geller's program was not canned.) I left them to get involved in a job in the garage. A few minutes later my wife came to call me to see "it." She stated that the spoon the elder daughter,

Elizabeth, was stroking, was bending upward. I went to the study and saw the bending spoon lying untouched on the table. I was amazed when it was obvious that it was still proceeding to bend further, although untouched by anybody. This I found a bit weird and uncanny. The spoon involved was a grapefruit spoon, made of stainless steel. I, as an adult, found I could only bend a similar spoon with two hands with an effort that would be difficult for a child of Elizabeth's age and size. We phoned neighbors, B. and V.M., to come over and see the event, and they arrived about five minutes later. The spoon continued to bend further in their presence.

Later that night, at about 8:40 P.M., Elizabeth bent another spoon just by gently stroking it. During the process, she was the epitome of concentration. Her eyes were closed. I must mention that the other participants, my wife and the other little daughter, were unsuccessful. My wife soon gave up and the other one tried for the best part of an hour.

On Friday night, the 12th July, Elizabeth bent another spoon, made of stainless steel, that a child of her physique would bend with extreme difficulty. This was done in the presence of my brother. She held the spoon in one hand and stroked it lightly with her finger. After my brother took it from her, the spoon continued to bend in his hand.

We watched Elizabeth in action. She once again concentrated hard; her eyes were closed and she had a serious look on her face. She wanted silence and nobody was allowed to talk when she was in action. Comments annoyed her. When I asked what she was thinking while bending a spoon, she stated that she was saying to herself all the time, "Bend . . . bend . . . bend . . ." She really believed that she could bend spoons.

On Saturday evening, the 13th July, while visiting her granny, Elizabeth managed to get a wrist watch going by stroking it gently. According to my mother-in-law, this watch stopped about six weeks before. She herself had tried without success to get it going again and was about to take it in for repairs. After two months now, it is still going.

On Sunday, the 14th July, Elizabeth bent another grapefruit spoon, also made of stainless steel, in the presence of a friend, Mr.

J.G. She was immensely annoyed when he pulled her leg by telling her that she bent the spoon by force.

In the following week she bent at least a dozen spoons either in the presence of us (my wife and myself) or her friends and neighbors. An interesting incident happened on Friday, the 19th July, in our presence. Elizabeth started the bending of a spoon by gently rubbing it. It continued bending down on its own where it was left, on a cupboard in the lounge. This continued until the stem was folded double and was nearly touching the bowl of the spoon. Suddenly it developed a second bend, which had as its axis the point where the stem was nearly touching the bowl.

By now social complications began showing up. Because of this we had to take the decision to discourage Elizabeth from any further spoon bending. Relations between Elizabeth and her younger sister became strained. The latter tried without success to bend spoons. A visit from Elizabeth's cousin ended with a very competitive situation because of spoon bending. At a later stage, we may consider experimenting again with Elizabeth.

It was definitely established that she could bend spoons for at least ten days after listening to Uri Geller on a live show.

We tried to encourage a certain procedure with Elizabeth when she was bending spoons for us. She had to stay in our presence all the time. We preferred that she gently stroke a spoon while it lay on a table. On a few occasions, she was rewarded with a small sum of money (10 to 20 cents a time) after she managed to bend a spoon.

(signed) Dr. D.C.P. (dated) 18th October, 1974.

P.S. This report is based on notes made during July and August, 1974. (signed) D.C.P.

Case No. 38

On August 14, 1974, we received a letter from Mrs. R.S.A. of Johannesburg, who is the mother of Master D.F., a young lad of sixteen and a scholar. It reads as follows:

My son, David, first began bending metal objects without force when he heard Uri Geller's broadcast over Springbok Radio on the 11th July at 8:15 P.M. At first his powers (except when Uri was on the air) did not seem to be very strong and seemed to come and go. But now, after almost four weeks of practice, he is metal-bending better than ever. At first he got very severe headaches from the concentration, but now he doesn't even seem to have to concentrate so hard all the time. However, he has complained of eyestrain. David has bent knives, spoons, keys, and a solid brass pestle about half an inch thick. (See Plate 57.)

In the interests of science I feel it my duty to advise you of David's metal-bending ability and to give my permission for further investigations as long as there is no interference with his schoolwork.

P.S. David is sixteen years old. He is my son by my first marriage.

David subsequently sent us a completed questionnaire. In it he stated that he first saw Uri Geller at a stage performance on July 10. His own personal first experience was at 8:15 on Thursday, July 11, following the broadcast by Uri Geller on "Deadline Thursday Night." He saw Uri Geller subsequently once more at a private meeting in his hotel suite.

I personally have since heard from many people that David continues to bend metal at parties and friends' homes with the greatest of ease.

Case No. 126

On July 26, 1974, and on July 29, 1974, news reports appeared in the *Natal Daily News*, and on July 30, 1974, in the *Natal Mercury*, about a child, Derek W., who can produce metal-bending feats similar to Uri Geller's. Derek is seven years old and lives in Wartburg, Natal. We wrote to the mother and on August 5 we received from her a letter in which she claims that Derek proved beyond any doubt that he could still perform as well as when he initially saw Uri Geller on the stage (August 9, 1974), listened to him on the radio (July 25, 1974, at 7:40 A.M.) and at a private meeting (August 9 at 8:30 P.M.). She thinks that his ability has improved even more since Uri Geller left Durban. She further says that

Derek states that he feels a sort of pulsing "power" in the head, arms, and hand. When he is wearing a wrist watch, the "power" goes as far as the watch only. Derek is a scholar in Standard 2.

We sent her a questionnaire and a request for further information, and on October 8, 1974, we received the following reply:

I wish to thank you for your correspondence of the 16th September, 1974. I herewith return the completed questionnaire as requested.

It would be a lengthy affair to describe in detail all the experiences Derek has had since hearing Uri Geller. Suffice it to say that he has bent in the region of three dozen items of cutlery. The most spectacular being spoons, which have been bent almost double and one of which actually cracked at the bend. Sometimes spoons go on bending after he has left them. He has had some success with making the hands of a watch move. At times the watch has started to "tick" but at other times appeared to move without starting to tick at all. Other bent items include nail files, a couple of Yale keys and a couple of three-inch nails. Many items were straightened but items of cutlery remained bent.

I trust these brief details will not merely serve to frustrate you. If further details are desired, I should be only too glad to elaborate on any particular cases which you choose.

Yours sincerely,
(signed) Mrs. R.W.

On August 9 the child was brought to Johannesburg by a newspaper to see Uri Geller and was introduced on the stage to Uri Geller. The following day the mother and the child were brought to see Professor Arthur Bleksley, who is known to be interested and involved in the research project on Uri Geller. Dr. A. Bleksley made the following notes after the visit:

"Derek is a seven-year-old boy. He is quiet and introverted. Likes to get bending started while he is alone (!); then carries on in front of observers."

We subsequently wrote again to Mrs. W. and asked for any progress notes and whether we could have for examination some metal objects Derek had bent. She sent us a number of objects (which are discussed together with other objects later on in this paper), and added the following notes, dated October 25, 1974:

In reply to your queries —

1. Yes, I shall send you some items for examination. I am only too eager to know your findings. Unfortunately, a lot of the cutlery was straightened out for table use as we were running short! Also, some of the items have been bent more than once. His first "victim" was a knife similar to the pearl-handled one I shall send you. The original bent nail was lost. He could not get the enclosed sample to go any further. The soup spoons bent most spectacularly. A couple actually dropped as we watched. The curved fork bent into that shape as Derek held it over his knee.

2. About the thermometer I can tell you very little except that I felt my blood pressure rising rapidly! Derek wasn't feeling well and wanted to stay off school. I felt that I should take his temperature although he had no cough or other obvious ailment. When first I looked it showed a reading of just below normal (about 90 degrees F). These thermometers seem to work slowly so I told Derek to leave it in his mouth just a little longer. I left him for about one minute and on return found the thermometer still in his mouth. On looking at it I got the shock of my life, as it read 110 degrees F. I phoned the doctor and a neighbor in a bit of a panic, I can tell you. Only hours later did it occur to me that Derek's "power" had affected the thing. (Note: at that time I had not read the book *Uri*) I asked Derek about the incident much later and he insists that he did not touch the thermometer. No one but myself saw the high reading as his father was at work and I shook it back as I normally would do, not realizing, as I had said, that Derek must have affected the thermometer. It was not a faulty thermometer as the doctor suggested. I tried to get Derek to repeat the performance only two days ago (23rd October, 1974). While he had the thermometer in his mouth, it cracked and broke. He insists he did not bite it. I shall send you the pieces of glass and the mercury I rescued.

3. A few points of interest in chronological order: *25th July, 1974.* Had interview with Uri Geller on Port Natal Radio and bent two knives (pearl-handled), Yale key, and four-inch nail. This was the only time he bent a Yale key convincingly.

12th August, 1974. Soup spoons started off by Derek continued to bend for at least one hour after he had left them. One spoon kept by N.P.B. staff at Midmar Dam did this until bent to a *U* shape. This still happens sometimes but not always.

15th September, 1974. Derek stopped rubbing metals and started bending objects by holding them and looking at them. He can always tell if something is going to "work." He feels a power in his head, which he says throbs, and extends into the metal. In the presence of some people this works well but in the presence of others, particularly myself, he loses his "power." I have to sit well away (approximately 10 ft.) or his power immediately goes. Yet, when we experimented with my watch, I held the watch in my hand and Derek did feel "power." The watch had stopped but Derek managed to move the hands half a minute at a time. Once they moved four minutes, continuing to move for twenty-four hours. In that time they moved on their own an hour.

Obviously, this action of bending needs quite a lot of concentration but Derek will do little or nothing when he is tired, e.g., after school plus one hour of homework. He seems to suffer no ill effects when he is in the mood and things do bend.

4. The date on your questionnaire, 21st September, 1974, was misleading. That was merely the date on which I completed the questions.

Trusting that what you were waiting to know has been successfully put over by me.

Yours sincerely,
(Mrs.) R.W.

We have reports from a total of ten mini-Gellers. The parents claim similar if not more spectacular results.

*

Evaluation of the Authenticity and Evidentiality of the Reports on the Uri Geller Effect

When discussing the genuineness or authenticity of the Uri Geller Effect, we must remember that we are not concerned here with authenticity or genuineness of Mr. Uri Geller, the man, or his purported psychic ability. Thus, all the arguments leveled against Uri Geller, namely, that he is a magician, that he uses sleight of hand, misdirection, or that certain magicians claim that they can perform similar "tricks," is irrelevant when evaluating the Uri Geller Effect. Uri Geller was never near the experient in a physical sense to influence directly the phenomena reported. The experiences were, however, indirectly associated with Uri Geller but they may have been merely triggered off by him. Furthermore, the power of suggestion may act as a triggering mechanism, the psychokinetic ability being within the experient. This would be analogous with the hypnotist and the hypnotized. Some of the reports would suggest that in certain instances this was the case (response to prerecorded broadcasts).

In the evaluation of the reports that reached us, we soon realized that our main problem is to assess the honesty and integrity of the "reporter" or "experient."

Laura Dale,[4] in discussing the evidentiality rating of "spontaneous" cases, quotes J. Fraser Nicol as stating that top-quality cases, which would be graded as A cases, must meet three minimal criteria:

1. That the experience be veridical, i.e., that it relate to an actual event that was occurring, had occurred, or would occur.

2. That there be an independent witness who would testify that recipient related his experience to him before he came to know by normal means that the experience had been veridical.

3. That not more than five years have passed before the experience and a written account of it.

From the above it became clear to us that the first and last criteria were met by all our cases. That is to say, all presented a definite physical event and were reported to us within weeks or months of their occurrence. None longer than five months.

The second criterion does not apply to the Uri Geller Effect reports, as none of the experients could possibly know, and hence relate, the possibility of their psychokinetic experience to an independent witness before it actually happened.

What remains to be assessed, therefore, is the quality, the honesty, and the integrity of the experient in the case of adults, or the writer of the report (usually a parent) in the case of children. In each case we have asked for corroborative evidence by witnesses. In many cases we have such corroborative statements. However, in many instances, no witnesses were present. Take the instance when a key bent in a person's pocket or by the bedside lamp following on Uri Geller's broadcast and the person lived alone and hence there could not be any witnesses.

In an effort to remedy this situation, I, with the assistance of two of my colleagues, read and reread each case. Those that we felt were vague or fragmentary, or were irrelevant or not referring to the Uri Geller Effect, we excluded from this series. I realize the inadequacy of such an assessment and I also realize that such reports are not conclusively evidential of the existence of a paranormal phenomenon. The reports' value, however, lies in their stimulating others to continue collecting and reporting such experiences. Various patterns and characteristics may become apparent, and conditions under which they occur may be identified. It is the volume and the quality of these reports that will ultimately shed more light on these phenomena, which in my mind are genuine and of tremendous importance in parapsychological research.

Analysis of Questionnaires and Case Reports

As no previous similar investigation was ever undertaken on this effect, I had no guidelines to follow. The present investigation has some similarities with various analyses of spontaneous cases as reported by Henry Sidgwick[12] and others in the *Census of Hallucinations*, 1894, or in the book written by Louisa E. Rhine,[10] *Hidden Channels of the Mind*, and her various articles in the *Journal of Parapsychology*; and by Celia Green[6] in the *Proceedings of the Society of Psychical Research* (November 1960), where she reported her analyses of 300 spontaneous cases that were collected over a period of a number of years. This followed the conference on spontaneous cases, which initiated a project undertaken by the American and British Societies of Psychical Research.

However, their methods and classifications were not quite applicable to our material and hence I attempted to devise my own method of analysis. I fully realize the shortcomings of an analysis of questionnaires and case reports. Nevertheless, I hope that future researchers will find this analysis useful and will greatly improve and enlarge on this method in the future.

Technique Employed

I was very fortunate in obtaining the assistance of Mr. John Shochot, senior lecturer of the Department for Applied Mathematics of the University of the Witwatersrand, Johannesburg, who, after discussing the aims and purpose of this analysis, proceeded to write a computer program for it. The data were collected from questionnaires, reports, and letters, and were recorded on the "take-on" forms according to Mr. Shochot's instructions. The coding was performed by two psychologists, Mrs. H. Pienaar and Mrs. J. Nestel. The analysis of the data was done as follows: The first card was not used, except for reference. The data on the second card is being stored on magnetic discs for future reference. A program was written in FORTRAN for running on an IBM 370 computer and this program was used to count and calculate the percentage of the various results, e.g., the absolute number of people reporting within an age group and the percentage of people within the age group, etc. The data are being kept for future reference.

Results of the Analysis

One hundred and forty-four individuals sent us written and signed reports of their experiences. One hundred and thirty-seven questionnaires were analyzed. A total of 183 experiences were reported, some individuals having reported more than one experience. The analysis was made on the 137 questionnaires. The specimen questionnaire will be seen in Appendix B (pages 309–311).

Age of Experients

The ages of the experients were analyzed in order to determine how many of them were children (0–10 years old), adolescents (11–20 years old), adults (21–50 years old), and middle-aged and elderly people (51–99 years old). Most ages of the experients were known accurately. Table 1 and Figure 1 represent the proportion of

Table 1. Proportion of experients in different age groups and related to the corresponding proportion in the 1970 census of the white population*

Age in years	*Percentage in sample*	*Number of age group in population*	*Percentage of group in population*	*Percentage of sample / Percentage in population*
0–10	5.11	848,600	22.00	0.23
11–20	12.41	705,110	18.92	0.65
21–50	45.26	1,469,860	39.44	1.15
51–100	30.66	737,290	19.78	1.55
Unknown	6.57	—	—	—

** The white population (male and female) according to the 1970 census was 3,726,540. The white population only was related, as all experients were white.*

experients in each age group as mentioned above, calculated in proportion to the population percentages of these groups according to the 1970 census.

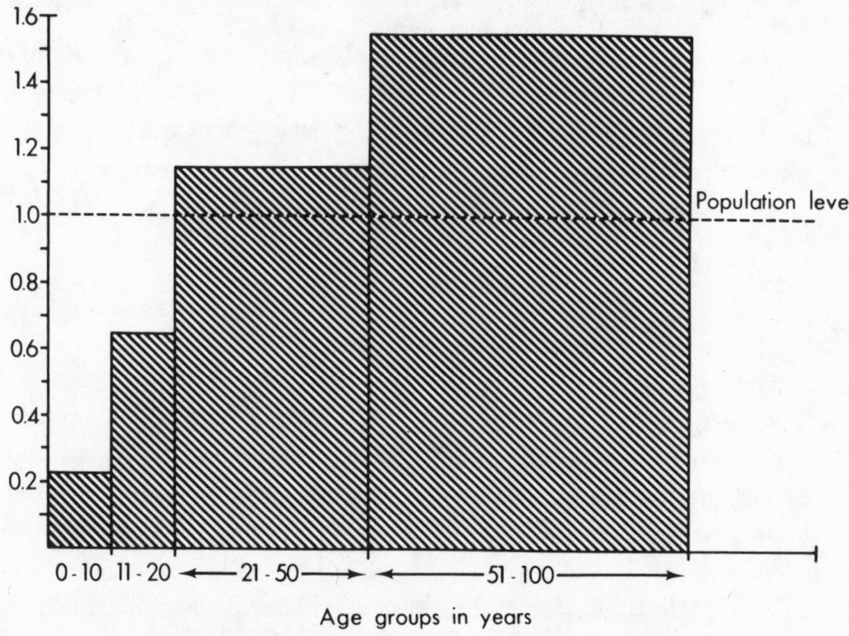

Fig. 1. Proportion of experients in different age groups divided by the corresponding proportion in the 1970 census

A study of the above table and histogram suggests that the number of Uri Geller Effect experients increases with age. This may be due to the fact that the older the person, the greater his interest in the paranormal, and the more likely he is to take the trouble to send in a report. However, it is also possible that the psychokinetic ability increases with age.

One has to point out, however, that almost all the so-called mini-Gellers, who claimed they could continue metal bending and had other psychokinetic ability, were children and adolescents under twenty years of age.

Sex of Experients

Table 2. Proportion of male and female experients related to the corresponding proportion in the white population based on the 1970 census

Sex	*Experients expressed as percentage of total sample*	*Percentage in general population*	*Percentage in sample / Percentage in population*
Males	47.45	49.8	0.953
Females	51.82	50.2	1.032
Unknown	0.73	—	—
Total	100.00	100.0	—

It would seem from the above that the sex distribution of the experients matches very closely that found in the general population. This is rather different from that found in studies of spontaneous psychic cases in England and reported by Celia Green[6] in the *Proceedings of the Society of Psychical Research* (November 1960). She reported an incidence of 18.74 percent males and 81.16 percent females in her large series of cases. The American Society for Psychical Research study of spontaneous cases reported an incidence of 24.47 percent males and 75.53 percent females. There appears to be a preponderance of female percipients in both series of cases. Louisa Rhine[10] states that, in her series of collected ESP experience, an estimate of ten psychic experiences for women to one for men would not be too high. Our series of cases, however, shows that the activation of psychokinesis and telepathy in the population by the Uri Geller Effect is proportional to the sex distribution in the general population. The Uri Geller Effect, therefore, does not seem to appear sex-linked.

Marital Status of Experients

Table 3

Marital status	Percentage of experients	Percentage in general population	Percentage of experients divided by corresponding proportion in population
1. Single	29.33	48.00	0.623
2. Married	53.28	45.39	1.17
3. Widowed	8.76	4.67	2.74
4. Divorced	4.38	1.60	1.87
5. Unknown	4.25	0.34	—
Total	100.00	100.00	—

Comment: That the proportion of experients who were never married is small is probably due to the fact that children and adolescents form a large segment of this group in the general population. In our previous analysis of the age groups (see Table 1)

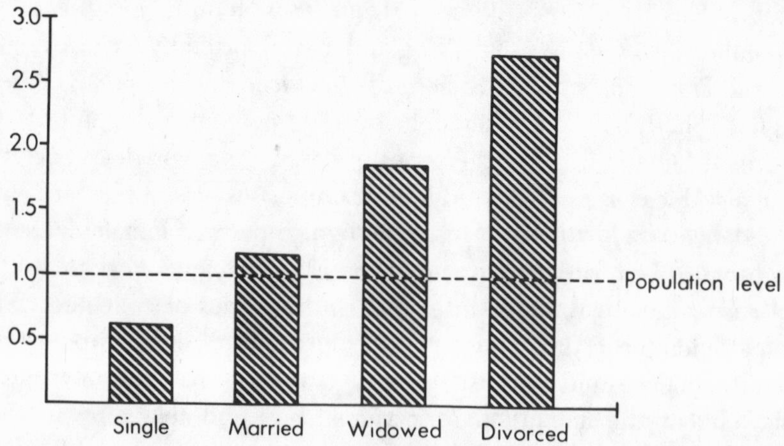

Fig. 2. Proportion of experients of various marital states divided by corresponding proportion in 1970 census

only a small percentage of the total sample were in the 1–20-year age group.

An interesting observation that comes out of this analysis (see Figure 2) is that there is the relatively large proportion of widowed and, especially, divorced experients. The possibility exists that certain psychological factors, such as tension, stress, frustration, and loneliness, may play a part in facilitating psychokinetic ability or stimulating greater interest in the paranormal.

The distribution in the married group is very close to that in the general population (1.17 to 1). That would indicate that being married does not significantly influence psychokinetic ability.

The Profession and Occupation of Experients

Table 4

Occupation	*Percentage of experients*
1. Scholars	16.79
2. Professionals	23.36
3. Tradesmen	2.19
4. Housewives	17.52
5. Civil servants	2.19
6. Others	37.95

It was difficult to compare with any accuracy the numbers and percentages of certain occupations within the general population from the statistical tables of the 1970 census. Nor was it considered that this information would contribute significantly to this paper. Thus, for example, the 1970 census does not list housewives or students as an occupation.

What is significant, however, is that the number of professional and technical workers based on the 1970 census is 202,390 white persons, or 5.43 percent of the population, whereas in our sample of experients the percentage is four times as high (23.36 percent). (See Table 4.)

This would suggest that a considerably larger proportion of professional persons than is present in the general population responded to the Uri Geller Effect. A rather small proportion of tradesmen and civil servants, on the other hand, reported such an effect.

Another significant observation that can perhaps be made is that, judging from their occupations, the experients would appear to belong to a socially reliable and responsible group of people.

Educational Qualifications of Experients

Table 5

Qualifications	*Percentage of experients*		*Percentage in population*	
1. Primary school	10.22		13.53	
2. High school graduates	27.74		22.84	
3. University undergraduates	24.09	59.86	1.46	32.24
4. Diplomats and postgraduates	8.03		7.94	
5. Unknown	29.92		—	
Total	100.00		—	

Comment: From the above table it can be seen that 32.12 percent were university graduates or postgraduates, while 27.74 percent were high school graduates. This is almost twice as many as in the general population (59.86 percent in our group and 32.24 percent in the population) and would indicate a fairly high percentage of reasonably educated people among those who reported the Uri Geller Effect experiences. The educational qualifications correlate well with the high percentage of professionals as seen in the analysis of occupations. This should not be taken to mean that the Uri

Geller Effect is more common in the more educated. It does, however, suggest that reporters of these experiences are reasonably good and reliable observers.

Classification into Types of Experiences

Table 6

Type of experience	*Percentage*
1. Telepathy	16.99
2. Metal bending	36.41
3. Fixing watches/clocks	30.00
4. Moving the hands of watches by PK	12.14
5. Others	4.46
Total	100.00

Comment: It can be noted from this table that only 16.99 percent were telepathic experiences. The remaining 83.01 percent are of a psychokinetic nature.

Where and When Did the Experience Occur in Relation to the Whereabouts of Uri Geller?

Comment: It would appear that only 18.25 percent of the experients were close to Uri Geller when the possibility of sleight of hand, misdirection, or other conjuring tricks could have been employed by Geller. In 81.75 percent of the cases there was no possibility of Geller personally being able to influence the experience by trickery.

In a number of cases there was delay in the manifestation of the Uri Geller Effect, but in a smaller number of cases the manifestation of the effect occurred prior to contact (audience or radio) with Geller. The total number of experiences that showed a "time-lag"

Table 7

Relation to Uri Geller	Percentage
1. When experient and Uri Geller were together	18.25
2. When experient was in the audience and Uri Geller was on the stage	15.33
3. When experient was at home and Geller's whereabouts were unknown to experient	3.65
4. When Geller was on the radio and experient was at home	23.36
5. Delayed occurrence of the Uri Geller Effect	7.30
6. Experience occurred prior to indirect contact with Geller	2.19
7. When experient was told about Uri Geller but neither saw him nor heard him on the radio or in the theater	3.65
8. Multiple experiences following more than one type of contact with Geller (radio stage or private meeting)	25.55
9. Unknown	0.72
Total	100.00

was twenty-two (16.4 percent). This number is larger than stated in Table 7 because some of the delayed experiences were included in the other groups.

Figure 3 (page 291) gives a breakdown of the time intervals involved in each of the cases where this "time difference" was reported.

It is difficult to understand this time difference in the manifestation of the effect in relation to the activation of it by Uri Geller. Tex G. Stanford,[13] in his article in the *Journal of the American Society for Psychical Research* (October 1974), "An experimentally testable model for spontaneous psi events: II psychokinetic events," states that the cessation of focusing on the desired objective and the abandoning of the effort may become effective in producing psychokinetic phenomena. This may well be the case in the above

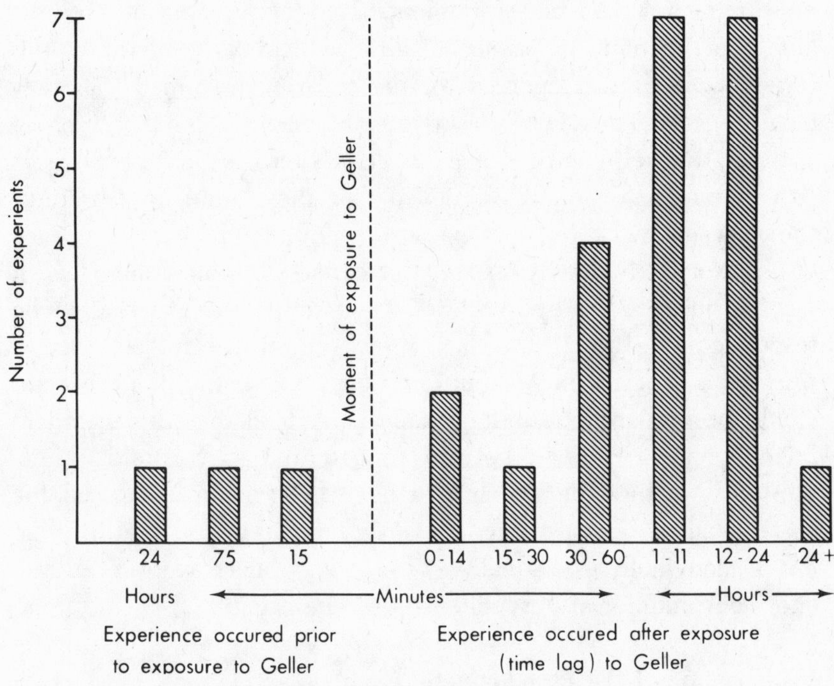

Fig. 3. Experiences manifested prior to (anticipated) or after (time-lag) exposure to Uri Geller

group, which demonstrates the time-lag phenomenon. This does not, however, explain the experiences that occurred prior to exposure to Geller.

Experients Who Had No Contact Whatsoever with Geller

In five cases (3.65 percent) the experient was merely told by his parent, or read in the newspaper, about Uri Geller. It would seem that in certain cases the mere knowledge that it can exist resulted in psychokinetic ability being released or activated.

Multiple Experiences

A large number of experients (25.55 percent) reported multiple experiences. This would suggest that repeatability occurred in a significant number of experients, and opens up the possibility of developing a repeatable experiment. The development of a repeatable experiment is the dream of all psychical researchers. In this series of cases, 20.44 percent of the experients claimed that they have repeated on numerous occasions the psychokinetic effect without the help or presence of Uri Geller. An additional 4.38 percent of the experients believed that they could now produce their psychokinetic phenomena on their own without the presence or assistance of Uri Geller, but have not attempted it. Thus, it would appear that 20 percent to 25 percent of the experients who responded to the Uri Geller Effect could be subjects for a repeatable experiment. To our question as to whether the experient would be prepared to undergo laboratory tests in order to obtain further evidence, 17.52 percent replied that they would. Here, then, is a method by which, if a huge net (mass media) and the correct bait (a true psychic or even an apparent psychic but who has a convincing personality of a Uri Geller) were used, an enormous number of "psychic fish" can be caught.

Visualization of the Psychokinetic Event

From the literature, one gains the impression that psychokinetic and poltergeist effects are rarely seen at the very moment that they occur. As J. Gaither Pratt states, in his report of the "Miami Case" (January 1967) mentioned in his book *ESP Research Today*:[8] "The disturbances persistently took place at points in space at which no one was looking at the precise moment when the motion occurred . . . As already stated, the actions were typical of poltergeists in that they seemed deliberately to hide from us."

In this series of cases, 22.63 percent of the experients stated that they saw the psychokinetic effect taking place, and some watched it for a few minutes as it continued. However, 35.77 percent of the experients stated that they did not see the effect at the moment when it occurred. In 41.61 percent of the cases, it was not possible to determine this fact either from the questionnaire or from the letter.

One has to mention that one should view the above figures with caution. It is always difficult to determine whether the experient who completed the questionnaire understood the importance of being absolutely certain that he noted the very moment at which the metal bending had taken place or the watch had started to work.

The Response to "Live" Radio Broadcasts as Compared to "Prerecorded" Radio Broadcasts

Uri Geller was on the radio four times and invited listeners to fetch watches, clocks, spoons, and keys and stroke them gently, repeating the words *bend, bend,* etc. Only one of these four broadcasts was a live broadcast: the other three were prerecorded. The experients who listened to the prerecorded programs were activated not by Uri Geller but by the taped electronic voice of Uri Geller.

Eighteen experients responded to Uri Geller's live radio program and fifteen responded to the prerecorded program.

I think this is one of the most significant findings that has emerged out of this investigation. It strongly suggests that it is not only the paranormal powers of the psychic Uri Geller that activated the psychokinetic response among the numerous experients scattered throughout the country. The mere belief that it was the psychic Uri Geller who was speaking to them was sufficient to activate and release the psychokinetic ability in the experient.

Rex G. Stanford[13] in the *JASPR* of October 1974 describes a number of inhibitory factors as well as enhancing factors that influence the appearance of psychokinesis. One such factor he calls "ownership inhibition." He claims that psychokinesis tends to be blocked when a person regards himself as responsible for the effect. He also describes a stimulating or activating factor that he refers to as "imitation or copying factor." In some of the experimental sittings of Batcheldor[1] and Brook-Smith,[2] these researchers deliberately employed deception. They arranged that one member of the group, unknown to the other sitters, intentionally produced phenomena by normal means (unbeknown to the others) after which presumably genuine paranormal psychokinetic phenomena took place.

The activation of the Uri Geller Effect by both live and prerecorded broadcasts suggests that a similar imitation or copying factor is manifesting itself. The ownership inhibitory factor may also be canceled out, as the experients believed that it is Uri Geller who is responsible for the effect and not they themselves. The presence of such a belief is confirmed by our finding that 78.10 percent of all experients stated that they are convinced that the paranormal (PK or telepathic) effect was induced by Uri Geller.

Associated Sensory or Emotional Subjective Feelings

Only 43.15 percent of the cases had an associated sensory or emotional experience coupled with the psychokinetic experience; 56.20 percent experienced nothing.

Table 8

Sensory or emotional feeling	*Percentage*
1. Feeling of warmth or tingling	13.87
2. Other emotional experiences	17.52
3. Tingling, warmth, and other emotional experiences	8.76
4. No sensory or emotional experiences	56.20
5. Unknown	3.65
Total	100.00

These findings are somewhat similar to those found by Celia Green[6] as described in the *Journal of the Society for Psychical Research* (November 1960) in her analysis of spontaneous cases. In 51.7 percent of her cases the percipient experienced no sensations.

Sense of Conviction

We were interested in determining the sense of conviction and the attitude of the experients, before and after the experience, toward the possibility that such a phenomenon would take place. The following tables were drawn up to analyze the incidence of this factor.

Table 9. Indicating sense of conviction before and after the experience

Type of attitude	*Percentage before*	*Percentage after*
1. Skeptical	12.41	6.57
2. Doubtful	36.50	12.41
3. Well disposed	37.96	27.74
4. Confirmed believer	13.13	53.28
Total	100.00	100.00

Table 10. Degree (in steps of 1, 2, 3) of change of conviction from one type of attitude to the others

Change of conviction	*Percentage*
1. No change	40.88
2. One step of change, e.g.,	41.61
i. skeptical to doubtful	
ii. doubtful to well disposed	
iii. well disposed to confirmed	
3. Two-step change	12.41
i. skeptical to well disposed	
ii. doubtful to confirmed	
4. Three-step change	3.65
i. skeptical to confirmed believer	
5. Negative change	1.45
Total	100.00

Comment: Only 13.13 percent of the experients were confirmed believers. This percentage is almost equal to the number of complete skeptics (12.41 percent). When the number of skeptics and doubtfuls (48.91 percent) are compared with the well disposed and confirmed believers (51.09 percent), one has to conclude that individuals with a negative attitude were closely balanced by those who had a positive attitude. There was, therefore, no obvious preponderance of sheep (believers) to goats (doubters), as so often occurs in ESP experiments and was so well described by Schmeidler and Murphy.[11] Our findings strongly suggest that a negative previous attitude need not be a bar to the activation of the PK abilities within an individual. This is further supported by our

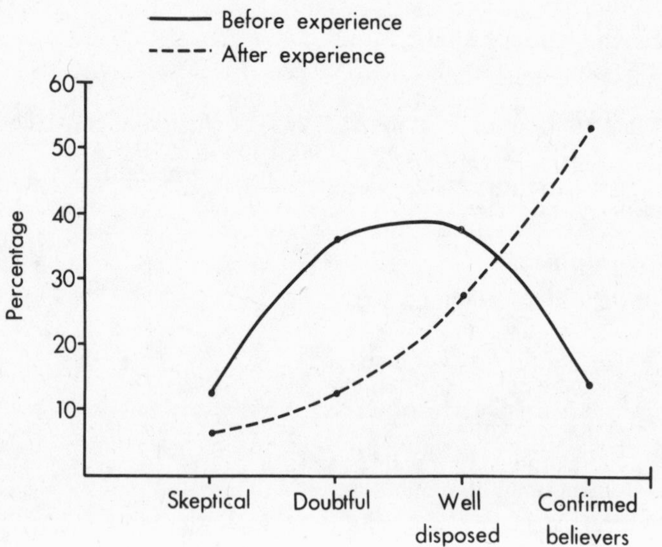

Fig. 4. Sense of conviction before and after the experience

finding that the percentage of experients who had previous psychical experiences was only 37.96. (This percentage, which is identical to the percentage of individuals who were well disposed before they had the experience, is merely fortuitous.) Two thirds of the experients, therefore, had no previous psychical experiences. This finding is contrary to the general impression held by many people that it is mostly the so-called psychics who would either have such experiences or write letters reporting such phenomena.

The dramatic change in conviction following a personal experience is well demonstrated in Table 9 and Figure 4. While 13.13 percent were confirmed believers before they experienced the phenomena, this percentage changed to 53.28 (almost quadrupled) after they had their personal experience. Once again this demonstrates a fact well known amongst parapsychologists, namely, that nothing will more readily convince an individual of the existence of the paranormal than a personal experience. Table 10 further confirms this observation. It indicates that 55.67 percent of the experients changed their attitude one or more steps up toward greater conviction. The negative change (1.45 percent) shown in this table is the result of two experients' having stated that they became less convinced after their experience.

Psychological Study

A psychological study of the personality of the experients would be useful in the investigation of those who responded to the Uri Geller Effect. It is, however, doubtful whether such a study can ever be carried out successfully on as large a number of experients as reported in this survey. Psychological investigations could be done on individuals who demonstrate a repeatable Uri Geller Effect ability, as seen among the mini-Gellers, if they could be persuaded to undergo the arduous and extensive psychological and neurological tests.

Activated Spontaneous Psychokinesis (ASPK) and Activated Recurrent Spontaneous Psychokinesis (ARSPK)

These are new terms, which I would like to coin in order to describe the Uri Geller Effect. This effect, as the above new terms imply, is not limited to Uri Geller. Any activating agent or object, whether he or she be a genuine psychic, a plausible showman using the power of suggestion to influence the experients, an able and clever experimenter, a tape-recorded voice or video-taped image, etc., may activate and precipitate a latent ability, present in many people, to demonstrate PK ability. In some of us this ability is greater than in others. It would appear to be produced more readily and to persist for longer periods in children and adolescents. When demonstrations of this ability are regularly repeatable over a period of time without further activation, one should refer to it as "activated recurrent spontaneous psychokinesis" (ARSPK).

Comparison of the Poltergeist Phenomena (SRPK) and the Uri Geller Effect.

1. In the poltergeist cases the events generally center on a single person. This is also the case in the Uri Geller Effect, where it centers on the experient.

2. Ordinarily, someone who is approaching, or has recently reached, puberty is found to be the agent responsible. In the Uri Geller phenomena almost all mini-Gellers are children or adolescents.

3. In the poltergeist cases nothing ever happens when the person on whom it centers is absent. The event starts unexpectedly, runs an unpredictable course, and suddenly fades away. The same type of behavior pattern is seen in most cases of adult Uri Geller Effect. In the mini-Geller phenomena, however, the effect did not fade away suddenly but persisted and even improved over a time.

4. Unexplained disturbances of the poltergeist phenomenon usually occur when they are not under direct visualization. This is also true of manifestations of the Uri Geller Effect; 77.4 percent of experients did not report seeing any changes taking place at the very moment they did occur.

5. As far as could be determined from a careful perusal of the reports of our cases, there was no evidence that suppressed hostility or release of pent-up feelings played a part in the production of the Uri Geller Effect. In individuals associated with a production of poltergeist phenomena, such hostility and release of pent-up feelings are said to be present.

Inhibitory and Enhancing Factors That May Play a Part in the Production of ASPK

Stanford[13] in his paper described certain inhibitory and activating factors that influence the production of PK. This is based largely on the work of Batcheldor[1] and Brook-Smith and Hunt.[3]

Inhibiting Factors

"Witness inhibition" appears to play a part in the production of the Uri Geller Effect, particularly in mini-Gellers. They find difficulty in getting started while observed, but once they have started without being unobserved, their metal-bending often continues under observation. However, the difficulty the experient encounters in demonstrating the effect while being observed often gives rise in others to the suspicion that cheating is taking place.

"Ownership inhibition" tends to block the production of PK when the person involved knows himself to be responsible for this effect. This ownership inhibition was probably canceled out in the experients, as the majority (78.10 percent) of all people reporting the phenomena were convinced that it was induced by Uri Geller and not by themselves. Owen & Sparrow[7] discuss this factor in their paper, "The generation of paranormal physical phenomena in connection with an imaginary communicator."

Factors That May Enhance the Production of PK

"Imitation or copying" factor: It is reported by Batcheldor[1] that genuine PK phenomena are often produced when the sitters observe such phenomena being produced by the leader or a member of their group. Batcheldor, unknown to the other sitters, sometimes deliberately produced phenomena by normal means, following which ostensibly genuine physical phenomena were produced by the rest of the sitters. This was particularly well observed and is possibly the most important factor responsible for success in the production of the Uri Geller Effect throughout the population. People listening to, or viewing, Uri Geller's performance (whether it was genuine or not), and believing that psychokinetic phenomena are taking place, were able to release their own inhibitions and successfully produced similar PK effects. Perhaps the prerecorded radio program response is the best example of the importance of this imitation or copying factor.

Other features that are present in the demonstration of PK ability were also noted in the production of the Uri Geller Effect. One of them is that both PK and the Uri Geller Effect occasionally become demonstrable after efforts to produce it are abandoned, e.g., the cessation of focusing on the desired objective. This would seem to have occurred on many occasions when delayed phenomena took place. Is this similar to the psychological block many of us have experienced when trying to recollect a name or event? No matter how hard we try, it eludes us. Then later, when we have abandoned the attempt to recollect, suddenly the memorized event surfaces in our consciousness.

How Can One Explain the Uri Geller Effect?

In truth, the method by which a given end-result is accomplished in the PK or the Uri Geller Effect phenomenon is uncomprehended.

The question is: How could any conceivable energy-form be directed to accomplish what is accomplished?

Certain explanations and theories are put forward by various people:

1. *The Rationalist Explanation.* The rationalist claims that the Uri Geller Effect does not exist. He maintains that Uri Geller is a clever conjurer, and by known or unknown techniques of misdirection, sleight of hand, and other illusionist's methods, he produces his apparently paranormal telepathic and psychokinetic results. Similarly, he maintains that the Uri Geller Effect in the population is a mass hysteria phenomenon, and the people who are reporting it are consciously or unconsciously cheating or lying.

Although it is possible in principle that in one or a few cases people may be cheating or lying, it is unreasonable to expect us to believe that literally thousands of responsible people — many of whom are of the highest academic, professional, and social status, and live in all parts of the world — who claim to have had these experiences personally, and were witnessed by independent observers, are suffering from illusions and hallucinations and are either consciously or unconsciously cheating. The perusal of our reports indicates that in most cases the phenomena occurred all over the country, very often in good light and in the presence of responsible, outside observers.

2. *The Physical Explanation.* It is suggested that electricity or magnetism channeled from the brain and perhaps through the muscles is the source of energy in the same way that some fish can send out strong electrical pulses. Some people claim that it is conceivable to suppose that certain individuals, more than others, are capable of generating this type of energy. The stimulation and direction of this energy may be influenced either by the individual himself or it may be triggered off by the power of suggestion from an outside agent. No such physical energy, however, has been identified as yet.

3. *The Parapsychological Theory.* Rhine and Pratt[9] suggest that

certain living systems possess an unknown facility, which they refer to as psi. It does not display space-time-mass properties. It is a "nonphysical" force that does not obey the laws that are so characteristic of physical energy forces. Thus, they claim that enough evidence appears to have been accumulated to suggest that the "information-gathering" and "transference" experience known as telepathy, precognition, etc. are all nonphysical and that psychokinesis, the poltergeist, and PK are similarly nonphysical phenomena. It is, therefore, conceivable that the Uri Geller Effect is a form of psi.

It remains to be determined whether the Uri Geller Effect is in every case required to be triggered off by an external agent and therefore the psi capacity is within the agent plus the experient, or whether it is due to the psychic powers of the agent alone, in this case Uri Geller, and the experient reporting the phenomena is a passive agent. A number of instances in our series of cases demonstrate this point, e.g., a person finding that the key was bent without his being aware of an outside force activating him or the key. Alternatively, it may be entirely within the experient, and the agent is a passive nonpsychic vehicle. In PK and RSPK the vehicle through which the psychokinetic effect occurs may be telepathy. In the Uri Geller Effect it is not certain whether telepathy is the chief vehicle. It may be completely nonpsychic. The instruction to the experient was usually transmitted by visual or auditory means in those instances where the experient was in the audience during a demonstration or at a private meeting, and by auditory means when the experient was listening to a live or prerecorded radio program. When the response occurred because of a television appearance, then again vision combined with voice may be the vehicle that transmits the instruction to the experient. Even in instances when the PK phenomena occurred without direct physical, visual, or auditory contact with Geller, the transmitting vehicle may not have been telepathy. The triggering effect may be the experient's psychological attitude; e.g., the knowledge that Geller is in the country and that other people in addition to Geller can do it was sufficient to produce the required psychological attitude.

General Remarks

The present investigation is not presented as final and conclusive evidence of the existence of the Uri Geller Effect, but rather claims that there is enough evidence to suggest that the Uri Geller Effect exists and is genuine. It may turn out to be the most significant happening in parapsychology in the past years and may open a fascinating and exciting new channel of research. Thus, it would seem possible that a large number of "experient-percipients" in a sizable population group could be activated through mass media and a psychic with the personality and ability of Uri Geller, and PK phenomena could be produced. The discovery of mini-Gellers, who may then be subjected to laboratory investigations, would open up a completely new avenue, a new prospect and dimension in psi research. This could produce as near a repeatable laboratory experiment as is possible in biological science.

In this type of work, the research worker, at this stage of the development of parapsychology, should be looking for understanding from other disciplines of science — not necessarily acceptance. Acceptance may come later.

APPENDIX A

Discussion About the Objects That Were Influenced by the Uri Geller Effect

It is of importance and of value to discuss the type and the nature of the objects that were affected both by Uri Geller personally, and by individuals other than Uri Geller, who claim to have been personally involved in the Uri Geller Effect.

Examination of Bent and Fractured Metal Objects

In our questionnaire we inquired whether the experient would be willing to send us the broken or bent keys, spoons, or other metal objects for examination. Of the experients, 44.53 percent replied that they are prepared to let us have the various objects in their possession for examination. Twenty-two experients sent in various objects for examination. Nine of these experients were mini-Gellers, who sent in seventy-four objects, which they claimed to have bent or broken over a period of months. Six experients sent in six metal objects, which were bent or broken by Uri Geller while they were holding them. Eight experients (adults) sent in thirteen objects, which they themselves had bent or broken while watching a demonstration in the theater or listening to Geller's radio broadcast. No watches were sent to us (most probably because they were too valuable). A total of ninety-three objects was sent to us for examination. (See Plate 58.)

Watches and Clocks

A total of sixty-two watches and clocks (30 percent) were reported to have been "fixed" by the Uri Geller Effect, and twenty-five watches (12.14 percent) had their hands moved without physical means. The following tables show the periods for which the watches were out of order and the

Table 11. Length of period for which the watches/clocks were out of order

Period	*Number of watches*
1. Less than 1 year	9
2. 1 to 5 years	11
3. 5 to 25 years	15
4. 25 to 100 years	3
5. More than 100 years	0
6. Unknown	24
Total	62

Table 12. Period for which watches/clocks worked following the "Uri Geller Effect-Fixing"

Period	*Number of watches*
1. Less than 1 hour	2
2. 1 to 12 hours	5
3. 12 to 48 hours	2
4. For more than 48 hours	48
5. Unknown	5
Total	62

periods for which the watches worked following the "Uri Geller Effect-fixing."

Comment: From Table 11 it becomes apparent that at least 42 percent of the watches and clocks that responded to Uri Geller or the Uri Geller Effect were out of order for 1–100 years. From Table 12 it is seen that at least 77 percent of the watches or clocks continued working for longer than forty-eight hours after they were "fixed" by Geller or the Uri Geller Effect. Forty-two percent of the watches were of sentimental value to the experient; 1.6 percent of watches were not of sentimental value. The rest (56.4 percent of those questioned did not answer this query.

Table 13. Type of objects sent to us for examination

Type of objects	*Number of objects*
1. Spoons (soup, dessert)	16
2. Teaspoons	21
3. Knives	4
4. Forks	9
5. Keys	39
6. Nail (4 inch)	1
7. Thermometer	1
8. Pestle (brass ¼-inch diameter)	1
9. Steel crowbar (1½-inch diameter)	1
Total	93

The metal in the "cutlery objects" was either stainless steel or nickel silver-plated steel; the items were of standard quality, found in most households. The keys were mostly Yale keys. A good number were wardrobe and garage keys.

Table 14. Type of deformation of objects

Type	*Number*
1. Bent	65
2. Twisted	9
3. Complete fracture	13
4. Incomplete fracture	8
Total	95

Some of the objects were bent and twisted at the same time, hence the total differs from the total in Table 13.

The degree of bending varied from five degrees to one hundred eighty degrees. We measured the degree of bending and twisting of each object, but no good purpose will be served in recording these details.

We submitted metal objects for examination to Professor G.V.R., Head of the Department of Material Science and Metallurgy of a South African University.* It required persistence to persuade the metallurgist to examine the objects. This is understandable, as much work is involved in the preparation, sectioning, and microscopic examination of metal objects. Furthermore, like many other scientists, he is convinced that metal bending by PK is impossible.

One of the objects submitted was a garage key that belonged to my good friend, Dr. D. Pienaar. This key had attached to it a personal object for the purpose of identification so that it could not be substituted by another key. The key was bent by Uri Geller in his hotel suite while Professor A. E. H. Bleksley held it in his hand. I was present in the room, sitting close to Professor Bleksley and Dr. Pienaar while Uri Geller attempted to bend the key. A newspaper photographer was taking photographs repeatedly. At no time could we see any evidence of misdirection or force being used by Geller to bend the key. Before sectioning the key, Professor

* Both the professor and the university wish to remain anonymous.

G.V.R. bent the key mechanically at a new site. The key was then sectioned and both sites (where Geller bent it and where it was bent mechanically in the laboratory) were sectioned and mounted in resin and examined microscopically. The following is a full report on this examination.

Report on Bending and Fracturing of Spoons, Keys, etc.

From the examination of a large number of objects that were submitted for examination, the following observations were made.

(a) Objects that were deformed were in all instances deformed to a greater extent at locations where the section was the weakest, as would be expected in the case of a mechanical loading.

(b) Deformation in some instances was so severe that small cracks developed. A number of objects were indeed deformed to such an extent that they fractured, as is commonly found when metals are mechanically deformed too far.

(c) Microscopic examination of the surfaces of the deformed specimens showed that the surface had an orange-peel appearance due to slip, the mechanism by which metals deform plastically when stressed excessively.

(d) The deformation of the specimens was found to be accompanied by work-hardening, a phenomenon associated with plastic deformation of metals at room temperature.

(e) Fracture-surface appearance was either brittle or ductile, depending on the hardness of the metal. The fracture-surface appearance was in all respects the same as that which is expected when a metal is deformed by a mechanical force until it fractures.

(f) A comparison of the metallographic structure of a key at the location where it was bent by Uri Geller with that at an adjacent location where it was bent mechanically showed that the sites were in all respects identical. No evidence of recrystallization or any softening could be found. At both the locations the brittle chromium plating on the surface, which was extended during bending, was cracked, as shown in Plate 59.

Conclusions

All the observations made are in accord with what is expected when a metal is deformed by the application of a force sufficient to cause plastic deformation.

(signed) Prof. G.V.R.

As no unusual change was noted in the bent objects that were submitted for metallurgical examination, one has at least excluded the possibility that chemicals, heat, laser beams, or an unknown physical radiation energy were employed. A negative finding is often just as important as a positive finding.

No scanning electron microscope examination of fractured surfaces was, however, done. It is, therefore, important to mention other work done in this field.

Dr. Wilbur Franklin of the Department of Physics, Kent State University, Ohio, U.S.A.,[5] has reported on a metallurgical analysis of two specimens of metal that were fractured in a room-temperature setting and were observed visually by the authors and others during the process of deformation and fracture. Franklin states that "the scanning electron microscope is especially useful in the examination of fractured surfaces since it has a good depth of field and since both low and high magnification can be utilized easily."

The following is an extract from a paper read by Dr. Wilbur Franklin[5] at the conference, "The Physics of Paranormal Phenomena," at Tarrytown, New York, in February 1975.*

The metallurgical analysis of three fractured surfaces in two metallic specimens broken by Uri Geller revealed two distinct types of fracturing surface microstructure in the SEM (scanning electron microscope) photographs. One type appeared quite similar to room-temperature ductile failure by mechanical loading, except for an unusual *viscous appearance* at the bottom of a small lateral crack. In the second type of fracture surface, the predominant microstructures were not typical of ductile failure, fatigue, or shear failure, nor of room-temperature cleavage. In the platinum ring specimen, localized sections of two types were observed on the same fracture surface. One type looked like incipient melting and the second like low-temperature cleavage, with inclusions or vacancy clusters also appearing in the field of view. These observations, which are not typical of SEM fractographs of failures by mechanical loading, indicate that the cause of fracture was neither mechanical in nature nor a result of usual mechanical methods of fracture. In fact, the possible methods of reconstruction of the fracture surface in the platinum ring by known techniques seem to require means such as cleavage at liquid nitrogen temperature followed by subsequent exposure to a small beam from a powerful laser in selected regions and shear in other regions.

* For full report by Wilbur Franklin, see pages 75–106.

APPENDIX B

The South African Institute for Parapsychology

P.O. Box 23154, Joubert Park 2044, Johannesburg
Republic of South Africa

QUESTIONNAIRE

1. Name of the person who underwent the experience reported. (In what follows, this person will be referred to as the Percipient.)
BLOCK LETTERS PLEASE.

....

2. ADDRESS: ....

....

....

3. TELEPHONE NUMBER: ....

4. Age of Percipient at time of experience .... years.

5. SEX: (a) Male ☐ (b) Female ☐

6. Marital Status: ....

7. Time at which experience occurred: date, hour, minute (if possible).

....

8. Was the experience related to Geller's
   (a) Stage performance? Date ....
   (b) Broadcast? Date and time ....
   (c) A private meeting? Date and time ....

9. Did the experience occur
   (a) When you and Geller were together? Yes ☐ No ☐
   (b) When you were in the audience and Geller on the stage? Yes ☐ No ☐
   (c) When you were at home or outside the theater and Geller elsewhere? Yes ☐ No ☐
   (d) When Geller was on the radio and you were at home? Yes ☐ No ☐
   (e) Some time after Geller's performance or broadcast? Yes ☐ No ☐

(f) If answer to (e) is yes, how long after? ....

10. Classification of experience:

(a) Telepathic	Yes ☐	No ☐
(b) Metal bending or breaking	Yes ☐	No ☐
(c) Starting of clock or watch	Yes ☐	No ☐
(d) Moving of hands of watch or clock	Yes ☐	No ☐
(e) Others	Yes ☐	No ☐

11. Was the experience accompanied by

(a) A feeling of warmth or tingling? Yes ☐ No ☐

(b) Any other emotional experience? ....

....

12. Profession, business, or trade of Percipient ....

....

....

13. Academic qualifications ....

14. Please categorize your state of conviction about the possibility of such an experience *before* it happened:

(a) Completely skeptical	Yes ☐	No ☐
(b) Doubtful but prepared to consider possibilities	Yes ☐	No ☐
(c) Well disposed to the possibility	Yes ☐	No ☐
(d) A confirmed belief in such experiences	Yes ☐	No ☐

15. What is your present state of belief after having had the experience?

(a) Completely skeptical	Yes ☐	No ☐
(b) Doubtful but prepared to consider possibilities	Yes ☐	No ☐
(c) Well disposed to the possibility	Yes ☐	No ☐
(d) A confirmed belief in such experience	Yes ☐	No ☐

16. Has the Percipient had previous experiences of a psychic nature? Yes ☐ No ☐

17. Does the Percipient believe that his experience was induced directly by Uri Geller? Yes ☐ No ☐

18. Does the Percipient believe that he is able to repeat the experience on occasions when Mr. Geller is not involved directly? Yes ☐ No ☐

19. If the answer to 18 above is Yes, has the experience in fact been repeated since the first occasion? Yes ☐ No ☐
20. If the answer to 19 above is Yes, would the Percipient be prepared to undergo laboratory tests in order to produce further evidence? Yes ☐ No ☐
21. If you have broken keys, bent spoons etc., drawings, or photographs in your possession, would you allow us to examine them? Yes ☐ No ☐
22. If you have had or witnessed more than one experience or observation associated with Mr. Geller's visit, would you please itemize them and describe them in detail on a separate sheet.

Signed: ....

Date: ....

BIBLIOGRAPHY

1. Batcheldor, K. J., "Report on a case of table levitation and associated phenomena," *Journal of the Society for Psychical Research,* 43, 339–356, 1966.
2. Brookes-Smith, C., "Data tape-recorded experimental PK phenomena," *Journal of the Society for Psychical Research,* 47, 68–89, 1973.
3. Brookes-Smith, C. and D. W. Hunt, "Some experiments in psychokinesis," *Journal of the Society for Psychical Research,* 45, 265–281, 1970.
4. Dale, Laura, A., Rhea White, and Gardner Murphy, "A selection of cases from a recent survey of spontaneous ESP phenomena," *Journal of the American Society for Psychical Research, LVI,* No. 1, January 1962.
5. Franklin, Wilbur, Physics Dept. Kent State University, Kent, Ohio, U.S.A., "Is there physics in ESP?" Paper read at the Tarrytown conference, "The Physics of Paranormal Phenomena," Feb. 1975.
6. Green, Celia, "Analysis of spontaneous cases," *Proceedings of the Society for Psychical Research,* 53, Part 191, 97–161, Nov. 1960.
7. Owen, I. M. and M. H. Sparrow, "Generation of paranormal physical phenomena in connection with an imaginary communicator," *New Horizons Journal,* 1, No. 3, 6–13, 1974.

8. Pratt, J. Gaither, *E.S.P. Research Today* (Metuchen, N.J.: The Scarecrow Press, Inc., 1973), p. 129.
9. Rhine, J. B. and J. G. Pratt, *Parapsychology: Frontier Science of the Mind* (Springfield, Ill.: Charles C Thomas, 1957), p. 74.
10. Rhine, Louisa E., *Hidden Channels of the Mind* (New York: William Sloan Associates, 1961), p. 132.
11. Schmeidler, G. R. and G. Murphy, "The influence of belief and disbelief in ESP upon individual scoring levels," *Journal of Experimental Psychology, 36*, 271–276, 1946.
12. Sidgwick, Henry and others, "Report on the census of hallucinations," 1894, *Society for Psychical Research Proceedings.*
13. Stanford, Rex G., "An experimentally testable model for spontaneous psi events: II psychokinetic events," *The Journal of the American Society for Psychical Research, 68*, No. 4, 321–357, Oct. 1974.
14. Targ, R. and H. Puthoff, "Information transmission under conditions of sensory shielding," *Nature, 251*, No. 5476, Oct. 18, 1974.

EPILOGUE

WHAT DOES IT ALL MEAN — both Geller's apparent ability to duplicate drawings and bend metals, and the evidence that certain individuals can muster enough "psychic energy," after seeing Geller perform, to reproduce many of his feats?

One editorial summed up the situation: A "challenge to scientists will arise if investigations continue to turn up signs of psychokinetic powers . . . It would then be urgently necessary for the scientific community to come to terms with something totally beyond its powers of explanation." That statement appeared in the traditionally conservative journal *Nature* in December 1973. Since then more evidence on paranormal phenomena — involving Geller and other individuals — *has* surfaced, and the scientific community *has* begun to turn its attention to research of the paranormal. Where the field of parapsychology once was the exclusive province of psychologists, today it has become an active arena for physical scientists as well: In August 1974, a group of physicists met in Geneva, Switzerland, to discuss how such arcane concepts of quantum physics as "time reversal" and "acausality" might be relevant to an understanding of psychical events; and in February 1975, a group of physicists and engineers met in Tarrytown, New York, at a conference entitled "The Physics of Paranormal Phenomena." It would have been impossible to convene such meetings just a decade ago, for reputable physical scientists were not interested in the field of parapsychology — or if they were, they kept it a well-guarded secret.

Why the turnabout? What has suddenly drawn so many physicists, chemists, and engineers into psychical research?

Certainly one reason has to do with the sophisticated electronic equipment used by modern psychical researchers. Devices such as electroencephalographs, temperature sensors, galvanic skin detectors, and others permit scientists to monitor a subject's brain waves, heart and respiration rates, and electrical skin conductivity during a test of paranormality, and to observe physiological correlations that accompany psychical happenings. Thus, in appearance, modern psychical research more closely parallels conventional scientific inquiry. And appearance is important. Another reason has to do with the willingness of scientists in the last decade to study humans in such altered states of consciousness as hypnosis, dreaming, and conditions of sensory deprivation and bombardment; paranormal perceptions are often found to spring naturally from such "twilight" levels of the mind.* But there is another factor that accounts for the recent influx of physical scientists to psychical research: Uri Geller. Regardless of one's personal attitude toward Geller, no one can deny the fact that in a mere four years Geller has focused more scientific attention on the field of parapsychology than it has seen in its entire ninety-year history. Further, research conducted with Geller has constituted the first parapsychological evidence to be published in an "establishment" scientific journal. To a large degree all of this attention has had positive effects on the quality of the work being done. But it has also raised a question that is being asked with great concern these days: Is the Geller-aroused interest in parapsychology really good for the field as a whole?

Some parapsychologists think it is not. "Many people think Uri Geller is all that there is to parapsychology today," says Charles

* For an overview of parapsychological research conducted in the last decade see: *The Roots of Coincidence*, Arthur Koestler (New York: Random House, 1972); *Dream Telepathy*, Montague Ullman, et al. (New York: Macmillan, 1973); *Supersenses: Our Potential for Parasensory Experience*, Charles Panati (New York: Quadrangle, 1974).

Unlike other psychics and ordinary individuals who have been studied for parasensory abilities, Geller claims that he experiences no shift in consciousness when he performs his feats. However, many scientists believe that Geller does undergo consciousness changes, but that, for some reason presently unknown, they are so slight that Geller himself is not aware of them. All attempts to measure alterations in Geller's brain-wave pattern during paranormal tests have yielded negative results.

Honorton, President of the Parapsychological Association and a leading psychical researcher at the Maimonides Medical Center in Brooklyn. Honorton feels that because of all the publicity Geller has generated, too strong, and unfounded, associations have been made in the minds of the public between Uri Geller and the entire field of psychical research. Honorton speaks for many other parapsychologists when he expresses one fear: "If Geller should ever be proved a fraud, or if it should ever be found that he uses magic when his paranormal talents fail him, the setback for the field of parapsychology could be the greatest in its history."

Other researchers, however, take a different view of Geller: they see him as a long-needed "superattraction" who is bringing attention to a field where research activity has always been minimal and results scarce. "The questions posed by paranormal phenomena are far too complex for psychologists alone to tackle," says physicist Wilbur Franklin. "It was important that physical scientists enter the field and conduct their own kind of research. Geller, I believe, has been one major factor for this happening."

Franklin and Honorton typify two different views, and figuratively speaking, at least, they head two opposing camps on the issue of Uri Geller and psychical research. But there is one point on which both sides agree: more research on Geller is necessary; first, to establish beyond any reasonable doubt the true nature of Geller's talents, then, assuming this is affirmatively established, to determine the exact extent of his abilities — not only what Geller *can* do, but what he *cannot* do. For this information is also of value in trying to understand the nature and origins of psychic abilities.

Geller himself is willing to participate in further scientific investigations. He has already undergone perceptual and PK experiments in Japan, Switzerland, and France. (They were conducted too late for the results to be included in this book.) Beyond this, there are the experiments proposed by Ronald Hawke, who, by using sound waves in metals, and light waves in plastics, hopes to understand the nature of the deformations in these materials, which Geller will attempt to bend. Eldon Byrd at the Naval Surface Weapons Center has suggested a series of experiments that would investigate whether there is a magnetic component to the energy that Geller uses in accomplishing his feats. Charles Honorton has designed a rigorous series of perceptual experiments to establish the extent of Geller's telepathic and clairvoyant ability. And shortly before this manuscript was completed, William Cox, at the Institute for Parapsychology in Durham, North Carolina, submitted to Geller an outline of the experiments he would like to conduct on both Geller's perceptual and psychokinetic abilities. These represent only a small fraction of the tests that have been proposed by qualified researchers in various scientific fields.

Another Geller-related area of study is the apparent PK abilities in adolescents and adults that develop spontaneously after some form of contact with Geller. Physicists Dr. John Hasted and Dr. John Taylor in England and medical psychologist Dr. Thelma Moss in the U.S. are just three of the researchers who are continuing to investigate this phenomenon. It has been suggested that the design of future research in the paranormal, with Geller and other psychics, can be greatly improved, and the protocols greatly tightened, by consultation with a skilled magician, who can impose experimental safeguards to prevent the possibility of fraud. An increasing number of psychical investigators are following this suggestion. And in the next few years it might become standard procedure to have a magician's name, and his recommendations, as an integral part of parapsychological research papers.

The plans for continued research with Geller and other individuals are exciting, but the efforts will be futile if the scientific community at large does not keep an open mind toward research on paranormal phenomena and if respected scientific journals do not publish the results of well-conducted psychical investigations. The appearance of the SRI paper in *Nature* overturned a century-old publishing hurdle; it can be hoped only that other journals will follow *Nature*'s lead.

What will it mean if further psychical research yields uneqivocally positive results? Parapsychologists have been saying for years that there exist human senses beyond the five ordinary ones — *parasenses,* or perceptual modalities that transcend our present understanding of space and time. Western science has really just begun to research the subject of human consciousness. Already it has determined that there are such things as parasenses, and that the parasenses of ordinary individuals can be aroused if changes in levels of consciousness are induced. Crudely now; feebly. But that's just for the present. Further research will refine our knowledge of our parasenses, and our ability to develop them — for the betterment of humankind and a clearer understanding of our place in the universe. Research on Uri Geller could greatly add to that knowledge, and lessen the time, by decades, before we have answers to the paranormal workings of the mind.